THE
HOLY
WAR

Frontispiece to the first edition of *The Holy War* (1682), engraved by Robert White
Reproduced by permission of the Trustees of the British Museum

THE  HOLY WAR

MADE BY SHADDAI
UPON DIABOLUS
FOR THE REGAINING
OF THE METROPOLIS
OF THE WORLD
                    OR
THE LOSING
AND TAKING AGAIN
OF THE TOWN OF MANSOUL

by
JOHN BUNYAN

edited by
JAMES F. FORREST
Associate Professor of English
University of Alberta

THE COPP CLARK PUBLISHING COMPANY

In Memoriam

Thomas Forrest

[1558]

FOREWORD

A new edition of Bunyan's *Holy War* is to be welcomed, not least because it is a book that teachers and historians of English literature ought to have close at hand as a reminder of the stubborn persistence of its ancient literary mode. Allegory, we often hear, had fallen out of fashion as the seventeenth century moved into the Age of Dryden. *Pilgrim's Progress,* it might seem, achieved its astonishing success almost in spite of its allegory, because of its powers of characterization, narrative, and conversation, its qualities as a forerunner of the novel. Milton, to be sure, included in *Paradise Lost* a vivid allegory of Sin and Death, together with his long allegory of the spiritual combat under the guise of the War in Heaven; but then Milton's muse was, we know, in some respects archaic, and such allegories were perhaps only a last, dying vestige of Milton's Spenserian allegiance.

Bunyan's *Holy War* helps to remind us that such uses of allegory were not eccentric, but that allegory maintained its hold on the popular imagination even as late as the year in the Restoration of the Sons of Belial, 1682. Like *Pilgrim's Progress,* Bunyan's *Holy War* depends for its success upon an audience trained in the understanding of the subtleties of Calvinist theology, and such an audience existed, in large numbers, trained by constant practice in listening to the Puritan preachers, hour after hour after hour. In this way Bunyan's readers were able to discern and enjoy the working of abstract principles within the world of daily experience, to grasp the intellectual structure of salvation as set forth by their own eloquent ministers. Bunyan's *Holy War* was thus able to give dramatic presentation to the structure of God's great design for man, as the Calvinist theologians conceived it. Through the simplest, most colloquial language, and through the commonest of settings, we can perceive the firm strand of a high intellectual argument, guiding Bunyan's style and plot toward a preordained conclusion, the salvation of the Elect.

The peculiar power of Bunyan's allegorical style lies in the way in which he can maintain an exploratory manner, a flexible, tentative, colloquial mode of speaking, even while he is dealing with firmly fixed theological issues. We may see this remarkable combination of colloquial flexibility and theological rigor in the following passage, which deals with the intrusion of the Doubters into the town of Mansoul:

But there were three of those that came from the land of Doubting, who after they had wandered and ranged the country a while, and perceived that they had escaped, were so hardy as to thrust themselves, knowing that yet there were in the town Diabolonians—I say, they were so hardy as to thrust themselves into Mansoul among them. (Three, did I say? I think there were four.) Now to whose house should these Diabolonian Doubters go, but to the house of an old Diabolonian in Mansoul, whose name was Evil-questioning; a very great enemy he was to Mansoul, and a great doer among the Diabolonians there. Well, to this Evil-questioning's house, as was said, did these Diabolonians come (you may be sure that they had directions how to find the way thither); so he made them welcome, pitied their misfortune, and succoured them with the best that he had in his house. Now after a little acquaintance (and it was not long before they had that), this old Evil-questioning asked the Doubters if they were all of a town (he knew that they were all of one kingdom); and they answered, No, *nor not of one shire, neither.* 'For I,' said one, 'am an Election-doubter.' 'I,' said another, 'am a Vocation-doubter.' Then said the third, 'I am a Salvation-doubter,' and the fourth said he was a Grace-doubter. 'Well,' quoth the old gentleman, 'be of what shire you will, I am persuaded that you are down boys: you have the very length of my foot, are one with my heart, and shall be welcome to me.' So they thanked him, and were very glad that they had found themselves an harbour in Mansoul.

Election, Vocation, Salvation, Grace: four principal terms in the puritan theological vocabulary are thus placed in the most familiar setting, while the narrator adopts the tone and manner of a friend telling a tale spontaneously, with all the hesitations and parentheses that everyone makes in oral rendition of a story being told for the first time. In this way Bunyan gives his stern and difficult version of truth an energetic, immediate life within the world of common men.

YALE UNIVERSITY
December, 1966

LOUIS L. MARTZ

INTRODUCTION

I

The Holy War, first published in 1682, is the product of an outlook that has had an enormous influence on the making of Western man. Even today the Puritanism that inspires it exerts great pressure on our culture, modifying, controlling, shaping, directing. As a literary force, its impact is incalculable. Whatever the deviations, the line with its heavy scoring of evil descends directly from Milton and Bunyan in the seventeenth century to Graham Greene and William Golding in the twentieth. The contemporary phenomenon of the "Theatre of the Absurd" also reveals an attitude that many have seen, albeit superficially, as most distinctively Puritan: the view that man's right to dignity is patently ridiculous. Nor are the checkmated worlds of *Waiting for Godot* and *Samson Agonistes* dissimilar, for Samuel Beckett, like Milton, provides no social mechanics for the working out of one's own destiny; the difference is that the modern writer finds this life as a total concept of reality manifestly absurd, whereas the older deprecates the absurdity of taking our existence as anything but shadow. For Milton (and for Bunyan) God is what human life is all about; and only in the context of the Divine is man seen to have a chance, only in the frame of the Eternal does the temporal, with all its goodness and joy, its suffering and evil, have any meaning. But although the visions of the Puritans and the Absurdists are thus separate, they are related; and much of our cultural conditioning, our habits of thought, what we read and the way we write and feel and speak, we owe to a view of life that was being formulated over three and a half centuries ago.

Clearly, then, *The Holy War* should have a peculiar relevance to our own time. It is no mere monument to dead opinion, but a book whose main ideas (notwithstanding distaste for a creed outworn) have taken on the quality of myth or legend to permeate the very fabric of modern civilization. The point needs emphasizing, because there is no other of Bunyan's major works so shamefully neglected to the extent that no textually reliable edition has appeared for over sixty years and no satisfactory annotated edition in this century. And why this should be is surely fit matter for speculation, since with increased interest in the history of ideas it might be supposed that *The Holy War* is documentary evidence too obvious to overlook. After all, "no other work," as the late E. M. W. Tillyard remarked, "has so good a claim to be called England's Puritan epic."[1] Perhaps one reason for the neglect is the form of the book itself. Allegory has not always appealed to the modern mind: it was under a cloud for most of the nineteenth century, with Hazlitt apologizing for Spenser, and the disrepute extended into the present age, when romantic antipathy to it was made explicit in the aesthetics of Croce. But tastes change, and slighted mercies are reclaimed. What the Renaissance, with its purer love of mystery and more profound respect for veiled truth, called a "darke conceit," has in recent years been vindicated. Spenser is reborn, Melville and Kafka appreciated anew—even the current vogue of Bergman's or Fellini's symbolical films stands as eloquent testimony to the renewed popularity of *allegoria* as a fruitful artistic procedure.

Nevertheless, allegory remains a stumbling-block for many, and its use ought somehow to be explained. The reader should first realise that allegory always has a serious purpose, and that allegory in the service of Christianity is entirely natural, because the Christian constantly sees this world in terms of the next, of which the present is only a pale reflection, "a moment of time, whereof dependeth eternity of life to come." Historically, the Christian's allegory of his soul's odyssey from this place to the other has been largely based on two metaphors, the warfare and the journey, which seem always to have been sympathetic vehicles for the mind's personifying tendency; at any rate, both antedate the appearance of the Seven Deadly Sins, although they are afterwards linked with that great religious concept. One of the oldest figures of Christian thought, the warfare appears in literature at least as early as the fifth-century *Psychomachia* of Prudentius and is a fascinating motif in the sermons and drama of the Middle Ages. When it is combined with the ancient image of the journey, a fertile soil is produced for the growth of the conflict between the Sins and the human soul. The battle is fought as early as the *Ancrene Riwle* (*ca.* 1200), a hortatory handbook for anchoresses living outside the nunnery walls, in which the Jerusalem-bound pilgrim is shown beset with seven fierce beasts; it flares up again in Lydgate's *Assembly of Gods* (*ca.* 1400) and in his translation of the unconscionably lengthy fourteenth-century poem, Guillaume de Deguilleville's *Le Pèlerinage de l'âme*. Spiritual warfare is also the backbone of the English morality play, as in *The Castell of Perseverance* (*ca.* 1425). In the seventeenth century, a whole army of artists besides Bunyan employ these antique emblems, either

---

[1] E. M. W. Tillyard, *The English Epic and its Background* (London, 1954), p. 406.

separately or together. John Downame in *The Christian Warfare* (1612), William Gouge in *The Whole Armour of God* (1616) and Richard Bernard in *The Isle of Man* (1627) are only three stout defenders of the faith, who discover in the war-image a strong ally in the battle of the Spirit. For others, a union of the two tropes, as in the theme of pilgrimage, forms a more advantageous medium; hence there exists a host of tracts and pamphlets suggestive of *The Pilgrim's Progress* (1678)—as, for instance, David Lindsey's *The Godly Mans Journey to Heaven* (1625) or John Welles' *The Soules's Progress to the Celestiall Canaan, or Heavenly Jerusalem* (1639) or Simon Patrick's *Parable of the Pilgrim* (1663). And certainly the popularity of these twin images is not really surprising, considering their plain ability to carry the burden of the Puritan saga.

In treating of war directly, just as four years earlier in *The Pilgrim's Progress* he had dealt with the conflict of journey, Bunyan was thus writing in a great tradition, sanctioned and sanctified by the New Testament itself. For not only had St. Paul vividly defined the nature of the moral struggle within ("For the flesh lusteth against the Spirit, and the Spirit against the flesh: and these are contrary the one to the other: so that ye cannot do the things that ye would," Gal. 5:17), but in enjoining the Ephesians to "put on the whole armour of God," he had also actually described the fearsome adversaries ("principalities" and "powers," Eph. 6:11-17; Rom. 8:38) in objective terms that were later on to fire the imaginations of medieval homilists and become part and parcel of their notion of angelic hierarchy. However, the development of Paul's literary practice in medieval times was frequently fantastic. From the merest scriptural hint the preacher often arbitrarily drew out the oddest significance, with the result that a number of the figures in the rich imagery of *The Holy War* owe their existence to really grotesque origins: hence the very core of Bunyan's allegorical structure, the conception of Mansoul as a stronghold besieged, can actually be traced to a medieval elaboration of the *castellum*, a village, according to the Vulgate version, like the one in which Mary and Martha lived (*Intravit Jesus in castellum*, Luke 10:38; Matt. 21:2).[2] Although apparently wayward or accidental, this growth of the symbol is thoroughly organic; and the branching out so unexpectedly into other interconnected images is a good illustration of the root metaphor's peculiar vitality, especially in its power to grasp and

[2] G. R. Owst, *Literature and Pulpit in Medieval England* (Cambridge, 1933), pp. 77-85. From the same source, combined with an interpretation of Cant. 4:4, sprang also the idea of the Virgin as a castle, into which the incarnate Saviour entered to protect Himself, until in due time He would sally forth to do battle against the Devil.

hold the mind. It is sometimes charged that the military metaphor is inferior to that of the journey. The war theme, it is claimed, is much less capable of representing life in all its fullness and diversity; inevitably it makes too severe a distinction by separating mankind into opposing camps, and thus abets the unlovely Calvinistic habit of depriving us of our interesting humanity; it suffers in addition from over-concentration and strain. If the charge were wholly true, it would be extremely damaging. But an allegory that treats of arms and man, of man in arms, can never be very restrictive. In the fortunes of war, sudden alarums and excursions may often give place to quiet diplomacy, lengthy negotiations, truces, uneasy peaces between hostilities—to periods, in short, where tension is markedly relaxed, and where the allegorist, if he so chooses, can conveniently deal with the underside of the moral life, triumph as well as defeat, hope and joy as well as despair and anguish. Moreover, battle alone provides better than pilgrimage the utmost polarization of human character. No matter the outcome, the struggle is never unavailing, because the contestants are inexorably committed to the one side or the other, and even deserters must tacitly enlist. And however extraordinary these soldiers may be, they are not on that account the less fit for allegorical service, since through them moral issues can be clarified more absolutely, and the nature of virtue and vice more plainly set down. Black and white may not rest the eyes, but their boldness can invigorate. At the very least, in literary art the sharp demarcation of good and bad is by no means always a defect—else wherein lies the strength of popular myth and folk-tale?

Ultimately the worth of Bunyan's vehicle can be judged only from experience of the allegory itself. We cannot go far in *The Holy War*, however, without realising how different its action is from that of *The Pilgrim's Progress*. It is not merely that the focus is a town rather than a person, but that its scope is so much broader. Where the earlier narrative limited itself to the adventures of fallen man, the war story presents no less than an account of how Paradise was lost and how it may be rewon.

II

Mansoul is first described. A beautiful town situated in the continent of Universe, it had been built for the delight of King Shaddai (God), who desired to live in a great castle at the heart of it. Shaddai had honoured the townsmen by entrusting this castle to their keeping, and so long as he lived within it, everyone was happy. But after a while an envious prince, the renegade giant Diabolus, resolved to gain possession of the town. Disguised as a dragon, he one day sat down with his host before Mansoul, and soon through knavery and violence persuaded the people to open their gates and let him enter. Forthwith Diabolus seized control. He occupied the castle, jailed or debauched some of the town's worthiest officials, and began to remodel the corporation along infernal lines. Shaddai, however, though removed to his court, had not forgotten his people; and presently, after covenanting to make Mansoul happier far than it had been, he sent an army, led by the redoubtable Captains Boanerges, Conviction, Judgment and Execution, to eject the invader. But doughty as these warriors proved, they could not shake the town. A plea was accordingly directed to Shaddai, who graciously responded by despatching an irresistible force under his son, Emmanuel. Desperately Diabolus tried to mitigate disaster, but the Prince would brook nothing short of unconditional surrender. The diabolonian hordes were routed, the usurper himself driven out in frightful disarray, and the town lay open to the will of the conqueror. Anticipating summary execution, the people were overwhelmed to receive pardon instead; also, a new charter was granted the town, and the Lord Chief Secretary (the Holy Spirit) to guide them. And so with bells and loud hosannas the folk joyously welcomed the triumphal entry of their glorious victor-lover into Mansoul.

All summer long Mansoul knew bliss beyond compare. But then the viper emerged from the bosom: one Carnal Security, ally of Diabolus, who began to squander the people's blessings by leading them into complacency. So successful was he that Emmanuel at length turned his face against the town and silently withdrew; other emboldened rascals slithered out of hiding, and Diabolus got ready to hazard another attack. The Mansoulians themselves gave him the victory. Betrayed by pride and ignorance, they made the grievous tactical error of clashing by night in open field; they were forced to retreat, whereupon Diabolus and his crew of Doubters shortly after assaulted the gates and won the town. The citadel alone held out (Mr. Godlyfear was keeper of that)—and luckily, for it gave essential sanctuary to Lord Willbewill, whom the Diabolonians most wanted to harm. A weary time ensued. Sorrow and misery lay all around, as petition after petition to Emmanuel met with no response. At last, however, the Prince was sufficiently moved by one inspired by the Lord Chief Secretary that he returned to Mansoul to decimate the Doubters and throw their champion back into the pit. But Diabolus was not yet done. He raised a second army, twenty-five thousand strong, Doubters and Bloodmen combined, and hurled it against Mansoul, only to have it shocked and soundly beaten, most of the Doubters slain outright, the Bloodmen taken and bound over for judgment. Some Doubters who had escaped to plot further treasons were caught, tried and sentenced to death. Now seemed the times set fair for peace. Emmanuel, however, in a magnificent closing exhortation called for alertness: some of the enemy would be suffered still to lurk within the walls, though not for ill but for good, to make Mansoulians fit through exercise in opposition: therefore they must hold fast.

Even from this brief outline it should be evident that Bunyan's narrative sustains considerable drift, with the allegory moving on several levels at once, though not always on every level uninterruptedly. The story essentially represents the strenuous processes of conversion and backsliding in the human soul, pulled this way and that by implacable contending forces. But man's fall and his subsequent history, the record of Shaddai's dealings with Mansoul, may also be read analogically as the making of God's covenant with Israel, its consummation in man's salvation through Christ, and the later trials of the Church. On another level there is a foreshadowing of the millennium, a crystallization of the hopes of the saints for the New Jerusalem, while yet another layer composes a minor topical allegory in allusions to events usually of the reign of Charles II. The incorporation of so many themes, with their dexterous manipulation within a single unified conception, presents an astonishing display of the creative imagination in one who was an unlettered "mechanick preacher"; but it should be recognised that Bunyan was not totally ill-equipped to handle complex allegory. He had, after all, been nurtured in a great allegorical tradition that persisted from the Middle Ages, and he was schooled at least in rudimentary hermeneutics, as his exposition of multiple layers of significance in the posthumously-published treatise on Genesis plainly shows.

Most "literal" of levels in The Holy War (and most personal, when we recall Grace Abounding) is the struggle of the individual soul, a theme that in its fascination for the interior drama of the mind, its concentration on the essential inwardness of true virtue, its concern with holiness in an imperfect world, breathes the noblest Puritan spirit. At a time when popular belief mistakenly equates Puritanism and Calvinism, Calvinism and rigorous Determinism, The Holy War can serve as a potent prophylactic, for here is a book in which Bunyan is ever the Christian humanist.

The note of personal responsibility is indeed struck early. From the initial description of Mansoul we learn that the city's walls and gates can never be breached except by consent of the people, nor will Shaddai live in his castle unless the townsfolk wish it. Diabolus then makes headway in the siege only when the inhabitants themselves agree to accept him. Nor can Captain Boanerges with his army thereafter penetrate the diabolonian defences so long as Lord Willbewill as governor continues to support the mayor, Lord Lustings, or his successor, Lord Incredulity. Bunyan is manifestly anxious to demonstrate the will's accountability for approving or disapproving the infiltration of evil, since after Emmanuel's force under the field command of Captain Credence has routed the enemy and humbled the town's administrative officials, Lord Willbewill promptly turns his coat to become an ardent supporter of the new regime, and thereupon toils as assiduously to subdue his erstwhile masters as he had formerly slaved to serve them. This situation is actually the only possible one for regenerate man, incessant labour being the price of experience. Intermarriage of Mansoulian and Diabolonian has produced a profusion of mixed breeds, every whit as confused and as difficult to cull and sort out as the Psyche seeds. Thus Mr. Self-conceit, having wed Willbewill's daughter, the Lady Fear-nothing, there was begat the dangerous Carnal Security: "Wherefore, there being then in Mansoul those strange kind of mixtures, 'twas hard for them in some cases to find out who were natives, who not; for Mr. Carnal Security sprang from my Lord Willbewill, by mother's side, though he had for his father a Diabolonian by nature." However, despite this conglomerate citizenry, a blameless order can be maintained so long as Lord Willbewill is enrolled on the side of right: the might of an external army of Doubters cannot rock the town, but traitorous pride inside the gates can overthrow it. And when surrender to that evil quality in fact occurs, chaos is come again: "And now did Mansoul seem to be nothing but a den of dragons, an emblem of Hell, and a place of total darkness. Now did Mansoul lie almost like the barren wilderness; nothing but nettles, briars, thorns, weeds, and stinking things seemed now to cover the face of Mansoul." Yet with a bold allegorical stroke Bunyan asserts that even now pardon involves a voluntary act of repentance. After their suit to Emmanuel has proved unavailing, the Mansoulians plead with the Lord Chief Secretary to entreat on their behalf:

'Well,' said the Lord Secretary, 'I will draw up a petition for you, and will also set my hand thereto.' Then said they, 'But when shall we call for it at the hands of our Lord?' But he answered, 'Yourselves must be present at the doing of it. Yes, you must put your desires to it. True, the hand and pen shall be mine, but the ink and paper must be yours; else how can you say it is your petition? Nor have I need to petition for myself, because I have not offended.'

Here is the heart of the book, the sum of Bunyan's answer to the problem of keeping the soul sure and steadfast. Aware as he is of the perils of lust, of the thousand natural shocks to which fallen man is daily heir, he is also alive to the integrity of the mind that refuses to acquiesce, but eschews iniquity by positively electing otherwise. To the soul thus committed, he brings the comfort of assurance that it never acts alone, but always in collaboration with the Holy Spirit, and that it is forever sustained by prevenient grace. It is indeed a divine consolation, capable of removing the sting from every diabolonian assault.

III

Of strictures most commonly made on *The Holy War* the most serious surely is that it is over-loaded and repetitive: the siege-metaphor (it is alleged) is expanded and developed to carry far too much allegorical significance, and eventually it totters beneath its own weight. There is a certain justness in this, for the work is decidedly ambitious, and unquestionably there is a repetitiveness about those incidents that illustrate the ups and downs of the Christian life in the process of sanctification—though it is hard to see how that doctrine could otherwise be put. However, the charge that the allegory is over-freighted can be valid only if the several themes do not harmonise or coalesce; but despite the discontinuity of the allegory in its separate layers, the book in fact achieves a unity in its "revelation of mysteries" and in the reader's apprehension of its vision of truth.

This unity can be illustrated in small compass by the trial of the Diabolonians after Mansoul has been regained. The episode reads fluently, and forcefully impresses itself on the mind by its ritualism, as delinquent after delinquent passes in processional review to and from the bar. Yet the scene is allegorically complex. On the surface level it presents on Pauline authority the soul's struggle to mortify its fleshly lusts and spiritual corruptions, while on another it represents the redemptive work of the Church in purifying itself as the body of Christ. A further personal layer appears in the court procedure that speaks of Bunyan's experience before the English assizes. Historical allegory is perhaps also present in the correspondences noted to some atrocities committed in the name of legality by Anabaptists of the sixteenth century against the people of Münster, Germany. And finally, on a political plane, the scene may depict the millennial theocracy of the Fifth Monarchists rigorously applying its own bloody Draconian code to the discomfiture of the wicked. (These Fifth Monarchists were misguided souls, who throughout the Commonwealth period believed that the advent of King Jesus' earthly reign was imminent and ought to be hastened by force.) Now all these strands may very well be there, but the point is that they are caught up and imaginatively reshaped in a grand design, whose import far transcends

xiv

the meaning even of the sum of them. And the consequence is interesting. It is simply that the critic's task of describing the allegory is impossible, since he is compelled to articulate a complex imaginative experience that is really inexpressible in terms other than the artist's own. Paradoxically, the more the critic succeeds in laying bare the particular layers, the more he fails to give an accurate account of the allegory in general. The dilemma is inescapable, and the only solution lies in recognising it. But it should caution us to beware of the partial and distorted view that can result from isolating a level and pushing a thesis to the limit—such as that *The Holy War* is a radically subversive political tract, advocating (in apocalyptic symbols) overthrow of the government of the Beast and establishment of the saints' millenary rule.

One need not dwell on other adverse criticisms of the piece, since there are virtues enough to explore. Tillyard has shown the great architectonic skill in Bunyan's fashioning of the structure, and has brilliantly perceived how the unlaboured start of a fresh movement, as in the deliberately quiet and casual introduction of Mr. Carnal Security, has a formal affinity with Shakespeare.[3] He might have added the exploitation of another device, characteristically Miltonic as well as Shakespearean, in the parallels and contrasts that organically relate the parts. For example, Diabolus's captains are presented in an emblematic fashion-parade, just as Emmanuel's had been earlier; and the parallel orderly cataloguing of names of followers, signs on scutcheons, colours of banners, and so on, is a means of marking the contrast between them through cunningly prolonging our perception. It is, of course, in this contrast that the pictures carry much of their comment: the diabolonian values (or lack of them) are exposed, and the battle's moral issues are thereby more adequately defined. A more basic contrast is the ironic turning of the root image of God's armour against itself, which occurs in Diabolus's early inspiriting speech to the townsfolk, who are alarmed by news of Shaddai's preparations to retake the town. "Armour for you I have, and by me it is," he tells them, and then goes on, in a grotesque parody of Paul's command to the Ephesians, to describe his own brand of spiritual war-harness ("My shield is unbelief," etc.). As Bunyan glosses, it is all "very deceivable language"; but its verve and blatant unselfconsciousness make it grimly humorous, and superbly, absurdly effective. Other instances, like the sending of petitions or the making of summonses or the constant playing of an official from one side against his opposite number on the other side, are perhaps too obvious to need elaboration; however, it should not be

[3]Tillyard, *op. cit.*, p. 401.

overlooked that such comparisons invariably qualify our responses, and thus form part of the organising principle of the book. They comprise, that is, but another aspect of Bunyan's art that reveals great structural control.

The master's grip is no less firm in its command of the allegory's *personae*. Bunyan's characters are conceived from an unshakeable moral assurance, a granitic integrity, that it would be as just to praise as it would be irrelevant to condemn. But even if the people of *The Holy War*, as some have argued, are mostly overwhelmed in the holocaust of conflicting ideologies, not all become pale flitting shades eternally tagged with symbolical labels. Often, indeed, some come on the scene with a massively disturbing substantiality that can only derive from our instantaneous recognition of the interesting human classifications to which they belong. In this way Lord Lustings, at his trial, is securely established by pedigree: he is "the son of one Beastly, and his mother bare him in Flesh Street; she was one Evil-Concupiscence's daughter." Similarly that old Diabolonian, Mr. Loth-to-stoop, is economically fixed in a phrase: "a stiff man in his way." (Why, incidentally, are Diabolonians like Loth-to-stoop, Prejudice and Ill-pause, whose beard "reached down to his girdle," so palsied with age? No doubt because hope is for the young, and these desiccated souls have none.) There is a valuable literary husbandry here, a deft trick of the ancient art of character-writing that was revived in Renaissance England; and Bunyan's delight in its practice is as excited as that of Shakespeare and Ben Jonson (to whose *personae* Bunyan's most closely compare), who also plan the recognition of their characters, so that we see at once the Machiavellian in Iago or Edmund or Volpone. The use of such "speaking pictures," or at least of traits that typify, is certainly not to be faulted as a means to a noble end, which in Bunyan's case is a thoroughly realistic account of the moral life. To achieve this goal, and yet be true to life's richness and diversity, is a mighty work; but Bunyan confidently marches armies across his canvas, and miraculously, in the bustling throng he never lets himself down on the depiction of a single man.

At every turn in *The Holy War* the same control operates to become part of the allegorical texture. And the style naturally reflects it. That well-known description of the drilling of Emmanuel's host, a passage hung heavy with reminiscence of Bunyan's own service in the Parliamentarian army, makes an ideal instance:

They marched, they counter-marched; they opened to the right and left; they divided, and subdivided; they closed, they wheeled, made good their front and rear with their right and left wings, and twenty things more, with that aptness, and then were all as they were again, that they took, yea, ravished the hearts that were in Mansoul to behold it. But add to this, the handling of their arms, the managing of their weapons of war, were marvellous taking to Mansoul and me.

The orderliness of the writing, with its progressive syntactical arrangements that open and close, thrust and withdraw, balance and counterbalance, nicely imitates the fine discipline of the army to hit off the experience magnificently. Another good example is the early speech of Diabolus to the Mansoulians, already mentioned. At this point Diabolus prefers the open palm to the closed fist, and whatever logic (or illogic) he employs is washed away in the flow of rhetoric; but it is rhetoric controlled and channelled. Or take the wonderful contrast that is developed through a sustained use of antithesis to describe the joyful return of the Mansoulians, who had earlier set out broken-heartedly to answer to Emmanuel for their sins:

At last they discerned that they were the prisoners; but can you imagine how their hearts were surprised with wonder—especially when they perceived also in what equipage, and with what honour they were sent home! They went down to the camp in black, but they came back to the town in white; they went down to the camp in ropes, they came back in chains of gold; they went down to the camp with their feet in fetters, but came back with their steps enlarged under them; they went also to the camp looking for death, but they came back from thence with assurance of life; they went down to the camp with heavy hearts, but came back again with pipe and tabor playing before them. So, so soon as they were come to Eyegate, the poor and tottering town of Mansoul adventured to give a shout; and they gave such a shout as made the captains in the Prince's army leap at the sound thereof. Alas! for them, poor hearts, who could blame them, since their dead friends were come to life again? For 'twas to them as life from the dead, to see the ancients of the town of Mansoul to shine in such splendour. They looked for nothing but the axe and the block; but behold! joy and gladness, comfort and consolation, and such melodious notes attending of them, that was sufficient to make a sick man well.

Here the elaborate insistence of the reiteration supports a meaningful play between the theological concepts of justice and mercy: the tension between them is resolved, and the whole culminates in the soaring evocation of grace, "sufficient to make a sick man well." From this extract, or from the wondrous raptures of the victor-lover's entry into Mansoul, we can see that even when restrained Bunyan's imagination ranges still like the nimble spaniel. If style should be answerable to theme, Bunyan in describing the soul's warfare has indeed found a Christian rhetoric fit.

Not all those separate excellences would draw us to The Holy War, however, were they not fused in a book of singularly compelling power. No doubt it was extravagant of Macaulay to say that The Holy War would be the supreme of religious allegories, were there no *Pilgrim's Progress*; yet there is much virtue in a claim that would rank it high among the greatest of such works. And it is to be valued, not just for bringing a crumb of comfort whenever our own little towns or castles (like Bunyan's in the frontispiece) suffer the nature of an insurrection, nor simply for enabling us to endure the drum in unremitting existential struggle: it is to be appreciated also for its mythic power, for its capacity to move our minds to the contemplation of things far beyond outmoded creed or narrow sectarian interest, and for its ability, above all, to make our relationship to the world infinitely deeper and richer than it was before. For this reason it is ultimately to be treasured as a fine work of art, a timeless human document composed by a great agonist of human nature, who drew his strength from the wounds and scars of his own heart.

It is pleasant to acknowledge a number of debts incurred in the preparation of this edition. First of my obligations must be to my editorial predecessors, from whose work I have constantly benefited. My thanks are due to Professor Louis Martz for his helpful reading of the manuscript and also for contributing the Foreword: such generosity, however, must exclude responsibility for any blunders perpetrated by my own waywardness. I am grateful also to Mrs. Darlene Tracie for her excellent typing of a text that was at times scarcely legible; to Mr. Felix Mnthali, a graduate student from Malawi, for aid in checking the typescript and for incidentally teaching me something about the nature of Bunyan's universal appeal; to Miss Linda McKnight of The Copp Clark Publishing Company for her editorial helpfulness; and to my wife, Ann, for her forbearance and help in correcting proofs. Finally, I record my appreciation of an award from the General Research Fund of the University of Alberta, which enabled me to pursue certain essential inquiries at the British Museum.

UNIVERSITY OF ALBERTA   JAMES F. FORREST
January, 1967

BIBLIOGRAPHICAL NOTE

Only two editions of *The Holy War* appeared in Bunyan's lifetime, and there is considerable doubt about the authenticity of the second, which came out in 1684. John Brown examined the Bodleian and British Museum copies of this curious issue in the course of preparing his own edition of 1905, and was inclined to believe them "pirated copies, similar to those of which Nathaniel Ponder [Bunyan's first publisher] complained so bitterly in the case of *The Pilgrim's Progress*. For both paper and typography are greatly inferior to those of the first edition; some of Bunyan's most characteristic marginalia are carelessly omitted; Bunyan's own title—'The Holy War made by Shaddai upon Diabolus for the regaining of the Metropolis of the World'—is altered to the feebler and more commonplace form—'The Holy War made by Christ upon the Devil for the regaining of Man'; and further, when a new edition was issued in 1696, the alterations and omissions of 1684 were ignored, and a simple reprint was made of the first edition of 1682."[1]

Brown's judgment is reasonable. Not only are the peculiarities of the 1684 text generally lamentable, but also abundant evidence exists of other anomalies in the publication of Bunyan's major works, unremarked by the outraged Ponder. (For instance, as recently as 1964, the present editor established that a purported copy of the extremely rare third edition of *The Pilgrim's Progress* was in fact a hybrid, the first gathering alone being that of the third edition, the remainder that of the fourth.) It seems best, then, to treat the 1684 edition with prudent circumspection, and to regard its emendations as valuable mainly in attesting the impact of Bunyan's original text on a contemporary mind.

The text of this edition is accordingly based on that of the first edition of 1682, collated with the texts of 1684 and 1696. (These three editions are referred to in the notes by order of publication: as, "first edition reads . . ." etc.). Spelling of the text has been modernized, the lavish seventeenth-century use of initial capitals particularly excised; in addition, the punctuation—a rich mixture of rhetorical and grammatical pointing—has been hopefully clarified by being brought more into line

---

[1] *Life and Death of Mr. Badman and The Holy War*, ed. John Brown (Cambridge, 1905), p. vii.

with current practice. However, no attempt has been made to improve Bunyan's grammar, so that the flavour of his colloquialism remains piquant.

Readers who wish to make a study of *The Holy War* will find the following selective book-list helpful:

EDITIONS

Brown, John (ed.). *Life and Death of Mr. Badman and The Holy War.* Cambridge, 1905.

Offor, George (ed.). *Complete Works of John Bunyan.* 3 vols. Glasgow and London, 1860-62. Vol. III.

Peacock, Mabel (ed.). *The Holy War and The Heavenly Footman.* Oxford, 1892.

CRITICISM

Lamont, Daniel. "Bunyan's *Holy War*: A Study in Christian Experience," *Theology Today*, III (1946-47), 459-72.

Sharrock, Roger. *John Bunyan.* London, 1954. pp. 118-37.

Talon, Henri. *John Bunyan, the Man and his Works.* London, 1951. pp. 240-56.

Tillyard, E. M. W. *The English Epic and its Background.* London, 1954. pp. 397-406.

Tindall, William York. *John Bunyan, Mechanick Preacher.* New York, 1934. pp. 144-65.

THE
Holy War,
MADE BY
SHADDAI
UPON
DIABOLUS,

For the Regaining of the

Metropolis of the World.

OR, THE

Losing and Taking Again

OF THE

Town of Manfoul.

By *JOHN BUNYAN*, the Author of the
Pilgrims Progress.

I have used Similitudes, Hof. 12.10.

LONDON, Printed for *Dorman Newman* at the *Kings Arms* in the *Poultry*; and *Benjamin Alfop* at the *Angel* and *Bible* in the *Poultry*, 1682.

Title page of the first edition of *The Holy War*
Reproduced by permission of the Trustees of the
British Museum

TO THE READER

'Tis strange to me, that they that love to tell
Things done of old, yea, and that do excel
Their equals in historiology,
Speak not of Mansoul's wars, but let them lie
Dead, like old fables, or such worthless things,
That to the reader no advantage brings;
When men, let them make what they will their own,
Till they know this, are to themselves unknown.
    Of stories, I well know there's divers sorts,
Some foreign, some domestic; and reports
Are thereof made, as fancy leads the writers;
(By books a man may guess at the inditers.)
    Some will again of that which never was,
Nor will be, feign (and that without a cause)
Such matter, raise such mountains, tell such things
Of men, of laws, of countries, and of kings;
And in their story seem to be so sage,
And with such gravity clothe ev'ry page,
That though their frontispiece say all is vain,
Yet to their way disciples they obtain.
    But, readers, I have somewhat else to do,
Than with vain stories thus to trouble you;

4   Bunyan's name for the town derives from a recurring image in medieval homilies. See G. R. Owst, *Literature and Pulpit in Medieval England* (Cambridge, 1933), pp. 56-109.

15   *raise such mountains*: give enthusiastic accounts of dangerous and exciting exploits.

True Christians. What here I say, some men do know so well,
They can with tears and joy the story tell.
    The town of Mansoul is well known to many,
Nor are her troubles doubted of by any
The Scriptures. That are acquainted with those histories,
That Mansoul and her wars anatomize.
    Then lend thine ear to what I do relate,
Touching the town of Mansoul and her state;
How she was lost, took captive, made a slave;
And how against him set, that should her save.   10
Yea, how by hostile ways, she did oppose
Her Lord, and with his enemy did close.
For they are true, him that will them deny,
Must needs the best of records vilify.
For my part, I (myself) was in the town,
Both when 'twas set up, and when pulling down,
I saw Diabolus in his possession,
And Mansoul also under his oppression.
Yea, I was there when she owned him for Lord,
And to him did submit with one accord.   20
    When Mansoul trampled upon things divine,
And wallowed in filth as doth a swine;
When she betook herself unto her arms,
His counsels. Fought her Emmanuel, despis'd his charms,
Then I was there, and did rejoice to see
Diabolus and Mansoul so agree.
    Let no man then count me a fable-maker,
Nor make my name or credit a partaker
Of their derision: what is here in view,
Of mine own knowledge I dare say is true.   30
    I saw the Prince's armed men come down
By troops, by thousands, to besiege the town.
I saw the captains, heard the trumpets sound,
And how his forces cover'd all the ground
Yea, how they set themselves in battle-ray;
I shall remember to my dying day.
    I saw the colours waving in the wind,
And they within to mischief how combin'd,
To ruin Mansoul, and to make away

17   *Diabolus*: the Devil. See Matt. 4:1; Luke 4:2; John 6:70.

Her *primum mobile* without delay.   Her soul.
  I saw the mounts cast up against the town,
And how the slings were plac'd, to beat it down.
I heard the stones fly whizzing by mine ears,
(What longer kept in mind than got in fears?)
I heard them fall, and saw what work they made,
And how old Mors did cover with his shade   Death.
The face of Mansoul; and I heard her cry,
'Woe worth the day, in dying I shall die!'

10   I saw the battering-rams, and how they play'd,
To beat ope Eargate and I was afraid,
Not only Eargate, but the very town,
Would by those battering-rams be beaten down.
  I saw the fights, and heard the captains shout,
And in each battle saw who fac'd about;
I saw who wounded were, and who were slain;   Lusts.
And who when dead, would come to life again.
  I heard the cries of those that wounded were,
(While others fought like men, bereft of fear)

20 And while they cry, 'Kill, kill,' was in mine ears,
The gutters ran, not so with blood as tears.
  Indeed the captains did not always fight,
But then they would molest us day and night;
Their cry, 'Up, fall on, let us take the town!'
Kept us from sleeping, or from lying down.
  I was there when the gates were broken ope,
And saw how Mansoul then was stripped of hope.
  I saw the captains march into the town,
How there they fought, and did their foes cut down.

30   I heard the Prince bid Boanerges go

---

1   *primum mobile*: lit. the first moving thing. In Ptolemaic astronomy, the ninth (later tenth) and outermost sphere, which revolved diurnally about the earth, carrying the other heavenly bodies with it. Hence, figuratively, something that indicates a complex system or gives impetus to other things; here, as Bunyan glosses, "the soul."

11 The concept of the senses as gateways to the soul appears long before Bunyan, as, for example, in the anonymous *Pilgrimage of Perfection* (1526).

30 *Boanerges*: "sons of thunder," the name given by Christ to the impetuous James and John, who wanted to "call down fire from heaven" to burn up the Samaritan villages for not receiving their Lord (see Mark 3:17; Luke 9:51-56); now a metaphor for a loud-mouthed orator or tub-thumping preacher.

Up to the castle, and there seize his foe,
And saw him and his fellows bring him down,
In chains of great contempt quite through the town.
    I saw Emmanuel, when he possess'd
His town of Mansoul, and how greatly bless'd
A town, his gallant town of Mansoul was,
When she receiv'd his pardon, liv'd his laws.
    When the Diabolonians were caught,
When tried, and when to execution brought,
Then I was there; yea, I was standing by,   10
When Mansoul did the rebels crucify.
    I also saw Mansoul clad all in white,
And heard her Prince call her his heart's delight
I saw him put upon her chains of gold,
And rings, and bracelets, goodly to behold.
    What shall I say? I heard the people's cries,
And saw the Prince wipe tears from Mansoul's eyes.
I heard groans, and saw the joy of many;
Tell you of all, I neither will, nor can I.
But by what here I say, you well may see   20
That Mansoul's matchless wars no fables be.
    Mansoul! the desire of both Princes was,
One keep his gain would, t'other gain his loss;
Diabolus would cry, 'The town is mine!'
Emmanuel would plead a right divine
Unto his Mansoul; then to blows they go,
And Mansoul cries, 'These wars will me undo.'
    Mansoul! her wars seem'd endless in her eyes,
She's lost by one, becomes another's prize.
And he again that lost her last would swear,   30
'Have her I will, or her in pieces tear.'
    Mansoul, it was the very seat of war,
Wherefore her troubles greater were by far,
Than only where the noise of war is heard,
Or where the shaking of a sword is fear'd,
Or only where small skirmishes are fought,
Or where the fancy fighteth with a thought.
    She saw the swords of fighting men made red,
And heard the cries of those with them wounded;
Must not their frights then be much more by far   40
Than theirs who to such doings strangers are?

Or theirs that hear the beating of a drum,
But not made fly for fear from house and home?
   Mansoul not only heard the trumpets sound,
But saw her gallants gasping on the ground.
Wherefore we must not think that she could rest
With them, whose greatest earnest is but jest;
Or where the blust'ring threat'ning of great wars
Do end in parleys, or in wording jars.
   Mansoul, her mighty wars, they did portend
Her weal or woe, and that world without end.
Wherefore she must be more concern'd than they
Whose fears begin and end the selfsame day;
Or where none other harm doth come to him
That is engag'd, but loss of life or limb,
As all must needs confess that now do dwell
In Universe, and can this story tell.
   Count me not then with them, that to amaze
The people, set them on the stars to gaze,
Insinuating with much confidence,
That each of them is now the residence
Of some brave creatures; yea, a world they will
Have in each star, though it be past their skill
To make it manifest to any man,
That reason hath, or tell his fingers can.
   But I have too long held thee in the porch,
And kept thee from the sunshine with a torch.
Well, now go forward, step within the door,
And there behold five hundred times much more
Of all sorts of such inward rarities
As please the mind will, and will feed the eyes
With those, which if a Christian, thou wilt see
Not small, but things of greatest moment be.
   Nor do thou go to work without my key,
(In mysteries men soon do lose their way;)

10

20

30

---

8   *wording jars*: verbal quarrels.
24 *tell*: count. These lines remind us that in the seventeenth century, no less than in the twentieth, men's minds were excited by speculation about the existence of life on other planets.
26 *kept thee from the sunshine with a torch*: deprived you of full understanding by giving you only a glimpse of the truth.

And also turn it right, if thou wouldst know
My riddle, and wouldst with my heifer plough.

The margent. It lies there in the window. Fare thee well,
My next may be to ring thy passing-bell.

JOHN BUNYAN

2 *with my heifer plough*: take advantage of my explanations. See Judg. 14:18.
3 *It lies there in the window*: the key to the allegory is to be found in the marginal references.   *margent*: margin.

A

RELATION

of

THE HOLY WAR, &c.

In my travels, as I walked through many regions and countries, it was my chance to happen into that famous continent of Universe; a very large and spacious country it is. It lieth between the two Poles, and just amidst the four points of the heavens. It is a place well watered, and richly adorned with hills and valleys, bravely situate; and for the most part (at least where I was) very fruitful, also well peopled, and a very sweet air.

The people are not all of one complexion, nor yet of one language, mode, or way of religion; but differ as much as ('tis said) do the planets themselves. Some are right, and some are wrong, even as it happeneth to be in lesser regions.

In this country, as I said, it was my lot to travel, and there travel I did, and that so long, even till I learned much of their mother-tongue, together with the customs, and manners of them among whom I was. And to speak truth, I was much delighted to see and hear many things which I saw and heard among them. Yea, I had, to be sure, even lived and died a

A natural state pleasing to the flesh.

---

7   *bravely*: splendidly.
10   *complexion*: character, temperament.

native among them (so was I taken with them and
Christ. their doings), had not my Master sent for me home to
his house, there to do business for him and to oversee
business done.

Now, there is in this gallant country of Universe,
Man. a fair and delicate town, a corporation, called Mansoul:
a town for its building so curious, for its situation so
commodious, for its privileges so advantageous—I
mean with reference to its original—that I may say of
it, as was said before, of the continent in which it is   10
placed, *There is not its equal under the whole Heaven.*

As to the situation of this town, it lieth just
between the two worlds, and the first founder, and
Scriptures. builder of it, so far as by the best, and most authentic
The Almighty. records I can gather, was one Shaddai; and he built it
for his own delight. He made it the mirror, and glory
Gen. 1:26. of all that he made even the top-piece beyond any
thing else that he did in that country; yea, so goodly
Created. a town was Mansoul, when first built, that it is said
Angels. by some, the gods at the setting up thereof, came   20
down to see it, and sang for joy. And as he made it
goodly to behold, so also mighty to have dominion
over all the country round about. Yea all was commanded to acknowledge Mansoul for their metropoli-
tan, all was enjoined to do homage to it. Ay, the town
itself had positive commission, and power from her
king to demand service of all, and also to subdue any,
that any ways denied to do it.

There was reared up in the midst of this town, a
The heart. most famous and stately palace. For strength, it might   30
Eccles. 3:11. be called a castle; for pleasantness, a paradise; for largeness, a place so copious as to contain all the world.
This place the King Shaddai intended but for himself
alone, and not another with him, partly because of his
own delights, and partly because he would not that

9   *original*: origin.
15   *Shaddai*: God Almighty. The Hebrew name manifests the awesomeness and
terror of God omnipotent and is employed in the King James version, esp.
in Job and Revelations.
20   *gods*: angels. This usage is found often in Renaissance literature.

the terror of strangers should be upon the town. This place Shaddai made also a garrison of, but committed the keeping of it, only, to the men of the town.

The powers of the Soul.

The wall of the town was well built; yea, so fast and firm was it knit and compact together, that had it not been for the townsmen themselves, they could not have been shaken, or broken for ever.

For here lay the excellent wisdom of him that built Mansoul, that the walls could never be broken down, nor hurt, by the most mighty adverse potentate, unless, the townsmen gave consent thereto.

The body.

This famous town of Mansoul had five gates, in at which to come, out at which to go, and these were made likewise answerable to the walls: to wit, impregnable, and such as could never be opened nor forced, but by the will and leave of those within. The names of the gates were these, Eargate, Eyegate, Mouthgate, Nosegate and Feelgate.

The five senses.

Other things there were that belonged to the town of Mansoul, which if you adjoin to these, will yet give farther demonstration to all, of the glory and strength of the place. It had always a sufficiency of provision within its walls; it had the best, most wholesome, and excellent law that then was extant in the world. There was not a rascal, rogue, or traitorous person then within its walls: they were all true men, and fast joined together; and this you know is a great matter. And to all these, it was always (so long as it had the goodness to keep true to Shaddai the King) his countenance, his protection, and it was his delight.

The state of Mansoul at first.

Well, upon a time there was one Diabolus, a mighty giant, made an assault upon this famous town of Mansoul, to take it, and make it his own habitation. This giant was King of the Blacks or Negroes, and a most raving prince he was. We will, if you please, first discourse of the original of this Diabolus, and then of his taking of this famous town of Mansoul.

The devil.

Sinners, the fallen angels.

The original of Diabolus.

14 *answerable*: corresponding, commensurate Cf. Milton, "answerable style."
30 *delight*: first edition reads "delight, &c."

This Diabolus is indeed, a great and mighty prince, and yet both poor and beggarly. As to his original, he was at first, one of the servants of King Shaddai, made, and taken and put by him into most high and mighty place—yea, was put into such principalities as belonged to the best of his territories and

Isa. 14:12.

dominions. This Diabolus was made *Son of the morning*, and a brave place he had of it: it brought him much glory, and gave him much brightness, an income that might have contented his Luciferian heart, had it not been insatiable, and enlarged as Hell itself.

Well, he seeing himself thus exalted to greatness and honour, and raging in his mind for higher state, and degree, what doth he but begin to think with himself, how he might be set up as Lord over all and have the sole power under Shaddai. Now *that* did the King

II Pet. 2:4.
Jude 6.

reserve for his Son—yea, and had already bestowed it upon him—wherefore he first consults with himself what had best to be done, and then breaks his mind to some other of his companions, to the which they also agreed. So in fine, they came to this issue, that they should make an attempt upon the King's Son to destroy him, that the inheritance might be theirs. Well, to be short, the treason (as I said) was concluded, the time appointed, the word given, the rebels rendezvoused, and the assault attempted. Now the King, and his Son being *All*, and always *Eye*, could not but discern all passages in his dominions; and he having always love for his Son, as for himself, could not, at what he saw, but be greatly provoked, and offended: wherefore what does he, but takes them in the very nick and first trip that they made towards their design, convicts them of the treason, horrid rebellion, and conspiracy that they had devised, and now attempted to put into practice, and casts them altogether out of all place of trust, benefit, honour, and preferment; this done, he banishes them the court,

10

20

30

---

7 *Son of the morning*: Lucifer.
32 *in the very nick and first trip*: at the instant they took their first step. "Nick" is an allusion to the early custom of marking time by means of notches or nicks. Cf. "in the nick of time."

turns them down into the horrible pits, as fast bound in chains, never more to expect the least favour from his hands, but to abide the judgment that he had appointed: and that forever.

Now they being thus cast out of all place of trust, profit, and honour, and also knowing that they had lost their Prince's favour for ever (being banished his court and cast down to the horrible pits), you may be sure they would now add to their former pride what malice and rage against Shaddai, and against his Son they could. Wherefore, roving and ranging in much fury from place to place, if perhaps they might find something that was the King's to revenge, by spoiling of that, themselves on him. At last they happened into this spacious country of Universe, and steer their course towards the town of Mansoul; and considering that that town was one of the chief works, and delights of King Shaddai what do they, but after counsel taken, make an assault upon that. I say they knew that Mansoul belonged unto Shaddai, for they were there when he built it, and beautified it for himself. So when they had found the place they shouted horribly for joy, and roared on it as a lion upon the prey, saying, 'Now we have found the prize, and how to be revenged on King Shaddai for what he hath done to us.' So they sat down and called a council of war, and considered with themselves what ways and methods they had best to engage in, for the winning to themselves this famous town of Mansoul; and these four things were then propounded to be considered of:

First, Whether they had best, all of them to show themselves, in this design to the town of Mansoul.

Secondly, Whether they had best to go and sit down against Mansoul, in their now ragged, and beggarly guise.

Thirdly, Whether they had best to show to Mansoul their intentions, and what design they came about, or whether to assault it with words and ways of deceit.

I Pet. 5:8.

A council of war held by Diabolus and his fellows against the town of Mansoul.

Proposals.

Fourthly, Whether they had not best, to some of their companions to give out private orders to take the advantage, if they see one, or more of the principal townsmen, to shoot them—if thereby they shall judge their cause and design will the better be promoted.

To the first proposal.

It was answered to the first of these proposals, in the negative, to wit, that it would not be best that all should show themselves before the town, because the appearance of many of them might alarm, and fright the town, whereas, a few or but one of them, was not so likely to do it. And to enforce this advice to take place, 'twas added further, that, if Mansoul was frighted, or did take the alarm, ' 'Tis impossible,' said Diabolus (for he spoke now) 'that we should take the town: for that none can enter into it without its own consent. Let therefore but few, or but one, assault Mansoul, and in mine opinion,' said Diabolus, 'let me be he.' Wherefore to this they all agreed, and then to the second proposal they came, namely, whether they had best to go and sit down before Mansoul, in their now ragged and beggarly guise. To which it was answered also in the negative, by no means; and that because, though the town of Mansoul had been made to know, and to have to do before now, with things that are invisible; they did never as yet see any of their fellow creatures in so sad, and rascal condition as they. And this was the advice of that fierce Alecto. Then said Apollyon, 'The advice is pertinent, for even one of us appearing to them as we are now, must needs, both beget, and multiply such thoughts in them, as will both put them into a consternation of spirit, and necessitate them to put themselves upon their guard. And if so,' said he, 'then as my Lord

The second proposal.

Alecto.
Apollyon.

10

20

30

27   *Alecto*: lit. implacable. The goddess of strife and vengeance, one of the three Furies of classical mythology, whose head was covered with snakes. As the agent of Juno, Alecto plays an important part in Virgil's Aeneid (Book VII), inciting the Latins to war against the Trojans by creating a series of provocative incidents.

28   *Apollyon*: Greek name of Abaddon, king of Hell and angel of the bottomless pit. (See Rev. 9:11.) Undoubtedly more memorable as the dragonish adversary of Christian in *The Pilgrim's Progress*.

Alecto said but now, 'tis in vain for us to think of taking the town.' Then said that mighty giant Beelzebub, 'The advice that already is given is safe, for though the men of Mansoul have seen such things as we once were, yet hitherto they did never behold such things as we now are. And 'tis best in mine opinion to come upon them in such a guise, as is common to, and most familiar among them.' To this when they had consented: the next thing to be considered was in what shape, hue or guise, Diabolus had best to show himself, when he went about to make Mansoul his own. Then one said one thing, and another the contrary; at last Lucifer answered, that in his opinion, 'twas best that his lordship should assume the body of some of those creatures that they of the town had dominion over. 'For,' quoth he, 'these are not only familiar to them, but being under them they will never imagine that an attempt should by them be made upon the town; and to blind all, let him assume the body of one of these beasts that Mansoul deems to be wiser than any of the rest.' This advice was applauded of all, so it was determined that the giant Diabolus should assume the dragon, for that he was in those days as familiar with the town of Mansoul as now is the bird with the boy. For nothing that was in its primitive state was at all amazing to them. Then they proceeded to the third thing, which was,

3. Whether they had best to show their intentions, or the design of his coming to Mansoul, or no? This also was answered in the negative; because of the weight that was in the former reasons, to wit, for that Mansoul were a strong people, a strong people in a strong town, whose wall and gates were impregnable (to say nothing of their castle), nor can they by any means be won but by their own consent. 'Besides,' said Legion, (for he gave answer to this), 'a discovery of

Marginal notes:
- Beelzebub.
- Lucifer.
- Gen. 3:1.
- Rev. 20:1,2.
- The third proposal.
- Legion.

---

2   *Beelzebub*: originally Baalzebul, a false idol worshipped and excoriated by the Jews who changed his name to Beelzebub (lit. lord of the flies). Matthew calls him "prince of devils" (12:24), while Milton gives him rank next to Satan "in power, and next in crime," (*Paradise Lost*, I, 79).

36   *Legion*: see Mark 5:9.

our intentions, may make them send to their King for aid, and if that be done, I know quickly what time of day 'twill be with us. Therefore let us assault them in all pretended fairness, covering of our intentions with all manner of lies, flatteries, delusive words; feigning of things that never will be, and promising of that to them, that they shall never find. This is the way to win Mansoul, and to make them of themselves to open their gates to us; yea, and to desire us too, to come in to them.

'And the reason why I think that this project will do is because the people of Mansoul now are every one simple and innocent; all honest and true: nor do they as yet know what it is to be assaulted with fraud, guile, and hypocrisy. They are strangers to lying and dissembling lips; wherefore, we cannot, if thus we be disguised, by them at all be discerned; our lies shall go for true sayings, and our dissimulations for upright dealings. What we promise them, they will in that believe us, especially if in all our lies and feigned words, we pretend great love to them, and that our design is only their advantage and honour.' Now there was not one bit of a reply against this; this went as current down, as doth the water down a steep descent. Wherefore they go to consider of the last proposal which was,

The fourth proposal. 4. Whether they had not best to give out orders to some of their company, to shoot some one or more of the principal of the townsmen, if they judge that their cause may be promoted thereby.

This was carried in the affirmative, and the man that was designed by this stratagem to be destroyed, *Of Capt. Resistance.* was one Mr. Resistance, otherwise called Captain Resistance. And a great man in Mansoul, this Captain Resistance was; and a man that the giant Diabolus and his band more feared than they feared the whole town of Mansoul besides. Now who should be the actor to do the murder? That was the next, and they appointed one Tisiphone, a fury of the lake, to do it.

39 *Tisiphone*: lit. the avenger of blood. Another of the classical Furies.

They thus having ended their council of war, rose up, and assay'd to do as they had determined; they marched towards Mansoul, but all in a manner invisible, save one—only one; nor did he approach the town in his own likeness, but under the shade, and in the body of the dragon.

The result of their counsel.

So they drew up, and sat down before Eargate, for that was the place of hearing for all without the town, as Eyegate was the place of perspection. So, as I said, he came up with his train to the gate, and laid his ambuscado for Captain Resistance within bow-shot of the town. This done, the giant ascended up close to the gate, and called to the town of Mansoul for audience. Nor took he any with him, but one Ill-pause, who was his orator in all difficult matters. Now, as I said, he being come up to the gate (as the manner of those times was), sounded his trumpet for audience. At which the chief of the town of Mansoul, such as my Lord Innocent, my Lord Willbewill, my Lord Mayor, Mr. Recorder, and Captain Resistance came down to the wall to see who was there, and what was the matter. And my Lord Willbewill, when he had looked over and saw who stood at the gate, demanded, what he was, wherefore he was come, and why he roused the town of Mansoul with so unusual a sound.

Diabolus marches up to the town and calls for audience.

The lords of Mansoul appeared.

DIAB. Diabolus then, as if he had been a lamb, began his oration and said, 'Gentlemen of the famous town of Mansoul, I am, as you may perceive, no far dweller from you, but near, and one that is bound by the King to do you my homage, and what service I can; wherefore that I may be faithful to myself, and to you, I have somewhat of concern to impart unto you. Wherefore grant me your audience and hear me patiently. And first, I will assure you, it is not myself but you; not mine, but your advantage that I seek by what I now do, as will full well be made manifest, by that I have opened my mind unto you. For gentlemen,

Diabolus his oration.

---

9   *perspection*: looking out.
11 *ambuscado*: ambush; an affectedly Spanish form of "ambuscade," common in the seventeenth century.

16

I am (to tell you the truth) come to show you how
you may obtain great, and ample deliverance from a
bondage that unawares to yourselves, you are captivated and enslaved under.' At this the town of Mansoul began to prick up its ears, and 'What is it? Pray,
what is it?' thought they. And he said, 'I have somewhat to say to you concerning your King, concerning
his law, and also touching yourselves. Touching your
King, I know he is great and potent, but yet all that
he hath said to you, is neither true, nor yet for your 10
advantage. 1. 'Tis not true, for that wherewith he
hath hitherto awed you, shall not come to pass, nor be
fulfilled, though you do the thing that he hath forbidden. But if there was danger, what a slavery is it to
live always in fear of the greatest of punishments, for
doing so small and trivial a thing, as eating of a little
fruit is. 2. Touching his laws, this I say further, they
are both unreasonable, intricate and intolerable. Unreasonable as was hinted before, for that the punishment is not proportioned to the offence. There is great 20
difference, and disproportion betwixt the life, and an
apple; yet the one must go for the other by the law of
your Shaddai. But it is also intricate, in that he saith,
first, you may eat of all; and yet after, forbids the eating of *one*. And then in the last place, it must needs
be intolerable, for as much as that fruit which you are
forbidden to eat of (if you are forbidden any) is that,
and that alone, which is able by your eating, to minister
to you, a good, as yet unknown by you. This is manifest by the very name of the tree: it is called the *tree* 30
of knowledge of good and evil, and have you that
knowledge as yet? No, no, nor can you conceive how
good, how pleasant, and how much to be desired to
make one wise it is, so long as you stand by your
King's commandment. Why should you be held in
ignorance and blindness? Why should you not be
enlarged in knowledge and understanding? And now!
Ah ye inhabitants of the famous town of Mansoul, to
speak more particularly to yourselves, you are not a
free people! You are kept both in bondage and 40
slavery, and that by a grievous threat; no reason being

annexed, but so I will have it, so it shall be. And is it not grievous to think on, that that very thing that you are forbidden to do, might you but do it, would yield you both wisdom and honour? For then your eyes will be opened, and you shall be as gods. Now since this is thus,' quoth he, 'can you be kept by any prince in more slavery, and in greater bondage than you are under this day? You are made underlings, and are wrapt up in inconveniencies, as I have well made appear. For what bondage greater than to be kept in blindness? Will not reason tell you that it is better to have eyes than to be without them; and so to be at liberty, to be better than to be shut up in a dark and stinking cave?'

And just now while Diabolus was speaking these words to Mansoul, Tisiphone shot at Captain Resistance, where he stood on the gate, and mortally wounded him in the head; so that he to the amazement of the townsmen, and the encouragement of Diabolus, fell down dead quite over the wall. Now when Captain Resistance was dead (and he was the only man of war in the town), poor Mansoul was wholly left naked of courage, nor had she now any heart to resist. But this was as the devil would have it. Then stood forth that he, Mr. Ill-pause, that Diabolus brought with him, who was his orator, and he addressed himself to speak to the town of Mansoul: the tenure of whose speech here follows.

ILL-PAUSE. 'Gentlemen,' quoth he, 'it is my master's happiness, that he has this day a quiet and teachable auditory; and it is hoped by us, that we shall prevail with you not to cast off good advice. My master has a very great love for you, and although, as he very well knows, that he runs the hazard of the anger of King Shaddai, yet love to you will make him do more than that. Nor doth there need that a word more

Captain Resistance slain.

Mr. Ill-pause his speech to the town of Mansoul.

25   *Ill-pause*: the name suggests one who habitually puts off doing the right thing until later.
28   *tenure*: tenor, drift.
31   *auditory*: audience.

should be spoken to confirm for truth what he hath said; there is not a word but carries with it self-evidence in its bowels. The very name of the tree may put an end to all controversy in this matter. I therefore at this time shall only add this advice to you, under, and by the leave of my lord'—and with that he made Diabolus a very low congee. 'Consider his words, look on the tree, and the promising fruit thereof; remember also that yet you know but little, and that this is the way to know more. And if your reasons be not conquered to accept of such good counsel, you are not the men that I took you to be.' But when the townsfolk saw that the tree was good for food, and that it was pleasant to the eye, and a tree to be desired to make one wise, they did as old Ill-pause advised; they took and did eat thereof. Now this I should have told you before, that even then, when this Ill-pause was making of his speech to the townsmen, my Lord Innocency (whether by a shot from the camp of the giant, or from sinking qualm that suddenly took him, or whether by the stinking breath of that treacherous villain old Ill-pause, for so I am most apt to think), sunk down in the place where he stood, nor could he be brought to life again. Thus these two brave men died. Brave men I call them, for they were the beauty and glory of Mansoul, so long as they lived therein; nor did there now remain any more, a noble spirit in Mansoul; they all fell down, and yielded obedience to Diabolus, and became his slaves and vassals, as you shall hear.

Now these being dead, what do the rest of the townsfolk, but as men that had found a fools' paradise, they presently, as afore was hinted, fall to prove the truth of the giant's words. And first they did as Ill-pause had taught them: they looked, they considered, they were taken with the forbidden fruit:

My Lord Innocency's death.

The town taken, and how.

10

20

30

---

7   *congee*: a low bow.
13ff. See Gen. 3:6.
35f. Bunyan's account of the process of the Fall—"they looked, they considered, they were taken"—is traditional. It is in keeping with St. Augustine's "three

they took thereof, and did eat; and having eaten, they
became immediately drunken therewith. So they
opened the gates, both Eargate, and Eyegate, and let in
Diabolus with all his bands, quite forgetting their
good Shaddai, his law, and the judgment that he had
annexed with solemn threat'ning to the breach
thereof.

Diabolus, having now obtained entrance in at the
gates of the town, marches up to the middle thereof,
to make his conquest as sure as he could; and finding
by this time the affections of the people warmly inclining to him, he as thinking 'twas best striking while
the iron is hot, made this further deceivable speech
unto them, saying, 'Alas my poor Mansoul! I have
done thee indeed this service, as to promote thee to
honour, and to greaten thy liberty. But alas! alas!
Poor Mansoul, thou wantest now one to defend thee,
for assure thyself that when Shaddai shall hear what
is done, he will come; for sorry will he be that thou
hast broken his bonds, and cast his cords away from
thee. What wilt thou do? Wilt thou after enlargement
suffer thy privileges to be invaded and taken away? Or
what wilt resolve with thyself?' Then they all with
one consent said to this bramble, 'Do then reign over

---

steps—suggestion, pleasure, consent" ("Our Lord's Sermon on the Mount,"
in *The Nicene and Post-Nicene Fathers*, ed. Philip Schaff [New York, 1886-
90], VI, 15-16), and Milton's reiteration of the "seeing, desiring, enjoying"
stages (*De Doctrina Christiana* [Of Christian Doctrine], in *Works of John
Milton*, eds. F. A. Patterson *et al.* [New York, 1931-40], XV, 181-83).

3   *gates*: first edition, "gate."
24   *this bramble*: see Judg. 9:7-21. From the top of Mount Gerizim, Jotham
relates his fable of the monarchy of the trees. After the olive, the fig, and the
vine in turn decline the honour of being monarch on the ground that they
are already occupied in valuable service, the position is offered to the useless
bramble who alone has time for it. The bramble, in accepting, promises
shelter to the faithful and punishment by fire to the disloyal; but these are
clearly vain boasts, since he cannot give "shade" and is moreover quite likely
to encompass the ruin of all through his own destruction by forest-fire. In
context, the fable is a bitterly ironic comment on the presumption of Abi-
melech to rule over the Shechemites, but it also reflects a more universal
feeling against the very notion of kingship, personified by worthless and des-
potic Eastern rulers of whom the bramble is here the exemplar. This brilliant
allusion to the old fable gives substance to the political allegory, and also fits
Diabolus to be placed beside Milton's Satan, another recognizably arrogant
and blandly deceitful Oriental potentate.

He is entertained for their King.

us.' So he accepted the motion and became the King of the town of Mansoul. This being done, the next thing was to give him possession of the castle, and so of the whole strength of the town. Wherefore, into the castle he goes: it was that which Shaddai built in Mansoul for his own delight, and pleasure. This now was become a den, and hold for the giant Diabolus.

He is possessed of the castle and fortified it for himself.

Now having got possession of this stately palace, or castle, what doth he, but make it a garrison for himself, and strengthens and fortifies it with all sorts of provision against the King Shaddai, or those that should endeavour the regaining of it to him and his obedience again. 10

This done, but not thinking himself yet secure enough, in the next place, he bethinks himself of new-modelling the town; and so he does, setting up one, and putting down another at pleasure. Wherefore my Lord Mayor, whose name was my Lord Understanding, and Mr. Recorder, whose name was Mr. Conscience, those he puts out of place and power. 20

He new-modelleth the town.

As for my Lord Mayor, though he was an understanding man, and one too that had complied with the rest of the town of Mansoul in admitting of the giant into the town; yet Diabolus thought not fit to let him abide in his former lustre and glory, because he was a seeing man. Wherefore he dark'ned it not only by taking from him his office and power, but by building of an high and strong tower, just between the sun's reflections, and the windows of my Lord's palace; by which means his house and all, and the whole of his habitation, was made as dark as darkness itself. And thus being alienated from the light, he became as one that was born blind. To this his house, my lord was confined, as to a prison; nor might he upon his parole go further than within his own bounds. And now, 30

My Lord Mayor put out of place.

II Cor. 10:4,5.

Eph. 4:18,19.

15f. *new-modelling*: a verb derived from "New Model Army," the name given to the Parliamentary army as reorganized in 1644-45. This re-forming of Mansoul suggests the re-shaping of Bedford Corporation (*ca.* 1681-84) to give the central government more control; see John Brown, *John Bunyan*, rev. by Frank Mott Harrison (London, 1928), pp. 310-32.
28gl. The second edition glosses II Cor. 4:4,5; also apt.

had he had an heart to do for Mansoul, what could
he do for it, or wherein could he be profitable to her?
So then, so long as Mansoul was under the power and
government of Diabolus—so long it was under him, as
it was obedient to him; which was, even until by a
war it was rescued out of his hand—so long my Lord
Mayor was rather an impediment in, than an advantage to, the famous town of Mansoul.

As for Mr. Recorder, before the town was taken,
he was a man well read in the laws of his King, and
also a man of courage and faithfulness to speak truth
at every occasion. And he had a tongue as bravely
hung, as he had an head filled with judgment. Now, **The Recorder**
this man Diabolus could by no means abide, because, **put out of place.**
though he gave his consent to his coming into the
town, yet he could not, by all wiles, trials, stratagems,
and devices that he could use, make him wholly his
own. True, he was much degenerated from his former
King, and also much pleased with many of the giant's
laws, and service; but all this would not do for as
much as he was not wholly his. He would now and
then think upon Shaddai, and have dread of his law
upon him, and then he would speak with a voice, as **He sometimes**
great against Diabolus, as when a lion roareth. Yea, **speaks for his**
and would also at certain times when his fits were **first King.**
upon him (for you must know that sometimes he had
terrible fits) make the whole town of Mansoul shake
with his voice; and therefore the now King of Mansoul could not abide him.

Diabolus therefore feared the Recorder more than
any that was left alive in the town of Mansoul,
because, as I said, his words did shake the whole town;
they were like the rattling thunder, and also like
thunder-claps. Since therefore the giant could not
make him wholly his own, what doth he do but
studies all that he could, to debauch the old gentleman, and by debauchery, to stupify his mind, and **He is more de-**
more harden his heart in ways of vanity. And as he **bauched than**
attempted, so he accomplished his design. He de- **before.**
bauched the man, and by little and little, so drew him
into sin and wickedness, that at last he was not only

debauched as at first, and so by consequence defiled, but
was almost (at last, I say) past all conscience of sin.
And this was the farthest Diabolus could go. Wherefore
he bethinks him of another project, and that was to
persuade the men of the town that Mr. Recorder was
mad, and so not to be regarded. And for this he urged
his fits, and said, 'If he be himself, why doth he not do
thus always? But,' quoth he, 'as all mad folk have
their fits, and in them their raving language, so hath
this old and doting gentleman.' Thus by one means or   10
another, he quickly got Mansoul to slight, neglect,

The town taken off from heeding of him.
and despise whatever Mr. Recorder could say. For
besides what already you have heard, Diabolus had a
way to make the old gentleman, when he was merry,
unsay and deny what he in his fits had affirmed. And
indeed, this was the next way to make himself ridiculous, and to cause that no man should regard him.

How conscience becomes so ridiculous, as with carnal men it is.
Also now he never spoke freely for King Shaddai, but
always by force and constraint. Besides, he would at
one time be hot against that at which at another he   20
would hold his peace. So uneven was he now in his
doings. Sometimes he would be, as if fast asleep, and
again sometimes as dead, even then when the whole
town of Mansoul was in her career after vanity, and
in her dance after the giant's pipe.

Wherefore, sometimes when Mansoul did use to
be frighted with the thund'ring voice of the Recorder
that was, and when they did tell Diabolus of it, he
would answer, that what the old gentleman said, was
neither of love to him, nor pity to them, but of a fool-   30
ish fondness that he had to be prating; and so would
hush, still, and put all to quiet again. And that he
might leave no argument unurged that might tend to
make them secure, he said, and said it often: 'O Mansoul! consider that notwithstanding the old gentleman's
rage, and the rattle of his high and thund'ring words,
you hear nothing of Shaddai himself'—when, liar and
deceiver that he was, every outcry of Mr. Recorder
against the sin of Mansoul was the voice of God in

2   *conscience*: knowledge, awareness.

him to them. But he goes on and says, 'You see that he values not the loss nor rebellion of the town of Mansoul, nor will he trouble himself with calling of his town to a reckoning for their giving of themselves to me. He knows that though ye were his, now you are lawfully mine; so leaving us one to another, he now hath shaken his hands of us.

'Moreover, O Mansoul!' quoth he, 'consider how I have served you, even to the uttermost of my power; and that with the best that I have, could get, or procure for you in all the world. Besides, I dare say that the laws and customs that you now are under, and by which you do homage to me, do yield you more solace and content, than did the paradise that at first you possessed. Your liberty also, as yourselves do very well know, has been greatly widened, and enlarged by me; whereas I found you a penn'd-up people. I have not laid any restraint upon you; you have no law, His flatteries. statute, or judgment of mine to fright you; I call none of you to account for your doings, except the madman Conscience. —you know who I mean; I have granted you to live, each man like a prince in his own, even with as little control from me, as I myself have from you.'

And thus would Diabolus hush up, and quiet the town of Mansoul, when the Recorder that was, did at times molest them. Yea, and with such cursed orations Men sometimes as these, would set the whole town in a rage, and fury angry with their against the old gentleman. Yea, the rascal crew at consciences. sometimes would be for destroying of him. They have often wished (in my hearing) that he had lived a thousand miles off from them: his company, his words, yea, the sight of him—and especially when they rememb'red how in old times he did use to threaten and condemn them—for all he was now so debauched, did terrify and afflict them sore.

But all wishes were vain for I do not know how, unless by the power of Shaddai, and his wisdom, he Ill thoughts. was preserved in being amongst them. Besides, his house was as strong as a castle, and stood hard to a stronghold of the town; moreover, if at any time any Of fears. of the crew or rabble attempted to make him away,

24

he could pull up the sluices, and let in such floods, as would drown all round about him.

But to leave Mr. Recorder, and to come to my

The will. Lord Willbewill, another of the gentry of the famous town of Mansoul. This Willbewill was as high born, as any man in Mansoul, and was as much if not more a freeholder than many of them were; besides, if I remember my tale aright, he had some privilege peculiar to himself in the famous town of Mansoul. Now together with these, he was a man of great strength, resolution, and courage, nor in his occasion could any turn him away. But I say, whether he was proud of his estate, privileges, strength or what (but sure it was through pride of something), he scorns now to be a slave in Mansoul; and therefore resolves to bear office under Diabolus, that he might (such an one as he was) be a petty ruler and governor in Mansoul. And headstrong man that he was!—thus he began betimes; for this man, when Diabolus did make his oration at Eargate, was one of the first that was for consenting to his words, and for accepting of his counsel as wholesome, and that was for the opening of the gate, and for letting him into the town: wherefore Diabolus had a kindness for him, and therefore he designed for him a place. And perceiving the valour and stoutness of the man, he coveted to have him for one of his great ones, to act and do in matters of the highest concern.

So he sent for him, and talked with him of that secret matter that lay in his breast, but there needed
The will takes place under Diabolus. not much persuasion in the case. For as at first he was willing that Diabolus should be let into the town, so now he was as willing to serve him there. When the tyrant, therefore, perceived the willingness of my lord to serve him, and that his mind stood bending that way, he forthwith made him the Captain of the

10

20

30

---

7   *freeholder*: one who has title (for life at least) to an estate on which no service or duty is due to any but the King.
11   *occasion*: need.
19   *betimes*: early.

Castle, Governor of the Wall, and Keeper of the Gates of Mansoul. Yea, there was a clause in his commission, *that nothing without him should be done in all the town of Mansoul.* So that now, next to Diabolus himself, who but my Lord Willbewill in all the town of Mansoul. Nor could anything now be done, but at his will and pleasure throughout the town of Mansoul. He had also one Mr. Mind for his clerk, a man to speak on, every way like his master; for he and his lord were in principle one, and in practice not far asunder. And now was Mansoul brought under to purpose, and made to fulfil the lusts of the will, and of the mind.

But it will not out of my thoughts, what a desperate one this Willbewill was, when power was put into his hand. First, he flatly denied that he owed any suit or service to his former Prince and Liege-Lord. This done in the next place he took an oath, and swore fidelity to his great master Diabolus, and then being stated and settled in his places, offices, advancements and preferments—oh! you cannot think, unless you had seen it, the strange work that this workman made in the town of Mansoul.

First, he maligned Mr. Recorder to death. He would neither endure to see him, nor to hear the words of his mouth; he would shut his eyes when he saw him, and stop his ears when he heard him speak. Also he could not endure that so much as a fragment of the law of Shaddai should be anywhere seen in the town. For example, his clerk Mr. Mind had some old, rent, and torn parchments of the law of good Shaddai in his house, but when Willbewill saw them, he cast them behind his back. True Mr. Recorder had some of the laws in his study, but my lord could by no means come at them. He also thought and said that the windows of my Lord Mayor's house, were always too light for the profit of the town of Mansoul. The light of a candle he could not endure. Now nothing at all pleased Willbewill but what pleased Diabolus his lord.

Marginal notes:
Heart.
Flesh.
Senses.

Rom. 8:7.

Mr. Mind, my lord's clerk.

Eph. 2:2-4.

The carnal will opposeth conscience.

Neh. 9:26.

Corrupt will loves a dark understanding.

17   *Liege-Lord*: lord receiving service and loyalty from a favoured retainer.

There was none like him to trumpet about the streets, the brave nature, the wise conduct, and great glory of the King Diabolus. He would range and rove throughout all the streets of Mansoul, to cry up his illustrious lord, and would make himself even as an abject, among the base and rascal crew, to cry up his valiant prince. And I say, when, and wheresoever he found these vassals, he would even make himself as one of them. In all ill courses he would act without bidding, and do mischief without commandment.

The Lord Willbewill also had a deputy under him, and his name was Mr. Affection, one that was also greatly debauched in his principles, and answerable thereto in his life. He was wholly given to the flesh, and therefore they called him Vile Affection. Now there was he, and one Carnal Lust, the daughter of Mr. Mind ('Like to like,' quoth the devil to the collier) that fell in love, and made a match, and were married; and as I take it, they had several children, as Impudent, Blackmouth and Hate-reproof—these three were black boys; and besides these they had three daughters, as Scorn-Truth, and Slight-God, and the name of the youngest was Revenge: these were all married in the town, and also begot and yielded many bad brats, too many to be here inserted. But to pass by this.

When the giant had thus engarrisoned himself in the town of Mansoul, and had put down and set up whom he thought good, he betakes himself to defacing. Now there was in the market-place in Mansoul, and also upon the gates of the castle, an image of the blessed King Shaddai. This image was so exactly engraven (and it was engraven in gold) that it did the most resemble Shaddai himself of anything that then

Marginal notes:

Vain thoughts.

Rom. 1:25.

A match betwixt vile affection and carnal lust.

Line numbers: 10, 20, 30

---

4   *cry up*: acclaim.
13   See also Rom. 1:26.
17   An old proverb, not confined to English, roughly meaning that like natures attract each other. Bunyan uses the proverb again in *The Life and Death of Mr. Badman*: "Hang them rogues, there is not a barrel better herring of all the holy brotherhood of them: *Like to like*, quoth the devil to the collier, this is your precise crew." (London, 1953), p. 263.

was extant in the world. This he basely commanded to be defaced, and it was as basely done by the hand of Mr. No-Truth. Now you must know, that as Diabolus had commanded, and that by the hand of Mr. No-Truth the image of Shaddai was defaced, he likewise gave order that the same Mr. No-Truth should set up in its stead the horrid and formidable image of Diabolus to the great contempt of the former King, and debasing of his town of Mansoul.

What No-Truth did.

Moreover, Diabolus made havoc of all remains of the laws and statutes of Shaddai that could be found in the town of Mansoul: to wit, such as contained either the doctrines of morals, with all civil and natural documents. Also relative severities he sought to extinguish. To be short, there was nothing of the remains of good in Mansoul, which he and Willbewill sought not to destroy; for their design was to turn Mansoul into a brute, and to make it like to the sensual sow by the hand of Mr. No-truth.

All law books destroyed that could be so.

When he had destroyed what law and good orders he could, then further to effect his design, namely, to alienate Mansoul from Shaddai her King, he commands, and they set up his own vain edicts, statutes and commandments, in all places of resort, or concourse in Mansoul, to wit, such as gave liberty to the lusts of the flesh, the lusts of the eyes, and the pride of life which are not of Shaddai, but of the world. He encouraged, countenanced and promoted lasciviousness, and all ungodliness there. Yea, much more did Diabolus to encourage wickedness in the town of Mansoul; he promised them peace, content, joy, and bliss in doing his commands, and that they should never be called to an account for their not doing the contrary. And let this serve to give a taste to them that love to hear tell of what is done beyond their knowledge, afar off in other countries.

I John 2.

Now Mansoul, being wholly at his beck, and

13f. *civil and natural documents*: precepts concerning legal and inherent rights. (document: f. Lat. *docere*, to teach.)
14 *relative severities*: punishments fitted to particular breaches of the laws.
19 *sensual sow*: see II Pet. 2:22.

brought wholly to his bow, nothing was heard or seen therein but that which tended to set up him.

But now, he having disabled the Lord Mayor and Mr. Recorder from bearing of office in Mansoul, and seeing that the town, before he came to it, was the most ancient of corporations in the world; and fearing, if he did not maintain greatness, they at any time should object that he had done them an injury, therefore, I say, (that they might see that he did not intend to lessen their grandeur, or to take from them any of their advantageous things), he did choose for them a Lord Mayor, and a Recorder, himself: and such as contented them at the heart, and such also as pleased him wondrous well.

They have a new Lord Mayor, and a new Recorder.

The name of the mayor that was of Diabolus's making was the Lord Lustings, a man that had neither eyes nor ears. All that he did, whether as a man or as an officer, he did it naturally as doth the beast. And that which made him yet the more ignoble, though not to Mansoul, yet to them that beheld and were grieved for its ruins, was, that he never could savour good, but evil.

The new Lord Mayor.

The Recorder was one whose name was Forget-good. And a very sorry fellow he was. He could remember nothing but mischief, and to do it with delight. He was naturally prone to do things that were hurtful; even hurtful to the town of Mansoul, and to all the dwellers there. These two therefore, by their power and practice, example and smiles upon evil, did much more grammar and settle the common people in hurtful ways. For who doth not perceive but when those that sit aloft are vile and corrupt themselves, they corrupt the whole region and country where they are?

The new Recorder.

Thoughts.

Besides these, Diabolus made several burgesses and aldermen in Mansoul, such as out of whom the

10

20

30

---

1   *being wholly at his beck, and brought wholly to his bow*: being immediately responsive to his every command or whim.

21   *savour*: here Brown's reproduction of the first edition is in error. The editor has confused *s* and *f* to print "favour."

30   *grammar and settle*: instruct and strengthen.

town, when it needed, might choose them officers, governors, and magistrates. And these are the names of the chief of them: Mr. Incredulity, Mr. Haughty, Mr. Swearing, Mr. Whoring, Mr. Hard-heart, Mr. Pitiless, Mr. Fury, Mr. No-Truth, Mr. Stand-to-lies, Mr. False-peace, Mr. Drunkenness, Mr. Cheating, Mr. Atheism—thirteen in all. Mr. Incredulity is the eldest, and Mr. Atheism the youngest of the company.

₁₀ There was also an election of common council men, and others, as bailiffs, serjeants, constables, and others; but all of them like to those aforenamed, being either fathers, brothers, cousins, or nephews to them— whose names, for brevity's sake, I omit to mention.

When the giant had thus far proceeded in his work, in the next place he betook him to build some strongholds in the town. And he built three that seemed to be impregnable. The first he called the hold of Defiance, because it was made to command the

₂₀ whole town, and to keep it from the knowledge of its ancient King. The second he called Midnight-hold, because it was builded on purpose to keep Mansoul from the true knowledge of itself. The third was called Sweet-sin-hold, because by that he fortified Mansoul against all desires of good. The first of these holds stood close by Eyegate, that as much as might be, light might be dark'ned there. The second was builded hard to the old castle, to the end that that might be made more blind, if possible. And the third stood in

₃₀ the market-place.

He that Diabolus made governor over the first of these, was one Spite-God, a most blasphemous wretch. He came with the whole rabble of them that came against Mansoul at first, and was himself one of themselves. He that was made the governor of Midnight-hold was one Love-no-light. He was also of them that came first against the town. And he that was made governor of the hold called Sweet-sin-hold, was one whose name was Love-flesh; he was also a very

₄₀ lewd fellow, but not of that country where the other are bound. This fellow could find more sweetness

He doth make them new aldermen, and who.

He buildeth three strongholds, their names, and governors.

when he stood sucking of a lust, than he did in all the paradise of God.

And now Diabolus thought himself safe. He had taken Mansoul; he had engarrisoned himself therein; he had put down the old officers, and had set up new ones; he had defaced the image of Shaddai, and had set up his own; he had spoiled the old law books, and had promoted his own vain lies; he had made him new magistrates, and set up new aldermen; he had builded him new holds, and had mann'd them for himself. And all this he did to make himself secure in case the good Shaddai, or his Son, should come to make an incursion upon him.

Diabolus has made his nest.

Now you may well think, that long before this time, word by some or other could not but be carried to the good King Shaddai, how his Mansoul in the continent of Universe was lost; and that the runagate giant Diabolus, once one of his Majesty's servants, had in rebellion against the King made sure thereof for himself. Yea, tidings were carried and brought to the King thereof, and that to a very circumstance.

Tidings carried to the court of what had happened to Mansoul.

As first, how Diabolus came upon Mansoul (they being a simple people and innocent) with craft, subtlety, lies and guiles. *Item*: That he had treacherously slain the right noble and valiant captain, their Captain Resistance, as he stood upon the gate with the rest of the townsmen. *Item*: How my brave Lord Innocent fell down dead (with grief some say, or with being poisoned with the stinking breath of one Illpause, as say others) at the hearing of his just Lord, and rightful Prince Shaddai, so abused by the mouth of so filthy a Diabolonian, as that varlet Ill-pause was. The messenger further told, that after this Ill-pause had made a short oration to the townsmen, in behalf of Diabolus his master, the simple town believing that what was said was true, with one consent did open Eargate, the chief gate of the corporation, and did let him with his crew into a possession of the famous

10

20

30

17   *runagate*: apostate.
21   *to a very circumstance*: in exact detail.

town of Mansoul. He further showed how Diabolus had served the Lord Mayor, and Mr. Recorder, to wit, that he had put them from all place of power and trust. *Item*: He showed also that my Lord Willbewill, was turned a very rebel and runagate, and that so was one Mr. Mind his clerk, and that they two did range and revel it all the town over, and teach the wicked ones their ways. He said moreover, that this Willbewill was put into great trust. And particularly that Diabolus had put into Willbewill's hand, all the strong places in Mansoul; and that Mr. Affection was made my Lord Willbewill's deputy in his most rebellious affairs. 'Yea,' said the messenger, 'this monster, Lord Willbewill, has openly disavowed his King Shaddai, and hath horribly given his faith and plighted his troth to Diabolus.

'Also,' said the messenger, 'besides all this, the new king or rather rebellious tyrant over the once famous, but now perishing town of Mansoul, has set up a Lord Mayor, and a Recorder of his own. For Mayor he has set up one Mr. Lustings, and for Recorder, Mr. Forget-good—two of the vilest of all the town of Mansoul.' This faithful messenger also proceeded and told what a sort of new burgesses Diabolus had made, also that he had builded several strong forts, towers, and strongholds in Mansoul. He told too, the which I had almost forgot, how Diabolus had put the town of Mansoul into arms, the better to capacitate them on his behalf to make resistance against Shaddai their King, should he come to reduce them to their former obedience.

Now this tidings-teller did not deliver his relation of things in private but in open court, the King and his Son, high lords, chief captains, and nobles, being all there present to hear. But by that they had heard the whole of the story, it would have amazed one, to have seen, had he been there to behold it, what sorrow and grief, and compunction of spirit there was among all sorts, to think that famous Mansoul was now taken; only the King, and his Son foresaw all this long before, yea, and sufficiently

Grief at court to hear the tidings.

provided for the relief of Mansoul, though they told not everybody thereof. Yet because they also would have a share in condoling of the misery of Mansoul, therefore they also did and that at a rate of the highest degree, bewail the losing of Mansoul. The King said

Gen. 6:5,6.

plainly that it grieved him at the heart, and you may be sure that his Son was not a whit behind him. Thus gave they conviction to all about them that they had love and compassion for the famous town of Mansoul. Well, when the King and his Son were retired into the privy-chamber, there they again consulted about what they had designed before, to wit,

The secret of his purpose.

that as Mansoul should in time be suffered to be lost; so as certainly it should be recovered again—recovered I say, in such a way as that both the King and his Son would get themselves eternal fame and glory thereby. Wherefore after this consult, the Son of

The Son of God.

Shaddai (a sweet and comely person, and one that had always great affection for those that were in affliction, but one that had mortal enmity in his heart against Diabolus, because he was designed for it, and because

Isa. 49:5.
I Tim. 1:15.
Hos. 13:14.

he sought his crown and dignity)—this Son of Shaddai, I say, having stricken hands with his Father, and promised that he would be his servant to recover his Mansoul again, stood by his resolution, nor would he repent of the same. The purport of which agreement

A brave design on foot for the town of Mansoul.

was this, to wit, *that at a certain time prefixed by both, the King's Son should take a journey into the country of Universe, and there in a way of justice and equity, by making of amends for the follies of Mansoul, he should lay a foundation of her perfect deliverance from Diabolus, and from his tyranny.*

Moreover, Emmanuel resolved to make, at a time convenient, a war upon the giant Diabolus, even while he was possessed of the town of Mansoul. And that

By the Holy Ghost.

he would fairly by strength of hand drive him out of his hold, his nest, and take it to himself, to be his habitation. This now being resolved upon, order was

23 The action accords with Jewish custom. See Job 17:3; Prov. 6:1, 17:18, 22:26.

given to the Lord Chief Secretary, to draw up a fair record of what was determined, and to cause that it should be published in all the corners of the kingdom of Universe. A short breviat of the contents thereof, you may if you please take here as follows.

Let all men know who are concerned, that the Son of Shaddai the great King, is engaged by covenant to his Father, to bring his Mansoul to him again. Yea, and to put Mansoul too, through the power of his matchless love, into a far better, and more happy condition than 'twas in before it was taken by Diabolus.

These papers therefore were published in several places, to the no little molestation of the tyrant Diabolus, 'for now,' thought he, 'I shall be molested, and my habitation will be taken from me.'

But when this matter, I mean this purpose of the King and his Son, did at first take air at court, who can tell how the high lords, chief captains, and noble princes that were there, were taken with the business? First, they whispered it one to another, and after that it began to ring out throughout the King's palace, all wond'ring at the glorious design that between the King and his Son was on foot for the miserable town of Mansoul. Yea, the courtiers could scarce do anything, either for the King or kingdom, but they would mix with the doing thereof, a noise of the love of the King and his Son, that they had for the town of Mansoul.

Nor could these lords, high captains, and princes, be content to keep this news at court; yea, before the records thereof were perfected, themselves came down and told it in Universe. At last it came to the ears, as I said, of Diabolus, to his no little discontent. For you must think it would perplex him to hear of such a design against him: well, but after a few casts in his mind, he concluded upon these four things.

The Holy Scriptures.

The contents.

Among the angels.

Diabolus perplexed at the news.

14   *molestation*: vexation.

First that this news, this good tidings, if possible, should be kept from the ears of the town of Mansoul. 'For,' said he, 'if they shall once come to the knowledge that Shaddai their former King, and Emmanuel his Son, are contriving of good for the town of Mansoul, what can be expected by me, but that Mansoul will make a revolt from under my hand and government, and return again to him?'

He concluded on several things.

Now to accomplish this his design, he renews his flattery with my Lord Willbewill, and also gives him strict charge and command, that he should keep watch by day and by night at all the gates of the town, especially Eargate and Eyegate. 'For I hear of a design,' quoth he, 'a design to make us all traitors, and that Mansoul must be reduced to its first bondage again. I hope they are but flying stories,' quoth he; 'however, let no such news by any means be let into Mansoul, lest the people be dejected thereat. I think, my lord, it can be no welcome news to you; I am sure it is none to me. And I think that at this time it should be all our wisdoms and care, to nip the head of all such rumors as shall tend to trouble our people. Wherefore I desire, my lord, that you will in this matter do as I say. Let there be strong guards daily kept at every gate of the town. Stop also and examine, from whence such come that you perceive do from far come hither to trade; nor let them by any means be admitted into Mansoul, unless you shall plainly perceive that they are favourers of our excellent government. I command, moreover,' said Diabolus, 'that there be spies continually walking up and down the town of Mansoul, and let them have power to suppress, and destroy any that they shall perceive to be plotting against us, or that shall prate of what by Shaddai and Emmanuel is intended.'

First how to keep the news from Mansoul.

The will engaged against the Gospel. Good thoughts must be kept out of the town of Mansoul.

All good thoughts and words in the town are to be suppressed.

This therefore was accordingly done. My Lord Willbewill heark'ned to his lord and master, went willingly after the commandment, and with all the diligence he could, kept any that would, from going

34   *prate of* : chatter about.

out abroad, or that sought to bring this tidings to Mansoul, from coming into the town.

Secondly, this done, in the next place, Diabolus, that he might make Mansoul as sure as he could, frames and imposes a new oath and horrible covenant upon the townfolk: to wit, *that they should never desert him, nor his government, nor yet betray him, nor seek to alter his laws: but that they should own, confess, stand by, and acknowledge him for their rightful king in defiance to any that do or hereafter shall, by any pretence, law, or title whatever lay claim to the town of Mansoul*—thinking belike that Shaddai had not power to absolve them from this covenant with death, and agreement with hell. Nor did the silly Mansoul stick or boggle at all at this most monstrous engagement, but as if it had been a sprat in the mouth of a whale, they swallowed it without any chewing. Were they troubled at it? Nay, they rather bragged and boasted of their so brave fidelity to the tyrant their pretended king, swearing that they would never be changelings, nor forsake their old lord for a new.

Thus did Diabolus tie poor Mansoul fast, but jealousy that never thinks itself strong enough, put him in the next place upon another exploit, which was yet more, if possible, to debauch this town of Mansoul. Wherefore he caused, by the hand of one Mr. Filth, an odious, nasty, lascivious piece of beastliness to be drawn up in writing, and to be set upon the castle gates, whereby he granted, and gave licence to all his true and trusty sons in Mansoul, to do whatsoever their lustful appetites prompted them to do; and that no man was to let, hinder, or control them, upon pain of incurring the displeasure of their prince.

A new oath imposed upon Mansoul.

Isa. 28:15.

Odious atheistical pamphlets and filthy ballads and romances full of baldry.

21   *changelings*: turncoats.
26gl. *baldry*: ribaldry.
27   Mr. Filth may be a satirical portrait of Sir Roger L'Estrange, appointed by Charles II as licenser of the press in Bunyan's time. Since Filth is selected for the job by Diabolus, the political implication of the allegory here is substantial.

Now this he did for these reasons:

1. That the town of Mansoul might be yet made weaker and weaker, and so more unable, should tidings come that their redemption was designed, to believe, hope, or consent to the truth thereof. For reason says, 'The bigger the sinner, the less grounds of hopes of mercy.'

2. The second reason was, if perhaps Emmanuel the Son of Shaddai their King, by seeing the horrible and profane doings of the town of Mansoul, might repent, tho' ent'red into a convenant of redeeming them, of pursuing that covenant of their redemption; for he knew that Shaddai was holy, and that his Son Emmanuel was holy—yea, he knew it by woeful experience; for, for the iniquity and sin of Diabolus, was he cast from the highest orbs. Wherefore what more rational than for him to conclude that thus, for sin, it might fare with Mansoul? But fearing also lest this knot should break, he bethinks himself of another, to wit:

3. Thirdly, to endeavour to possess all hearts in the town of Mansoul that Shaddai was raising of an army, to come to overthrow, and utterly to destroy this town of Mansoul. And this he did to forestall any tidings that might come to their ears, of their deliverance. 'For,' thought he, 'if I first bruit this, the tidings that shall come after, will all be swallowed up of this. For what else will Mansoul say, when they shall hear that they must be delivered, but that the true meaning is, Shaddai intends to destroy them?' Wherefore, he summons the whole town into the market-place, and there with deceitful tongue thus he addresses himself unto them:

'Gentlemen, and my very good friends, you are all as you know my legal subjects, and men of the famous town of Mansoul. You know how, from the

Reasons of his thus doing.

The place of hearing and of considering.

---

15   Second edition, "for for his iniquity and sin was Diabolus cast from the highest Orbs." Third edition, "For the iniquity and sin of Diabolus, was he cast from the highest Orbs."

26   *bruit*: report.

first day that I have been with you until now, I have
behaved myself among you, and what liberty, and
great privileges you have enjoyed under my government, I hope to your honour and mine, and also to
your content and delight. Now my famous Mansoul,
a noise of trouble there is abroad, of trouble to the
town of Mansoul—sorry I am thereof for your sakes.
For I received but now by the post from my Lord
Lucifer—and he useth to have good intelligence—that
your old King Shaddai is raising of an army to come
against you, to destroy you root and branch. And this,
O Mansoul! is now the cause, that at this time I have
called you together; namely to advise what in this
juncture is best to be done. For my part, I am but one,
and can with ease shift for myself, did I list to seek
my own ease, and to leave my Mansoul in all the
danger. But my heart is so firmly united to you, and
so unwilling am I to leave you, that I am willing to
stand and fall with you, to the utmost hazard that
shall befall me. What say you? O my Mansoul! will
you now desert your old friend, or do you think of
standing by me?' Then as one man, with one mouth,
they cried out together, 'Let him die the death that
will not!'

    Then said Diabolus again: ' 'Tis in vain for us to
hope for quarter, for this king knows not how to
show it. True perhaps, he at his first sitting down
before us, will talk of and pretend to mercy, that
thereby, with the more ease and less trouble, he may
again make himself the master of Mansoul. Whatever,
therefore, he shall say, believe not one syllable or
tittle of it, for all such language is but to overcome
us, and to make us, while we wallow in our blood, the
trophies of his merciless victory. My mind is, therefore, that we resolve to the last man to resist him, and
not to believe him upon any terms, for in at that door
will come our danger. But shall we be flattered out of
our lives? I hope you know more of the rudiments of

Very deceiv-
able language.

9   *useth to have*: usually has.
26   *quarter*: clemency granted a surrendering foe.

politics than to suffer yourselves so pitifully to be
served.

'But suppose he should, if he gets us to yield,
save some of our lives, or the lives of some of them
that are underlings in Mansoul, what help will that be
to you that are the chief of the town, especially of you
whom I have set up, and whose greatness has been
procured by you through your faithful sticking to me?
And suppose again, that he should give quarter to
every one of you, be sure he will bring you into that
bondage under which you were captivated before, or
a worse, and then what good will your lives do you?
Shall you with him live in pleasure as you do now?
No, no; you must be bound by laws that will pinch
you, and be made to do that which at present is hate-
ful to you. I am for you if you are for me, and it is
better to die valiantly, than to live like pitiful slaves.
But I say, the life of a slave, will be counted a life too
good for Mansoul now. Blood, blood, nothing but
blood is in every blast of Shaddai's trumpet against
poor Mansoul now. Pray be concerned; I hear he is
coming. Up, and stand to your arms, that now while
you have any leisure, I may learn you some feats of
war. Armour for you I have, and by me it is. Yea, and
it is sufficient for Mansoul from top to toe; nor can
you be hurt by what his force can do, if you shall
keep it well girt and fast'ned about you. Come therefore to my castle and welcome, and harness yourselves
for the war. There is helmet, breast-plate, sword and
shield, and what not, that will make you fight like
men.

1. 'My helmet, otherwise called an head-piece, is
hope of doing well at last what lives soever you live.
This is that which they had, who said, that they
should have peace tho' they walked in the wickedness
of their heart, to add drunkenness to thirst. A piece of
approved armour this is, and whoever has it and can
hold it, so long no arrow, dart, sword or shield can

Lying language.

*He is afraid
of losing of
Mansoul.*

*He puts them
upon arming of
themselves.*

*His helmet.
Deut. 29:19.*

10

20

30

33   *what lives soever you live*: no matter how you live.

hurt him. This therefore keep on, and thou wilt keep off many a blow, my Mansoul.

2. 'My breast-plate is a breast-plate of iron. I had it forged in mine own country, and all my soldiers are armed therewith. In plain language, it is an hard heart, an heart as hard as iron, and as much past feeling as a stone, the which if you get, and keep, neither mercy shall win you, nor judgment fright you. This, therefore, is a piece of armour most necessary for all to put on that hate Shaddai, and that would fight against him under my banner.

His breast-plate. Rev. 9:9.

3. 'My sword is a tongue that is set on fire of hell, and that can bend itself to speak evil of Shaddai, his Son, his ways, and people. Use this; it has been tried a thousand times twice told. Whoever hath it, keeps it, and makes that use of it as I would have him, can never be conquered by mine enemy.

His sword. Ps. 57:4. Ps. 64:3. Jas. 3.

4. 'My shield is unbelief, or calling into question the truth of the word, or all the sayings that speak of the judgment that Shaddai has appointed for wicked men. Use this shield; many attempts he has made upon it, and sometimes, 'tis true, it has been bruised; but they that have writ of the wars of Emmanuel against my servants, have testified that he could do no mighty work there because of their unbelief. Now to handle this weapon of mine aright, it is, not to believe things because they are true, of what sort or by whomsoever asserted. If he speaks of judgment, care not for it; if he speaks of mercy, care not for it; if he promises, if he swears that he would do to Mansoul, if it turns, no hurt but good, regard not what is said, question the truth of all, for it is to wield the shield of unbelief aright, and as my servants ought and do; and he that doth otherwise loves me not, nor do I count him but an enemy to me.

His shield. Job. 15:26. Ps. 76:3 Mark 6:5,6.

5. 'Another part or piece,' said Diabolus, 'of mine excellent armour is, a dumb and prayerless spirit, a spirit that scorns to cry for mercy. Wherefore be you,

15   *a thousand times twice told*: two thousand times.

my Mansoul, sure that you make use of this. What! Cry for quarter? Never do that, if you would be mine. I know you are stout men, and am sure that I have clad you with that which is armour of proof; wherefore to cry to Shaddai for mercy, let that be far from you. Besides all this, I have a maul, fire-brands, arrows and death, all good hand-weapons, and such as will do execution.'

He backs all
with a speech
to them.

After he had thus furnished his men with armour and arms, he addressed himself to them in such like words as these: 'Remember,' quoth he, 'that I am your rightful King, and that you have taken an oath, and ent'red into covenant to be true to me and my cause. I say remember this, and show yourselves stout and valiant men of Mansoul. Remember also the kindness that I have always showed to you, and that without your petition. I have granted to you external things, wherefore the privileges, grants, immunities, profits and honours wherewith I have endowed you, do call for at your hands, returns of loyalty, my lion-like men of Mansoul. And when so fit a time to show it, as when another shall seek to take my dominion over you, into their own hands? One word more and I have done. Can we but stand, and overcome this one shock or brunt, I doubt not but in little time, all the world will be ours. And when that day comes, my true hearts, I will make you kings, princes and captains—and what brave days shall we have then!'

Diabolus having thus armed and forearmed his servants and vassals in Mansoul, against their good and lawful King Shaddai, in the next place he

10

20

30

---

6   *maul*: club. In the Second Part of *The Pilgrim's Progress* Giant Maul almost breaks Mr. Greatheart's skull with blows of his club.

15   *stout*: resolute.

28   Diabolus' speech is surely one of the high points of the book. Here is a great satanic parody of Paul's urging the Ephesians to put on "the whole armour of God" (Eph. 6); this is the background against which the speech should be read, though the devil naturally employs scriptural reminiscences more suited to his purposes. Here also is a most telling mockery of the elaborate ritual traditionally associated with the arming of the epic hero. In its use of a variety of rhetorical devices, in its cajolery and flattery, the speech at certain moments reveals a dramatic power essentially Shakespearean.

doubleth his guards at the gates of the town, and he takes himself to the castle, which was his stronghold. His vassals also, to show their wills, and supposed (but ignoble) gallantry, exercise themselves in their arms every day, and teach one another feats of war; they also defied their enemies, and sang up the praises of their tyrant; they threat'ned also what men they would be, if ever things should rise so high, as a war between Shaddai and their king.

They of Mansoul show their loyalty to the giant.

Now all this time the good King, the King Shaddai, was preparing to send an army to recover the town of Mansoul again from under the tyranny of their pretended King Diabolus. But he thought good at the first, not to send them by the hand and conduct of brave Emmanuel his Son, but under the hand of some of his servants, to see first by them the temper of Mansoul, and whether by them they would be won to the obedience of their King. The army consisted of above forty thousand—all true men, for they came from the King's own Court, and were those of his own choosing.

Shaddai prepareth an army for the recovery of Mansoul.

The words of God.

They came up to Mansoul under the conduct of four stout generals, each man being a captain of ten thousand men, and these are their names and their signs. The name of the first was Boanerges. The name of the second was Captain Conviction. The name of the third was Captain Judgment. And the name of the fourth was Captain Execution. These were the captains that Shaddai sent to regain Mansoul.

The captains' names.

These four captains, as was said, the King thought fit in the first place to send to Mansoul, to make an attempt upon it; for indeed generally in all his wars he did use to send these four captains in the van, for they were very stout and roughhewn men, men that were fit to break the ice, and to make their way by dint of sword; and their men were like themselves.

Ps. 60:4.

To each of these captains the King gave a banner that it might be displayed, because of the goodness of his cause, and because of the right that he had to Mansoul.

First to Captain Boanerges, for he was the chief; to him, I say, was given ten thousand men. His ensign was Mr. Thunder, he bare the black colours, and his scutcheon was the three burning thunder-bolts.

Mark 3:17.

The second captain was Captain Conviction; to him also was given ten thousand men. His ensign's name was Mr. Sorrow, he did bear the pale colours, and his scutcheon was the book of the law wide open, from whence issued a flame of fire.

Deut. 33:2.

The third captain was Captain Judgment; to him was given ten thousand men. His ensign's name was Mr. Terror; he bare the red colours, and his scutcheon was a burning fiery furnace.

Matt. 13:40,41.

The fourth captain was Captain Execution; to him was given ten thousand men. His ensign was one Mr. Justice; he also bare the red colours, and his scutcheon was a fruitless tree with an axe lying at the root thereof.

Matt. 3:10.

These four captains, as I said, had every one of them under his command ten thousand men, all of good fidelity to the King, and stout at their military actions.

Well, the captains and their forces, their men and under-officers, being had upon a day by Shaddai into the field, and there called all over by their names, were then and there put into such harness, as became their degree and that service that now they were going about for their King.

Now, when the King had mustered his forces—for it is he that mustereth the host to the battle—he gave unto the captains their several commissions, with charge and commandment in the audience of all the

---

4 *scutcheon*: escutcheon, a shield with armorial bearings.
17 *fruitless tree*: the first of several references to a spiritual emblem, enormously influential in Western thought, and beloved by Bunyan and the Puritans generally. Bunyan even devotes an entire work, *The Barren Fig-Tree* (1682), to the image of the barren tree (Luke 12:6-9) as a symbol of the fruitless professor, one who talks mightily of religion but does not make his faith concrete in action. The popularity of the figure and its continuing validity for the Puritans is not really hard to understand when one recalls the significative aspect of Calvinism: the insistence that good works are tokens of faith, hence of election, and vice versa.

soldiers that they should take heed faithfully and courageously to do and execute the same. Their commissions were for the substance of them the same in form, though as to name, title, place and degree of the captains there might be some, but very small variation. And here let me give you an account of the matter and sum contained in their commission.

A Commission from the great Shaddai, King of Mansoul, to his trusty and noble captain, the Captain Boanerges, for making war upon the Town of Mansoul.

O, thou Boanerges, one of my stout and thund'ring captains, over one ten-thousand of my valiant and faithful servants! Go thou in my name with this thy force to the miserable town of Mansoul, and when thou comest thither, offer them first conditions of peace; and command them, that casting off the yoke and tyranny of the wicked Diabolus, they return to me their rightful Prince and Lord. Command them also that they cleanse themselves from all that is his in the town of Mansoul—and look to thyself that thou hast good satisfaction touching the truth of their obedience. Thus when thou hast commanded them, if they in truth submit thereto, then do thou to the uttermost of thy power, what in thee lies, to set up for me a garrison in the famous town of Mansoul. Nor do thou hurt the least native that moveth or breatheth therein, if they will submit themselves to me, but treat thou such as if they were thy friend or brother; for all such I love, and they shall be dear unto me. And tell them that I will take a time to come unto them, and to let them know that I am merciful.
But if they shall, notwithstanding thy summons and the producing of thy authority, resist, stand out against thee, and rebel, then do I command thee to make use of all thy cunning, power, might, and force, to bring them under by strength of hand. Farewell.

Their commission.
Mark 10:11.
Luke 10:5.

I Thess. 2:7-11.

Thus you see the sum of their commissions, for as

I said before, for the substance of them, they were the same that the rest of the noble captains had.

Wherefore they, having received each commander his authority at the hand of their King, the day being appointed, and the place of their rendezvous prefixed, each commander appeared in such gallantry as became his cause and calling. So after a new entertainment from Shaddai, with flying colours they set forward to march towards the famous town of Mansoul. Captain Boanerges led the van; Captain Conviction and Captain Judgment made up the main body, and Captain Execution brought up the rear. They, then, having a great way to go (for the town of Mansoul was far off from the court of Shaddai), they marched through the regions and countries of many people, not hurting or abusing any, but blessing wherever they came. They also lived upon the King's cost in all the way they went.

Having travelled thus for many days, at last they came within sight of Mansoul, the which when they saw, the captains could for their hearts do no less than for a while bewail the condition of the town; for they quickly saw how that it was prostrate to the will of Diabolus, and to his ways and designs.

Well, to be short, the captains came up before the town, march up to Eargate, sit down there, for that was the place of hearing. So when they had pitched their tents, and entrenched themselves they addressed themselves to make their assault.

Now the townsfolk at first, beholding so gallant a company, so bravely accoutred, and so excellently disciplined, having on their glittering armour, and displaying of their flying colours, could not but come out of their houses and gaze. But the cunning fox Diabolus, fearing that the people, after this sight should on a sudden summons, open the gates to the captains, came down with all haste from the castle, and made them retire into the body of the town, who, when he

10

20

30

6   *gallantry*: magnificence.

had them there, made this lying and deceivable speech
unto them:

'Gentlemen,' quoth he, 'although you are my
trusty and well beloved friends, yet I cannot but a
little chide you for your late uncircumspect action in
going out to gaze on that great and mighty force, that
but yesterday sat down before, and have now entrenched themselves in order to the maintaining of a
siege against the famous town of Mansoul. Do you
know who they are, whence they come, and what is
their purpose in sitting down before the town of
Mansoul? They are they of whom I have told you
long ago, that they would come to destroy this town,
and against whom I have been at the cost to arm you
with cap-a-pe for your body, besides great fortifications for your mind. Wherefore, then, did you not
rather, even at the first appearance of them, cry out,
Fire the beacons! and give the whole town an alarm
concerning them, that we might all have been in a
posture of defence, and a been ready to have received
them with the highest acts of defiance? Then had
you showed yourselves men to my liking; whereas, by
what you have done, you have made me half afraid—
I say, half afraid—that when they and we shall come
to push a pike, I shall find you want courage to stand
it out any longer. Wherefore have I commanded a
watch, and that you should double your guards at the
gates? Wherefore have I endeavoured to make you as
hard as iron, and your hearts as a piece of the nether
millstone? Was it, think you, that you might show

*Diabolus alien-
ates their minds
from them.*

*That's false
Satan.*

*Satan greatly
afraid of God's
minsters, that
they will set
Mansoul against
him.*

10

20

30

---

15 *cap-a-pe*: (accoutrements) from head to foot. Cf. *Hamlet*: "A figure like
your father, /Armed at point exactly, cap-a-pe" (I,ii, 199-200). (From Fr.
cap, head; *pied*, foot.)

20 *a*: a worn-down form of *have*, frequent in Bunyan and in other colloquial
or dialectal writers between the thirteenth and seventeenth centuries. On
this see OED, which gives usual spelling as *ha* or *ha'*.

25 *come to push a pike*: come at close quarters. The pike was a long lance used
by infantry until the eighteenth century, when it was superseded by the
bayonet.

29 *as a piece of the nether millstone*: i.e., insensible, obdurate. The figure is
taken from Job 41:24, which in the Geneva Bible (the version Bunyan knew
best) reads, "His heart is as strong as a stone and as hard as the nether
millstone." The allusion is to the firmness and hardness of the lower, fixed,

yourselves women, and that you might go out like a company of innocents to gaze on your mortal foes? Fie, fie! put yourselves into a posture of defence, beat up the drum, gather together in warlike manner, that our foes may know that, before they shall conquer this corporation, there are valiant men in the town of Mansoul.

He stirs them up to bid defiance to the ministers of the Word.

'I will leave off now to chide, and will not further rebuke you. But I charge you, that henceforwards, you let me see no more such actions. Let not henceforward a man of you, without order first obtained from me, so much as show his head over the wall of the town of Mansoul. You have now heard me. Do as I have commanded, and you shall cause me that I dwell securely with you, and that I take care as for myself, so for your safety and honour also. Farewell.'

Now were the townsmen strangely altered; they were as men stricken with a panic fear: they ran to and fro through the streets of the town of Mansoul, crying out, 'Help, help! The men that turn the world upside down are come hither also.' Nor could any of them be quiet after, but still as men bereft of wit, they cried out, 'The destroyers of our peace and people are come!' This went down with Diabolus. 'Ay!' quoth he to himself, 'this I like well. Now it is as I would have it. Now you show your obedience to your prince. Hold you but here, and then let them take the town if they can.'

When sinners hearken to Satan they are set in a rage against godliness.

Well, before the King's forces had sat before Mansoul three days, Captain Boanerges commanded his trumpeter to go down to Eargate, and there in the name of the great Shaddai to summon Mansoul to give audience to the message that he in his Master's name was to them commanded to deliver. So the trumpeter, whose name was Take-heed-what-you-hear, went up as he was commanded to Eargate, and there sounded his trumpet for a hearing. But there was none

The King's trumpet sounded at Eargate.

10

20

30

---

circular millstone, around which the other millstone revolves, grinding the grain against it.

2   *innocents*: simpletons, idiots.

that appeared, that gave answer or regard; for so had Diabolus commanded. So the trumpeter returned to his captain, and told him what he had done, and also how he had sped. Whereat the captain was grieved, but bid the trumpeter go to his tent.

They will not hear.

Again Captain Boanerges sendeth his trumpeter to Eargate, to sound as before for an hearing. But they again kept close, came not out, nor would they give him an answer, so observant were they of the command of Diabolus their king.

A second summons repulsed.

Then the captains, and other field-officers, called a council of war to consider what further was to be done for the gaining of the town of Mansoul, and after some close and thorough debate upon the contents of their commissions, they concluded yet to give to the town, by the hand of the forenamed trumpeter, another summons to hear. 'But if that shall be refused,' said they, 'and that the town shall stand it out still'—then they determined, and bid the trumpeter tell them so, that they would endeavour, by what means they could, to compel them by force to the obedience of their King.

A council of war.

Luke 14:23.

So Captain Boanerges commanded his trumpeter to go up to Eargate again, and in the name of the great King Shaddai to give it a very loud summons to come down without delay to Eargate, there to give audience to the King's most noble captains. So the trumpeter went, and did as he was commanded. He went up to Eargate, and sounded his trumpet, and gave a third summons to Mansoul. He said, moreover, that if this they should still refuse to do, the captains of his Prince would with might come down upon them, and endeavour to reduce them to their obedience by force.

A third summons.

Isa. 58:1.

Then stood up my Lord Willbewill, who was the governor of the town (this Willbewill was that apostate of whom mention was made before), and the

4   *sped*: fared.
8   *kept close*: kept themselves shut up within the town.
18   *that the town shall stand it out still*: should the town still ignore or reject that summons.

keeper of the gates of Mansoul. He, therefore, with big and ruffling words demanded of the trumpeter who he was, whence he came, and what was the cause of his making so hideous a noise at the gate, and speaking such insufferable words against the town of Mansoul?

The trumpeter answered, 'I am servant to the most noble captain, Captain Boanerges, general of the forces of the great King Shaddai, against whom both thyself with the whole town of Mansoul have re-belled, and lift up the heel; and my master the captain hath a special message to this town, and to thee as a member thereof; the which if you of Mansoul shall peaceably hear, so; and if not, you must take what follows.'

Then said the Lord Willbewill, 'I will carry thy words to my lord, and will know what he will say.'

But the trumpeter soon replied, saying, 'Our message is, not to the giant Diabolus, but to the miserable town of Mansoul; nor shall we at all regard what answer by him is made; nor yet by any for him. We are sent to this town to recover it from under his cruel tyranny, and to persuade it to submit, as in former times it did, to the most excellent King Shaddai.'

Then said the Lord Willbewill, 'I will do your errand to the town.'

The trumpeter then replied, 'Sir, do not deceive us, lest in so doing, you deceive yourselves much more.' He added moreover, 'For we are resolved, if in peaceable manner you do not submit yourselves, then to make a war upon you, and to bring you under by force. And of the truth of what I now say, this shall be a sign unto you, you shall see the black flag with its hot, burning thunderbolts set upon the mount tomorrow, as a token of defiance against your prince, and of our resolutions to reduce you to your Lord, and rightful King.'

2   *big and ruffling words*: rough and arrogant speech.
11   *lift up the heel*: kicked. See Ps. 41:9.

So the said Lord Willbewill returned from off the wall, and the trumpeter came into the camp. When the trumpeter was come into the camp, the captains and officers of the mighty King Shaddai came together to know, if he had obtained a hearing, and what was the effect of his errand. So the trumpeter told, saying, 'When I had sounded my trumpet, and had called aloud to the town for a hearing, my Lord Willbewill the governor of the town, and he that hath charge of the gates came up, when he heard me sound, and looking over the wall, he asked me what I was, whence I came, and what was the cause of my making this noise? So I told him my errand, and by whose authority I brought it. Then, said he, *I will tell it to the governor and to Mansoul.* And then I returned to my lords.'

The trumpeter returns to the camp.

Then said the brave Boanerges, 'Let us yet for a while lie still in our trenches, and see what these rebels will do.'

Now when the time drew nigh that audience by Mansoul must be given to the brave Boanerges and his companions, it was commanded that all the men of war throughout the whole camp of Shaddai, should as one man stand to their arms, and make themselves ready, if the town of Mansoul shall hear, to receive it forthwith to mercy; but if not, to force a subjection. So the day being come, the trumpeters sounded, and that throughout the whole camp, that the men of war might be in a readiness for that which then should be the work of the day. But when they that were in the town of Mansoul, heard the sound of the trumpets throughout the camp of Shaddai, and thinking no other, but that it must be in order to storming the corporation, they at first were put to great consternation of spirit; but after they a little were settled again, they also made what preparation they could for a war, if they did storm; else, to secure themselves.

Carnal souls make a wrong interpretation of the design of a Gospel ministry.

Well, when the utmost time was come, Boanerges was resolved to hear their answer; wherefore he sent out his trumpeter again to summons Mansoul to a hearing of the message that they had brought from

Zech. 7:11.

Shaddai. So he went and sounded, and the townsmen came up, but made Eargate as sure as they could. Now when they were come up to the top of the wall, Captain Boanerges desired to see the Lord Mayor; but my Lord Incredulity was then Lord Mayor, for he came in the room of my Lord Lustings. So Incredulity, he came up and showed himself over the wall; but when the Captain Boanerges had set his eyes upon him, he cried out aloud, 'This is not he. Where is my Lord Understanding, the ancient Lord Mayor of the town of Mansoul, for to him I would deliver my message?'

Then said the giant—for Diabolus was also come down—to the captain: 'Mr. Captain, you have by your boldness given to Mansoul at least four summons to subject herself to your King, by whose authority I know not; nor will I dispute that now. I ask therefore what is the reason of all this ado, or what would you be at, if you knew yourselves?'

Then Captain Boanerges, whose was the black colours, and whose scutcheon was the three burning thunderbolts, taking no notice of the giant or of his speech, thus addressed himself to the town of Mansoul: 'Be it known unto you, O unhappy and rebellious Mansoul, that the most gracious King, the great King Shaddai, my Master, hath sent me unto you with commission'—and so he showed to the town his broad seal—'to reduce you to his obedience. And he hath commanded me, in case you yield, upon my summons, to carry it to you as if you were my friends, or brother; but he also hath bid, that if after summons to submit, you still stand out and rebel, we should endeavour to take you by force.'

Then stood forth Captain Conviction, and said (his was the pale colours, and for a scutcheon he had the book of the law wide open, etc.), 'Hear O Mansoul! Thou, O Mansoul, wast once famous for innocency, but now thou art degenerated into lies and deceit. Thou hast heard what my brother, the Captain Boanerges, hath said; and it is your wisdom, and will

Side notes: Boanerges refuses to make Incredulity a judge of what he had to deliver to the famous town of Mansoul. Boanerges obtains a hearing. His speech. The speech of Captain Conviction. Rom. 3:10-19, 23; 16:17-18. Ps. 50:21,22.

29   *carry it to you*: behave toward you.

be your happiness to stoop to, and accept of conditions of peace and mercy when offered—specially when offered by one, against whom thou has rebelled, and one who is of power to tear thee in pieces, for so is Shaddai, our King; nor when he is angry, can anything stand before him. If you say you have not sinned, or acted rebellion against our King, the whole of your doings since the day that you cast off his service (and there was the beginning of your sin) will sufficiently testify against you. What else means your hark'ning to the tyrant, and your receiving him for your king? What means else your rejecting of the laws of Shaddai, and your obeying of Diabolus? Yea, what means this your taking up of arms against, and the shutting of your gates upon us, the faithful servants of your King? Be ruled then, and accept of my brother's invitation, and overstand not the time of mercy, but agree with thine adversary quickly. Ah Mansoul, suffer not thyself to be kept from mercy, and to be run into a thousand miseries, by the flattering wiles of Diabolus. Perhaps that piece of deceit may attempt to make you believe that we seek our own profit in this our service; but know 'tis obedience to our King, and love to your happiness, that is the cause of this undertaking of ours.

Luke 12:58,59.

'Again, I say to thee, O Mansoul, consider if it be not amazing grace that Shaddai should so humble himself as he doth, now he by us reasons with you, in a way of entreaty and sweet persuasions, that you would subject yourselves to him. Has he that need of you, that we are sure you have of him? No, no; but he is merciful, and will not that Mansoul should die, but turn to him and live.'

II Cor. 5:18-21.

Then stood forth Captain Judgment (whose was the red colours, and for a scutcheon he had the burning fiery furnace), and he said: 'O ye the inhabitants of the town of Mansoul that have lived so long in rebellion and acts of treason against the King Shaddai, know that we come not today to this place, in this

Captain Judgment his speech to Mansoul.

17   *overstand*: outstay.

manner, with our message of our own minds, or to revenge our own quarrel; it is the King, my Master, that hath sent us to reduce you to your obedience to him, the which if you refuse, in a peaceable way to yield, we have commission to compel you thereto. And never think of yourselves, nor yet suffer the tyrant Diabolus to persuade you to think, that our King by his power is not able to bring you down, and to lay you under his feet, for he is the former of all things, and if he touches the mountains they smoke. Nor will the gate of the King's clemency stand always open, for the day that shall burn like an oven is before him; yea it hasteth greatly, it slumb'reth not.

'O Mansoul! is it little in thine eyes that our King doth offer thee mercy, and that after so many provocations? Yea, he still holdeth out his golden scepter to thee, and will not yet suffer his gate to be shut against thee: wilt thou provoke him to do it? If so, consider of what I say: To thee it is opened no more for ever. If thou sayest thou shalt not see him, yet judgment is before him; therefore trust thou in him. Yea, because there is wrath, beware lest he take thee away with his stroke; then a great ransom cannot deliver thee. Will he esteem thy riches? No, not gold, nor all the forces of strength. He hath prepared his throne for judgment, for he will come with fire, and with his chariots like a whirlwind, to render his anger with fury, and his rebukes with flames of fire. Therefore, O Mansoul, take heed, lest after thou hast fulfilled the judgment of the wicked, justice and judgment should take hold of thee.' Now while the Captain Judgment was making of this oration to the town of Mansoul, it was observed by some that Diabolus trembled. But he proceeded in his parable and said, 'O thou woeful town of Mansoul! Wilt thou not yet set open thy gate to receive us, the deputies of thy King, and those that would rejoice to see thee live? Can thine heart endure, or can thy hands be strong in

Mal. 4:1.
II Pet. 2:3.

Job 36:14.
II Chron. 36:18.
Ps. 9:7.
Isa. 66:15.

10

20

30

9   *former*: creator.
16f.   *golden scepter*: see Esther 5:2.

the day that he shall deal in judgment with thee? I
say, canst thou endure to be forced to drink, as one
would drink sweet wine, the sea of wrath that our
King has prepared for Diabolus and his angels? Consider, betimes consider.'

Ezek. 22:14.

Then stood forth the fourth captain, the noble
Captain Execution, and said: 'O town of Mansoul,
once famous, but now like the fruitless bough; once
the delight of the high ones, but now a den for
Diabolus; hearken also to me, and to the words that
I shall speak to thee in the name of the great Shaddai.
*Behold the axe is laid to the root of the trees; every
tree therefore that bringeth not forth good fruit, is
hewn down and cast into the fire.*

The speech of
Captain Execu-
tion.

Matt. 3:7-10.

'Thou, O town of Mansoul, hast hitherto been
this fruitless tree; thou barest nought but thorns and
briars. Thy evil fruit fore-bespeaks thee not to be a
good tree: thy grapes are grapes of gall, thy clusters
are bitter. Thou hast rebelled against thy King, and
lo! we, the power and force of Shaddai, are the axe
that is laid to thy roots. What sayest thou? Wilt thou
turn? I say again—tell me before the first blow is
given: wilt thou turn? Our axe must first be laid *to*
thy root, before it be laid *at* thy root; it must first be
laid *to* thy root *in a way of threat'ning*, before it is
laid *at* thy root *by way of execution*; and between
these two is required thy repentance, and this is all the
time that thou hast. What wilt thou do? Wilt thou
turn? Or shall I smite? If I fetch my blow, Mansoul,
down you go. For I have commission to lay my axe *at*,
as well as *to* thy roots, nor will anything, but yielding
to our King, prevent doing of execution. What art
thou fit for, O Mansoul, if mercy preventeth not, but
to be hewn down, and cast into the fire and burned?

Deut. 32:32.

'O Mansoul! patience and forbearance do not act
for ever: a year, or two, or three they may; but if thou
provoke by a three years' rebellion—and thou hast
already done more than this—then what follows but

29   *fetch*: strike.

Luke 13. *Cut it down? nay, After that thou shalt cut it down.*
And dost thou think that these are but threat'nings,
or that our King has not power to execute his words?
O Mansoul! thou wilt find that in the words of our
King, when they are by sinners made little or light of,
there is not only threat'ning, but burning coals of fire.

'Thou hast been a cumber-ground long already,
and wilt thou continue so still? Thy sin has brought
this army to thy walls, and shall it bring it in judgment to do execution into thy town? Thou hast heard
what the captains have said, but as yet thou shuttest
thy gates. Speak out, Mansoul; wilt thou do so still, or
wilt thou accept of conditions of peace?'

These brave speeches of these four noble captains, the town of Mansoul refused to hear, yet a
sound thereof did beat against Eargate, though the
force thereof could not break it open. In fine, the town

Mansoul desires time to make answer. desired a time to prepare their answer to these
demands. The captains then told them that if they
would throw out to them one Ill-pause, that was in
the town, that they might reward him according to
his works, then they would give them time to con-

Upon what conditions the captains would give them time. sider; but if they would not cast him to them over the
wall of Mansoul, then they would give them none.
'For,' said they, 'we know that so long as Ill-pause
draws breath in Mansoul, all good consideration will
be confounded, and nothing but mischief will come
thereon.'

Then Diabolus, who was there present, being loth

Diabolus interrupts them and sets Incredulity to answer them. to lose his Ill-pause, because he was his orator (and
yet be sure he had, could the captains have laid their
fingers on him), was resolved at this instant to give
them answer by himself; but then changing his mind,
he commanded the then Lord Mayor, the Lord Incredulity, to do it, saying: 'My Lord, do you give these
runagates an answer, and speak out that Mansoul may
hear and understand you.'

10

20

30

---

1   The sense of the first edition reading is obscure: "what follows, but cut it
down, nay after that thou shalt cut it down." Our punctuation follows that
of the second edition.

7   *cumber-ground*: whatever occupies space unprofitably. See Luke 13:7.

So Incredulity at Diabolus's command began and said: 'Gentlemen, you have here, as we do behold, to the disturbance of our prince, and the molestation of the town of Mansoul, camped against it: but from whence you come, we will not know; and what you are, we will not believe. Indeed you tell us in your terrible speech, that you have this authority from Shaddai, but by what right he commands you to do it, of that we shall yet be ignorant.

His speech.

'You have also by the authority aforesaid, summoned this town to desert her lord, and for protection, to yield up herself to the great Shaddai your King; flatteringly telling her, that if she will do it, he will pass by and not charge her with her past offences.

'Further, you have also to the terror of the town of Mansoul, threat'ned with great and sore destructions to punish this corporation if she consents not to do as your wills would have her.

'Now captains, from whence soever you come, and though your designs be never so right; yet know ye, that neither my Lord Diabolus, nor I his servant Incredulity, nor yet our brave Mansoul, doth regard either your persons, message, or the King that you say hath sent you. His power, his greatness, his vengeance we fear not; nor will we yield at all to your summons.

The true picture of unbelief.

'As for the war that you threaten to make upon us, we must therein defend ourselves as well as we can: and know ye, that we are not without wherewithal to bid defiance to you. And in short (for I will not be tedious), I tell you that we take you to be some vagabond runagate crew, that having shaken off all obedience to your King, have gotten together in tumultuous manner, and are ranging from place to place to see, if, through the flatteries you are skilled to make on the one side, and threats wherewith you think to fright on the other, to make some silly town, city, or country, to desert their place and leave it to you. But Mansoul is none of them.

'To conclude: we dread you not, we fear you not,

20 *never*: second edition, "ever."

nor will we obey your summons. Our gates we keep shut upon you, our place we will keep you out of. Nor will we long thus suffer you to sit down before us.

Luke 11:21. Our people must live in quiet: your appearance doth disturb them. Wherefore arise with bag and baggage,

Flesh. and be gone, or we will let fly from the walls against you.'

This oration made by old Incredulity, was seconded by desperate Willbewill, in words to this effect.

The speech of the Lord Willbewill. 'Gentlemen, we have heard your demands, and the noise of your threats, and have heard the sound of your summons, but we fear not your force, we regard not your threats, but will still abide as you found us. And we command you, that in three days' time you cease to appear in these parts, or you shall know what it is once to dare offer to rouse the lion Diabolus, when asleep in his town of Mansoul?'

The speech of Forget-good the Recorder. The Recorder whose name was Forget-good, he also added as followeth. 'Gentlemen, my lords, as you see, have with mild and gentle words answered your rough and angry speeches; they have moreover, in my hearing, given you leave quietly to depart as you came. Wherefore take their kindness and be gone. We might have come out with force upon you, and have caused you to feel the dint of our swords; but as we love ease and quiet ourselves, so we love not to hurt or molest others.'

Then did the town of Mansoul shout for joy, as if by Diabolus and his crew some great advantage had been gotten of the captains. They also rang the bells, and made merry, and danced upon the walls.

The town resolved to withstand the captains. Diabolus also returned to the castle, and the Lord Mayor and Recorder to their place. But the Lord Willbewill took special care that the gates should be secured with double guards, double bolts, and double locks and bars; and that Eargate especially might the better be looked to, for that was the gate in at which the King's forces sought most to enter. The Lord Willbewill made one old Mr. Prejudice, an angry and ill-conditioned fellow, captain of the ward at that gate, and put under his power sixty men, called Deaf-men—men advantageous for that service, for as much as they mattered no words of the captains, nor of their soldiers.

The band of Deaf-men set to keep Eargate.

Now when the captains saw the answer of the great ones, and that they could not get an hearing from the old natives of the town, and that Mansoul was resolved to give the King's army battle, they prepared themselves to receive them, and to try it out by the power of the arm. And first they made their force more formidable against Eargate; for they knew that unless they could penetrate that, no good could be done upon the town. This done, they put the rest of their men in their places. After which they gave out the word, which was, *Ye must be born again.* Then they sounded the trumpet; then they in the town made them answer, with shout against shout, charge against charge, and so the battle began. Now they in the town had planted upon the tower over Eargate, two great guns, the one called High-mind, and the other Heady. Unto these two guns they trusted much: they were cast in the castle by Diabolus's founder, whose name was Mr. Puff-up, and mischievous pieces they were. But so vigilant and watchful, when the captains saw them, were they, that though sometimes their shot would go by their ears with a *whizz*, yet they did them no harm. By these two guns the townsfolk made no question but greatly to annoy the camp of Shaddai, and well enough to secure the gate, but they had not much cause to boast of what execution they did, as by what follows will be gathered.

The captains resolved to give them battle.

The battle begun.

Two guns planted upon Eargate.

The famous Mansoul had also some other small pieces in it, of the which they made use against the camp of Shaddai.

They from the camp also, did as stoutly, and with as much of that as may in truth be called valour, let fly as fast at the town, and at Eargate; for they saw that unless they could break open Eargate, 'twould be but in vain to batter the wall. Now the

The sentence and power of the word.

2 *mattered no words of the captains*: regarded the captains' words as of no importance.

58

King's captains had brought with them several slings and two or three battering-rams; with their slings, therefore, they battered the houses and people of the town, and with their rams they sought to break Eargate open.

The town stoutly stands out and the captains return to their winter quarters.

The camp and the town had several skirmishes, and brisk encounters, while the captains with their engines made many brave attempts to break open or beat down the tower that was over Eargate, and at the said gate to make their entrance. But Mansoul stood it out so lustily, through the rage of Diabolus, the valour of the Lord Willbewill, and the conduct of old Incredulity the Mayor, and Mr. Forget-good the Recorder, that the charge and expense of that summer's wars, on the King's side seemed to be almost quite lost, and the advantage to return to Mansoul. But when the captains saw how it was, they made a fair retreat, and entrenched themselves in their winter quarters. Now in this war, you must needs think there was much loss on both sides, of which be pleased to accept of this brief account following.

An account of this war with reference to the loss on both sides.

The King's captains, when they marched from the Court to come up against Mansoul to war, as they came crossing over the country, they happened to light upon three young fellows that had a mind to go for soldiers—proper men they were, and men of courage and skill, to appearance. Their names were Mr. Tradition, Mr. Human-wisdom, and Mr. Man's-invention. So they came up to the captains, and proffered their service to Shaddai. The captains then told them of their design, and bid them not to be rash in their offers; but the young men told them they had considered the thing before, and that hearing they were upon their march for such a design, came hither on purpose to meet them, that they might be listed under their excellencies. Then Captain Boanerges, for that they were men of courage, listed them into his company, and so away they went to the war.

Three new soldiers.

Now when the war was begun, in one of the briskest skirmishes, so it was, that a company of the Lord

10

20

30

40

Willbewill's men sallied out at the sally-port or postern of the town, and fell in upon the rear of Captain Boanerges' men, where these three fellows happened to be; so they took them prisoners, and away they carried them into the town, where they had not lain long in durance, but it began to be noised about the streets of the town what three notable prisoners the Lord Willbewill's men had taken, and brought in prisoners out of the camp of Shaddai. At length tidings thereof was carried to Diabolus to the castle, to wit, what my Lord Willbewill's men had done, and whom they had taken prisoners.

They are taken prisoners.

Then Diabolus called for Willbewill, to know the certainty of this matter. So he asked him, and he told him. Then did the giant send for the prisoners, who when they were come, demanded of them who they were, whence they came, and what they did in the camp of Shaddai; and they told him. Then he sent them to ward again. Not many days after, he sent for them to him again, and then asked them if they would be willing to serve him against their former captains. They then told him, that they did not so much live by religion, as by the fates of fortune. And that since his lordship was willing to entertain them, they should be willing to serve him. Now while things were thus in hand, there was one Captain Anything, a great doer in the town of Mansoul, and to this Captain Anything did Diabolus send these men, with a note under his hand to receive them into his company; the contents of which letter were thus—

They are brought before Diabolus, and are content to fight under his banner.

Anything.

He therefore sends them to Captain Anything with a letter.

Anything, my darling: the three men that are the bearers of this letter have a desire to serve me in the war; nor know I better to whose conduct to commit them than to thine. Receive them, therefore, in my name, and as need shall require, make use of them against Shaddai and his men. Farewell.

1   *sally-port*: gate through which the besieged soldiers rushed out upon the enemy.

So they came, and he received them, and he made of two of them sergeants, but he made Mr. Man's-invention, his ancient-bearer. But thus much for this; and now to return to the camp.

They of the camp did also some execution upon the town, for they did beat down the roof of the old Lord Mayor's house, and so laid him more open than he was before. They had almost with a sling slain my Lord Willbewill outright; but he made a shift to recover again. But they made a notable slaughter among the aldermen, for with one only shot they cut off six of them; to wit, Mr. Swearing, Mr. Whoring, Mr. Fury, Mr. Stand-to-lies, Mr. Drunkenness, and Mr. Cheating.

They also dismounted the two guns that stood upon the tower over Eargate, and laid them flat, in the dirt. I told you before that the King's noble captains had drawn off to their winter quarters, and had there entrenched themselves and their carriages, so as with the best advantage to their King, and the greatest annoyance to the enemy, they might give seasonable warm alarms to the town of Mansoul. And this design of them did so hit, that I may say they did almost what they would to the molestation of the corporation.

For now could not Mansoul sleep securely as before, nor could they now go to their debaucheries with that quietness as in times past. For they had from the camp of Shaddai such frequent, warm, and terrifying alarms—yea, alarms upon alarms, first at one gate and then at another, and again, at all the gates at once, that they were broken as to former peace. Yea, they had their alarms so frequently, and that when the nights were at longest, the weather coldest, and so consequently the season most unseasonable, that that winter was to the town of Mansoul a winter by itself. Sometimes the trumpets would sound, sometimes the slings would whirl the stones into the town. Sometimes ten thousand of the King's

10

20

30

3   *ancient-bearer*: standard-bearer.

soldiers would be running round the walls of Mansoul at midnight, shouting, and lifting up the voice for the battle. Sometimes again, some of them in the town would be wounded, and their cry and lamentable voice would be heard, to the great molestation of the now languishing town of Mansoul. Yea, so distressed with those that laid siege against them were they, that I dare say, Diabolus their king had in these days his rest much broken.

In these days, as I was informed, new thoughts, and thoughts that began to run counter one to another, began to possess the minds of the men of the town of Mansoul. Some would say, 'There is no living thus.' Others would then reply, 'This will be over shortly.' Then would a third stand up and answer, 'Let us turn to the King Shaddai, and so put an end to these troubles.' And a fourth would come in with a fear saying, 'I doubt he will not receive us.' The old gentleman too, the Recorder that was so before Diabolus took Mansoul, he also began to talk aloud, and his words were now to the town of Mansoul, as if they were great claps of thunder. No noise now so terrible to Mansoul as was his, with the noise of the soldiers and shoutings of the captains.

Also things began to grow scarce in Mansoul; now the things that her soul lusted after, were departing from her. Upon all her pleasant things there was a blast, and burning instead of beauty. Wrinkles now, and some shows of the shadow of death, were upon the inhabitants of Mansoul. And now, O how glad would Mansoul have been to have enjoyed quietness, and satisfaction of mind, though joined with the meanest condition in the world!

The captains also, in the deep of this winter, did send by the mouth of Boanerges' trumpeter, a summons to Mansoul to yield up herself to the King, the great King Shaddai. They sent it once, and twice, and thrice; not knowing but that at some times there might be in Mansoul some willingness to surrender up

Marginal notes:
- The town much molested.
- Change of thoughts in Mansoul.
- Conscience speaks.
- A famine in Mansoul.
- Luke 15:14,15.
- They are summoned again to yield.

28   *blast*: blight. Cf. "blasted heath" in *Macbeth*.

themselves unto them, might they but have the colour of an invitation to do it under. Yea, so far as I could gather, the town had been surrend'red up to them before now, had it not been for the opposition of old Incredulity, and the fickleness of the thoughts of my Lord Willbewill. Diabolus also began to rave; wherefore Mansoul, as to yielding, was not yet all of one mind; therefore they still lay distressed under these perplexing fears.

Mansoul in distress.

I told you but now that they of the King's army had this winter sent three times to Mansoul, to submit herself.

The first time the trumpeter went, he went with words of peace, telling of them, that the captains, the noble captains of Shaddai, did pity and bewail the misery of the now perishing town of Mansoul, and was troubled to see them so much to stand in the way of their own deliverance. He said, moreover, that the captains bid him tell them that if now poor Mansoul would humble herself, and turn, her former rebellions and most notorious treasons should by their merciful King be forgiven them—yea, and forgotten too. And having bid them beware that they stood not in their own way, that they opposed not themselves, nor made themselves their own losers, he returned again into the camp.

The contents of the first summons.

Secondly, the second time the trumpeter went, he did treat them a little more roughly. For, after sound of trumpet, he told them that their continuing in their rebellion did but chafe and heat the spirit of the captains, and that they were resolved to make a conquest of Mansoul, or to lay their bones before the town walls.

The contents of the second summons.

Thirdly, he went again the third time, and dealt with them yet more roughly; telling of them that now, since they had been so horribly profane, he did not know, not certainly know, whether the captains were inclining to mercy or judgment. 'Only,' said he, 'they commanded me to give you a summons to open the gates unto them.' So he returned, and went into the camp.

The contents of the third summons.

10

20

30

40

These three summons and especially the two last, did so distress the town that they presently call a consultation, the result of which was this, that my Lord Willbewill should go up to Eargate, and there with sound of trumpet call to the captains of the camp for a parley. Well, the Lord Willbewill sounded upon the wall; so the captains came up in their harness, with their ten thousands at their feet. The townsmen then told the captains, that they had heard and considered their summons, and would come to an agreement with them, and with their King Shaddai, upon such certain terms, articles, and propositions as, with and by the order of their Prince, they to them were appointed to propound. To wit, they would agree upon these grounds to be one people with them:

The town sounds for a parley.

They propound conditions of agreement.

1. If that those of their own company, as the now Lord Mayor, and their Mr. Forget-good, with their brave Lord Willbewill, might under Shaddai be still the governors of the town, castle, and gates of Mansoul.

Proposition the first.

2. Provided that no man that now serveth under their great giant Diabolus, be by Shaddai cast out of house, harbor, or the freedom that he hath hitherto enjoyed in the famous town of Mansoul.

Proposition the second.

3. That it shall be granted them, that they of the town of Mansoul shall enjoy certain of their rights, and privileges: to wit, such as have formerly been granted them, and that they have long lived in the enjoyment of, under the reign of their King Diabolus, that now is and long has been their only lord, and great defender.

Proposition the third.

4. That no new law, officer, or executioner of law or office, shall have any power over them, without their own choice and consent.

Proposition the fourth.

'These be our propositions, or conditions of peace; and upon these terms,' said they, 'we will submit to your King.'

2 *presently*: immediately.

64

But when the captains had heard this weak and feeble offer of the town of Mansoul, and their high and bold demands, they made to them again by their noble captain, the Captain Boanerges, this speech following—

O ye inhabitants of the town of Mansoul, when I heard your trumpet sound for a parley with us, I can truly say I was glad; but when you said you were willing to submit yourselves to our King and Lord, then I was yet more glad. But when by your silly provisoes, and foolish cavils, you lay the stumbling-block of your iniquity before your own faces, then was my gladness turned into sorrows, and my hopeful beginnings of your return, into languishing, fainting fears.

'I count that old Ill-pause, the ancient enemy of Mansoul, did draw up those proposals that now you present us with, as terms of an agreement; but they deserve not to be admitted to sound in the ear of any man that pretends to have service for Shaddai. We do therefore jointly, and that with the highest disdain, refuse, and reject such things as the greatest of iniquities.

'But, O Mansoul, if you will give yourselves into our hands, or rather into the hands of our King, and will trust him to make such terms with and for you, as shall seem good in his eyes—and I dare say they shall be such as you shall find to be most profitable to you—then we will receive you, and be at peace with you. But if you like not to trust yourselves in the arms of Shaddai our King, then things are but where they were before, and we know also what we have to do.'

Then cried out old Incredulity the Lord Mayor, and said, 'And who, being out of the hands of their enemies, as ye see we are now, will be so foolish as to put the staff out of their own hands, into the hand of they know not who? I, for my part, will never yield to so unlimited a proposition. Do we know the manner and temper of their King? 'Tis said by some, that he will be angry with his subjects, if but the

Boanerges his answer.

II Tim. 2:19.

Old Incredulity's reply.

Unbelief never is profitable in talk, but always speaks mischievously.

10

20

30

40

breadth of an hair they chance to step out of the way; and of others, that he requireth of them much more than they can perform. Wherefore it seems, O Mansoul, to be thy wisdom to take good heed what thou dost in this matter. For if you once yield, you give up yourselves to another, and so you are no more your own. Wherefore, to give up yourselves to an unlimited power is the greatest folly in the world. For now you indeed may repent, but can never justly complain. But do you indeed know, when you are his, which of you he will kill, and which of you he will save alive? Or whether he will not cut off every one of us, and send out of his own country another new people, and cause them to inhabit this town?'

This speech of the Lord Mayor undid all, and threw flat to the ground their hopes of an accord. Wherefore the captains returned to their trenches, to their tents, and to their men, as they were; and the Mayor to the castle, and to his king.

> This speech undid all, but it did please the devil.

Now Diabolus had waited for his return, for he had heard that they had been at their points. So when he was come into the chamber of state, Diabolus saluted him with, 'Welcome my Lord. How went matters betwixt you today?' So the Lord Incredulity (with a low congy), told him the whole of the matter, saying, '*Thus and thus*, said the captains of Shaddai, and *thus and thus* said I.' The which when 'twas told to Diabolus, he was very glad to hear it, and said, 'My Lord Mayor, my faithful Incredulity, I have proved thy fidelity above ten times already, but never yet found thee false. I do promise thee, if we rub over this brunt, to prefer thee to a place of honour, a place far better than to be Lord Mayor of Mansoul. I will make thee my Universal Deputy, and thou shalt, next to me, have all nations under thy hand; yea, and thou shalt lay bands upon them that they may not resist thee, nor shall any of our vassals walk

21   *at their points*: in fierce debate (lit. fighting with swords).
25   *congy*: bow. A variant form of *congee*.
31f. *rub over this brunt*: clear this hurdle.

more at liberty, but those that shall be content to walk in thy fetters.'

Now came the Lord Mayor out from Diabolus, as if he had obtained a favour indeed; wherefore to his habitation he goes in great state, and thinks to feed himself well enough with hopes, until the time came that his greatness should be enlarged.

But now, though the Lord Mayor and Diabolus did thus well agree, yet this repulse to the brave captains put Mansoul into a mutiny. For while old Incredulity went into the castle to congratulate his lord with what had passed, the old Lord Mayor that was so before Diabolus came to the town, to wit, my Lord Understanding, and the old Recorder Mr. Conscience, getting intelligence of what had passed at Eargate (for you must know that they might not be suffered to be at that debate, lest they should then have mutinied, for the captains; but, I say, they got intelligence what had passed there, and were much concerned therewith), wherefore they, getting some of the town together, began to possess them with the reasonableness of the noble captains' demands, and with the bad consequences that would follow upon the speech of old Incredulity, the Lord Mayor: to wit, how little reverence he showed therein, either to the captains, or to their King; also how he implicitly charged them with unfaithfulness, and treachery. For what less, quoth they, could be made of his words, when he said he would not yield to their proposition, and added moreover a supposition, that he would destroy us, when before he had sent us word that he would show us mercy? The multitude, being now possessed with the conviction of the evil that old Incredulity had done, began to run together by companies in all places, and in every corner of the streets of Mansoul; and first they began to mutter, then to talk openly, and after that they run to and fro, and cried as they run, 'O the brave captains of Shaddai! Would we were under the government of the captains, and of Shaddai their King!' When the Lord Mayor had intelligence that Mansoul was in an uproar, down he comes to appease

The understanding and conscience begin to receive conviction, and they set the soul in a hubbub.

A mutiny in Mansoul.

10

20

30

40

the people, and thought to have quashed their heat
with the bigness and the show of his countenance.
But when they saw him, they came running upon
him, and had doubtless done him a mischief, had he
not betaken himself to house. However, they strongly
assaulted the house where he was, to have pulled it
down about his ears; but the place was too strong,
so they failed of that. So he, taking some courage, *Incredulity*
addressed himself, out at a window, to the people in *seeks to quiet*
the people.
this manner—

'Gentlemen, what is the reason, that there is here
such an uproar to-day?'

UND. Then answered my Lord Understanding *My Lord Un-*
'It is even because that thou and thy master have *derstanding an-*
carried it not rightly, and as you should, to the cap- *swers him.*
tains of Shaddai; for in three things you are faulty.
First, in that you would not let Mr. Conscience and
myself be at the hearing of your discourse. Secondly,
in that you propounded such terms of peace, to the
captains, that by no means could be granted, unless
they had intended that their Shaddai should have
been only a titular Prince, and that Mansoul should
still have had power by law to have lived in all lewdness and vanity before him, and so by consequence
Diabolus should still here be king in power, and the
other, only King in name. Thirdly, for that thou didst
thyself, after the captains had showed us upon what
conditions they would have received us to mercy,
even undo all again with thy unsavory, and unseasonable, and ungodly speech.'

INCRED. When old Incredulity had heard this *Sin and the*
speech, he cried out, 'Treason! Treason! To your arms! *soul at odds.*
To your arms! O ye, the trusty friends of Diabolus in
Mansoul!'

UND. 'Sir, you may put upon my words what
meaning you please, but I am sure that the captains
of such an high lord as theirs is, deserved a better
treatment at your hands.'

INCRED. Then said old Incredulity, 'This is but
little better. But sir,' quoth he, 'what I spake, I spake
for my prince, for his government, and the quieting

of the people, whom by your unlawful actions, you
have this day set to mutiny against us.'

Cons. Then replied the old Recorder, whose name
was Mr. Conscience, and said, 'Sir, you ought not thus
to retort upon what my Lord Understanding hath said.
'Tis evident enough that he hath spoken the truth,
and that you are an enemy to Mansoul. Be convinced,
then, of the evil of your saucy and malapert language,
and of the grief that you have put the captains to;
yea, and of the damages that you have done to Mansoul thereby. Had you accepted of the conditions, the
sound of the trumpet and the alarm of war had now
ceased about the town of Mansoul; but that dreadful
sound abides, and your want of wisdom in your speech
has been the cause of it.'

Incred. Then said old Incredulity: 'Sir, if I live
I will do your errand to Diabolus, and there you shall
have an answer to your words. Meanwhile we will
seek the good of the town, and not ask counsel of
you.'

Und. 'Sir, your prince and you are both foreigners
to Mansoul, and not the natives thereof. And who
can tell but that when you have brought us into
greater straits (when you also shall see that yourselves can be safe by no other means than by flight),
you may leave us and shift for yourselves, or set us
on fire, and go away in the smoke, or by the light of
our burning, and so leave us in our ruins?'

Incred. 'Sir, you forget that you are under a
governor, and that you ought to demean yourself like
a subject; and know ye, when my lord the king shall
hear of this day's work, he will give you but little
thanks for your labour.'

Now while these gentlemen were thus in their
chiding words, down comes from the walls and gates
of the town, the Lord Willbewill, Mr. Prejudice, old
Ill-pause, and several of the new-made aldermen and
burgesses, and they asked the reason of the hubbub,
and tumult. And with that every man began to tell
his own tale, so that nothing could be heard distinctly.
Then was a silence commanded, and the old fox In-

10

20

30

40

credulity began to speak: 'My lord,' quoth he, 'here are a couple of peevish gentlemen, that have, as a fruit of their bad dispositions, and as I fear, through the advice of one Mr. Discontent, tumultuously gathered this company against me this day, and also attempted to run the town into acts of rebellion against our prince.'

Then stood up all the Diabolonians that were present, and affirmed these things to be true.

Now when they that took part with my Lord Understanding, and with Mr. Conscience, perceived that they were like to come to the worst, for that force and power was on the other side, they came in for their help and relief; so a great company was on both sides. Then they on Incredulity's side would have had the two old gentlemen presently away to prison; but they on the other side said they should not. Then they began to cry up parties again. The Diabolonians cried up old Incredulity, Forget-good, the new aldermen, and their great one Diabolus; and the other party, they as fast cried up Shaddai, the captains, his laws, their mercifulness, and applauded their conditions and ways. Thus the bickerment went a while; at last they passed from words to blows, and now there were knocks on both sides. The good old gentleman, Mr. Conscience, was knocked down twice by one of the Diabolonians, whose name was Mr. Benumbing. And my Lord Understanding had like to have been slain with an harquebus, but that he that shot wanted to take his aim aright. Nor did the other side wholly escape, for there was one Mr. Rashhead, a Diabolonian, that had his brains beaten out by Mr. Mind, the Lord Willbewill's servant; and it made me laugh to see how old Mr. Prejudice was kicked and tumbled about in the dirt. For though a while since he was made captain of a company of the Diabolonians, to the hurt and damage of the town, yet now

Marginal notes:

A great confusion.

They fall from words to blows.

A hot skirmish.

---

2   *peevish*: perverse.
29   *harquebus*: an early model of portable gun, which rested on a tripod by a hook attached to the barrel. (From Fr. *arquebuse*; ult. f. MHG *haken*, hook; *bühse*, gun.)

they had got him under their feet; and, I'll assure you, he had by some of the Lord Understanding's party, his crown soundly cracked to boot. Mr. Anything also, he became a brisk man in the broil; but both sides were against him, because he was true to none. Yet he had for his malapertness one of his legs broken, and he that did it, wished it had been his neck. Much harm

Harm done on both sides.

more was done on both sides, but this must not be forgotten: it was now a wonder to see my Lord Willbewill so indifferent as he was; he did not seem to take one side more than another, only it was perceived that he smiled to see how old Prejudice was tumbled up and down in the dirt. Also when Captain Anything came halting up before him, he seemed to take but little notice of him.

Now when the uproar was over, Diabolus sends for my Lord Understanding, and Mr. Conscience, and

The two old gentlemen put in prison as the authors of this revel-rout.

claps them both up in prison as the ringleaders and managers of this most heavy riotous rout in Mansoul. So now the town began to be quiet again, and the prisoners were used hardly; yea, he thought to have made them away, but that the present juncture did not serve for that purpose, for that war was in all their gates.

But let us return again to our story. The captains,

The captains call a council and consult what to do.

when they were gone back from the gate, and were come into the camp again, called a council of war, to consult what was further for them to do. Now some said, 'Let us go up presently and fall upon the town; but the greatest part thought rather better 'twould be to give them another summons to yield; and the reason why they thought this to be best, was, because, that so far as could be perceived, the town of Mansoul now was more inclinable than heretofore. 'And if,' said they, 'while some of them are in a way of inclination, we should by ruggedness give them distaste, we

10

20

30

18gl. *revel-rout*: disorderly brawl.
21 *used hardly*: punished severely.
34 *inclinable*: favourably disposed.
36 *ruggedness*: harshness.

may set them further from closing with our summons, than we would be willing they should.'

Wherefore to this advice they agreed, and called a trumpeter, put words into his mouth, set him his time, and bid him 'God speed.' Well, many hours were not expired before the trumpeter addressed himself to his journey. Wherefore coming up to the wall of the town, he steereth his course to Eargate, and there sounded, as he was commanded. They then that were within came out to see what was the matter, and the trumpeter made them this speech following—

'O hard-hearted and deplorable town of Mansoul! How long wilt thou love thy sinful, sinful simplicity, and ye fools delight in your scorning? As yet despise you the offers of peace and deliverance? As yet will ye refuse the golden offers of Shaddai, and trust to the lies and falsehoods of Diabolus? Think you when Shaddai shall have conquered you, that the remembrance of these your carriages towards him, will yield you peace, and comfort, or that by ruffling language, you can make him afraid as a grasshopper? Doth he entreat you for fear of you? Do you think that you are stronger than he? Look to the heavens, and behold, and consider the stars, how high are they? Can you stop the sun from running his course, and hinder the moon from giving her light? Can you count the number of the stars, or stay the bottles of heaven? Can you call for the waters of the sea, and cause them to cover the face of the ground? Can you behold every one that is proud, and abase him? And bind their faces in secret? Yet these are some of the works of our King, in whose name this day we come up unto you, that you may be brought under his authority. In his

The result is they send another trumpeter to summon the town to yield.

The summons itself.

---

1   *closing with our summons*: doing as we have commanded.
14   *your*: first edition, "their." See Prov. 1:22.
19   *carriages*: behaviour.
26f. See Job 38:37: "Who can number the clouds in wisdom? or can stay the bottles of heaven?"—i.e., who by himself can tell the number of the clouds or make the rain fall? The metaphor depicts heavy clouds as vast water-skins, from which, if one were to "stay" (lay down or tilt) them, the water would pour down as rain.

name, therefore, I summon you again to yield up
yourselves to his captains.'

At this summons the Mansoulians seemed to be
at a stand, and knew not what answer to make.
Wherefore Diabolus forthwith appeared, and took
upon him to do it himself; and thus he begins, but
turns his speech to them of Mansoul:

'Gentlemen,' quoth he, 'and my faithful subjects,
if it is true that this summoner hath said concerning
the greatness of their King, by his terror you will 10
always be kept in bondage, and so be made to sneak.
Yea, how can you now, though he is at a distance,
endure to think of such a mighty one? And if not to
think of him while at a distance, how can you endure
to be in his presence? I, your prince, am familiar with
you, and you may play with me, as you would with a
grasshopper. Consider, therefore, what is for your
profit, and remember the immunities that I have
granted you.

'Farther, if all be true that this man hath said, 20
how comes it to pass that the subjects of Shaddai are
so enslaved in all places where they come? None in the
Universe so unhappy as they, none so trampled upon
as they.

'Consider, my Mansoul: would thou wert as loth
to leave me, as I am loth to leave thee. But consider,
I say, the ball is yet at thy foot. Liberty you have, if
you know how to use it. Yea, a king you have too,
if you can tell how to love and obey him.'

Upon this speech, the town of Mansoul did again 30
harden their hearts, yet more against the captains of
Shaddai. The thoughts of his greatness did quite quash
them, and the thoughts of his holiness sunk them in
despair. Wherefore after a short consult they—of the
Diabolonian party they were—sent back this word
by the trumpeter, that for their parts, they were resolved to stick to their King, but never to yield to

*The town at a
stand.*

*Diabolus makes
a speech to the
town, and en-
deavours to ter-
rify it with the
greatness of
God.*

*He drives Man-
soul into des-
pair.*

---

11   *sneak*: crawl in servility.
27   *the ball is yet at thy foot*: you still have the initiative or opportunity. The
metaphor is taken from football.

Shaddai. So it was but in vain to give them any further summons, for they had rather die upon the place than yield. And now things seemed to be gone quite back, and Mansoul to be out of reach or call. Yet the captains who knew what their Lord could do, would not yet be beat out of heart; they therefore send them another summons, more sharp and severe than the last, but the oftener they were sent to, to reconcile to Shaddai, the further off they were. As they called them, so they went from them—yea, though they called them to the Most High.

So they ceased that way to deal with them any more, and inclined to think of another way. The captains, therefore, did gather themselves together, to have free conference among themselves, to know what was yet to be done to gain the town, and to deliver it from the tyranny of Diabolus; and one said after this manner, and another after that. Then stood up the right noble the Captain Conviction, and said 'My brethren, mine opinion is this:

'First, that we continually play our slings into the town, and keep it in a continual alarm, molesting of them day and night. By thus doing we shall stop the growth of their rampant spirit; for a lion may be tamed by continual molestation.

'Secondly, this done, I advise that in the next place we with one consent draw up a petition to our Lord Shaddai, by which, after we have showed our King the condition of Mansoul, and of affairs here, and have begged his pardon for our no better success, we will earnestly implore his Majesty's help, and that he will please to send us more force and power, and some gallant and well-spoken commander to head them, that so his Majesty may not lose the benefit of these his good beginnings, but may complete his conquest upon the town of Mansoul.'

To this speech of the noble Captain Conviction, they as one man consented, and agreed that a petition should forthwith be drawn up, and sent by a fit man, away to Shaddai with speed. The contents of the petition were thus:

Mansoul grows worse and worse.

Hos. 11:2.

The captains leave off to summons and betake themselves to prayer.

Most gracious, and glorious King, the Lord of the
best world, and the builder of the town of Mansoul:

We have, dread Sovereign, at thy commandment, put
our lives in jeopardy, and at thy bidding made a war,
upon the famous town of Mansoul. When we went
up against it, we did according to our commission, first
offer conditions of peace unto it. But they, great
King, set light by our counsel, and would none of our
reproof. They were for shutting of their gates, and
for keeping us out of the town. They also mounted
their guns, they sallied out upon us, and have done us
what damage they could; but we pursued them,
with alarm upon alarm, requiting of them with such
retribution as was meet, and have done some
execution upon the town.

Diabolus, Incredulity, and Willbewill, are the
great doers against us. Now we are in our winter
quarters, but so as that we do yet with an high hand
molest and distress the town.

Once, as we think, had we had but one
substantial friend in the town, such as would but have
seconded the sound of our summons, as they ought,
the people might have yielded themselves. But there
were none but enemies there, nor any to speak in
behalf of our Lord to the town. Wherefore, though we
have done as we could, yet Mansoul abides in a state
of rebellion against thee.

Now, King of Kings, let it please thee to pardon
the unsuccessfulness of thy servants, who have been
no more advantageous in so desirable a work as the
conquering of Mansoul is. And send, Lord, as we
now desire, more forces to Mansoul, that it may be
subdued; and a man to head them, that the town
may both love and fear.

We do not thus speak, because we are willing to
relinquish the wars (for we are for laying of our bones
against the place), but that the town of Mansoul
may be won for thy Majesty. We also pray thy
Majesty for expedition in this matter, that, after their
conquest, we may be at liberty to be sent about

Matt. 22:5.
Prov. 1.
Zech. 7:10-13.

10

20

30

40

other thy gracious designs. Amen.

The petition thus drawn up, was sent away with
haste to the King, by the hand of that good man,
Mr. Love-to-Mansoul.

Who carried
this petition.

When this petition was come to the palace of the
King, who should it be delivered to, but to the King's
Son. So he took it and read it, and because the contents of it pleased him well, he mended, and also in
some things, added to the petition himself. So after
he had made such amendments and additions as he
thought convenient, with his own hand he carried it
in to the King; to whom, when he had with obeisance
delivered it, he put on authority, and spake to it
himself.

To whom it was
delivered.

The King re-
ceives it with
gladness.

Now the King, at the sight of the petition, was
glad; but how much more, think you, when it was
seconded by his Son! It pleased him also to hear that
his servants that camped against Mansoul, were so
hearty in the work, and so steadfast in their resolves,
and that they had already got some ground upon the
famous town of Mansoul.

Wherefore the King called to him Emmanuel his
Son, who said, 'Here am I, my Father.' Then said the
King, 'Thou knowest, as I do myself, the condition of
the town of Mansoul, and what we have purposed,
and what thou hast done to redeem it. Come now,
therefore, my Son, and prepare thyself for the war,
for thou shalt go to my camp at Mansoul. Thou shalt
also there prosper, and prevail, and conquer the town
of Mansoul.'

The King calls
his Son, and
tells him that
he shall go to
conquer the
town of Man-
soul, and he is
pleased at it.

Then said the King's Son: 'Thy Law is within my
heart. I delight to do thy will. This is the day that I
have longed for, and the work that I have waited for
all this while. Grant me therefore what force thou
shalt in thy wisdom think meet; and I will go, and
will deliver from Diabolus, and from his power, thy
perishing town of Mansoul. My heart has been often

Heb. 10.
He solaceth
himself in the
thoughts of this
work.

8   *mended* : revised.

pained within me for the miserable town of Mansoul. But now 'tis rejoiced, but now 'tis glad.' And with that he leaped over the mountains for joy, saying:

Heb. 2:10.

'I have not, in my heart, thought anything too dear for Mansoul: the day of vengeance is in mine heart for thee, my Mansoul; and glad am I, that thou my Father, hast made me the Captain of their Salvation. And I will now begin to plague all those that have been a plague to my town of Mansoul, and will deliver it from their hand.'

10

When the King's Son had said thus to his Father, it presently flew like lightning round about at court; yea, it there became the only talk, what Emmanuel was to go to do for the famous town of Mansoul. But you cannot think how the courtiers, too, were taken with this design of the Prince. Yea, so affected were they with this work, and with the justness of the war, that the highest lord and greatest peer of the Kingdom did covet to have commissions under Emmanuel, to go to help to recover again to Shaddai the miserable town of Mansoul.

The highest peer in the Kingdom covets to go on this design.

20

Then was it concluded that some should go and carry tidings to the camp, that Emmanuel was to come to recover Mansoul, and that he would bring along with him so mighty, so impregnable a force that he could not be resisted. But, oh! how ready were the high ones at court, to run like lacqueys to carry these tidings to the camp that was at Mansoul. Now when the captains perceived that the King would send Emmanuel his Son, and that it also delighted the Son to be sent on this errand by the great Shaddai his Father; they also, to show how they were pleased at the thoughts of his coming, gave a shout that made the earth rend at the sound thereof. Yea, the mountains did answer again by echo, and Diabolus himself did totter and shake.

30

The camp shouts for joy when they hear the tidings.

For you must know, that though the town of Mansoul itself was not much, if at all, concerned with the project (for, alas for them! they were woefully

3   See Cant. 2:8.

besotted, for they chiefly regarded their pleasure and their lusts), yet Diabolus their governor was; for he had his spies continually abroad, who brought him intelligence of all things, and they told him what was doing at court against him, and that Emmanuel would shortly certainly come with a power to invade him. Nor was there any man at court, nor peer of the Kingdom, that Diabolus so feared, as he feared this Prince. For if you remember, I showed you before that Diabolus had felt the weight of his hand already. So that, since it was he that was to come this made him the more afraid. Well, you see how I have told you that the King's Son was engaged to come from the court to save Mansoul, and that his Father had made him the captain of the forces. The time therefore of his setting forth, being now expired, he addressed himself for his march, and taketh with him for his power, five noble captains and their forces.

1. The first was that famous captain, the noble Captain Credence. His were the red colours, and Mr. Promise bare them; and for a scutcheon, he had the *holy lamb* and *golden shield*. And he had ten thousand men at his feet.

2. The second was that famous captain, the Captain Goodhope. His were the blue colours; his standard bearer was Mr. Expectation, and for a scutcheon he had the *three golden anchors*. And he had ten thousand men at his feet.

3. The third captain was that valiant captain, the Captain Charity. His standard bearer was Mr. Pitiful; his were the green colours; and for his scutcheon, he had *three naked orphans embraced in the bosom*. And he had ten thousand men at his feet.

4. The fourth was that gallant commander, the Captain Innocent. His standard bearer was Mr. Harmless; his were the white colours, and for his scutcheon, he had the *three golden doves*.

5. The fifth was the truly loyal, and well beloved captain, the Captain Patience. His standard bearer was Mr. Suffer-long; his were the black colours, and for a

Diabolus afraid at the news of his coming.

The Prince addresses himself for his journey.

John 1:29.
Eph. 6:16.

Heb. 6:19.

I Cor. 13.

Matt. 10:16.

scutcheon, he had *three arrows through the golden heart.*

Faith and Patience do the work. Heb. 6:12.

These were Emmanuel's captains, these their standard bearers, their colours, and their scutcheons, and these the men under their command. So, as was said, the brave Prince took his march, to go to the town of Mansoul. Captain Credence led the van, and Captain Patience brought up the rear. So the other three with their men made up the main body, the Prince himself riding in his chariot at the head of them.

10

Their march.

But when they set out for their march, Oh! how the trumpets sounded, their armour glittered, and how the colours waved in the wind! The Prince's armour was all of gold, and it shone like the sun in the firmament. The captains' armour was of proof and was in appearance like the glittering stars. There were also some from the court that rode reformades, for the love that they had to the King Shaddai, and for the happy deliverance of the town of Mansoul.

20

The Holy Bible containing 66 books.

Emmanuel also, when he had thus set forwards to go to recover the town of Mansoul, took with him at the commandment of his Father, forty-four battering-rams, and twelve slings to whirl stones withal. Every

1   See Pss. 38:2, 45:5.
4   The colour symbolism is ecclesiastically traditional: red for faith; blue for hope; green for youth; white for innocence; black for suffering. Less clear are the emblems of the "scutcheons." Of the five, four are readily explicable in terms of the scriptural glosses; but the other, the third, is a little more mysterious. Perhaps Bunyan is aware of the traditional representation of Charity in medieval and renaissance iconography as a mother-figure surrounded by infants. If so, he has adapted the emblem to his own purposes, orphaning the babes to point Mr. Pitiful's concern.
18   *reformades*: angelic officers, serving voluntarily out of love. The word is derived from Sp. *reformado*, a military term applied to a disbanded officer, who retains his rank and full or half pay. See OED and *Notes and Queries*, clxvii, 440; clxviii, 52.
23f.   Here something is plainly wrong arithmetically: forty-four plus twelve does not total sixty-six, as Bunyan's marginal gloss would argue. But how to alter? Indeed, as George Offor, Bunyan's dedicated Victorian editor, remarks, "it would be a task for Aquinus [sic] to discover which are rams and which are slings." (*Complete Works of John Bunyan* [Glasgow and London, 1860-62], III, 286.) Yet Offor himself proposes a way out. Assuming the error to lie in the printer's "mistaking Mr. Bunyan's figures, 22 for 12," he suggests that

one of these was made of pure gold, and these they carried with them in the heart and body of their army, all along as they went to Mansoul.

So they marched till they came within less than a league of the town; and there they lay till the first four captains came thither to acquaint him with matters. Then they took their journey to go to the town of Mansoul, and unto Mansoul they came; but when the old soldiers that were in the camp saw that they had new forces to join with, they again gave such a shout before the walls of the town of Mansoul that it put Diabolus into another fright. So they sat down before the town, not now as the other four captains did, to wit, against the gates of Mansoul only; but they environed it round on every side, and beset it behind and before; so that now, let Mansoul look which way it will, it saw force and power lie in siege against it. Besides, there were mounts cast up against it.

The Mount Gracious was on the one side, and Mount Justice was on the other. Further, there were several small banks, and advance ground, as Plain-truth-hill, and No-sin-banks, where many of the slings were placed against the town. Upon Mount Gracious were planted four, and upon Mount Justice were placed as many; and the rest were conveniently placed in several parts round about the town. Five of the best battering-rams, that is, of the biggest of them, were placed upon Mount Hearken, a mount cast up hard by Eargate, with intent to break that open.

Now when the men of the town saw the multitude of the soldiers that were come up against the

Side notes:
- The forces joined with rejoicing.
- Mansoul beleaguered round.
- Mounts cast up against it.

---

the division can be made as follows: the forty-four battering-rams are "the 39 books of the Old Testament, with the Gospels and the Acts," and the twenty-two slings the "Epistles and Revelations." This is an agreeably ingenious solution, especially considering past sorry attempts at resolving the difficulty. In the second edition the issue is evaded by omitting the entire paragraph, while later editions incorporate the passage and repeat the error. After a mid-eighteenth-century edition tacitly alters to "fifty-four battering-rams," this emendation is established and followed by apparently all subsequent editors, including Mabel Peacock in her 1892 Clarendon Press edition. But no modern editor can hope for so easy a cutting of this Gordian knot.

place, and the rams and slings, and the mounts on
which they were planted, together with the glittering
of the armour and the waving of their colours, they
were forced to shift, and shift, and again to shift their
thoughts; but they hardly changed for thoughts more
stout, but rather for thoughts more faint. For though
before they thought themselves sufficiently guarded,
yet now they began to think that no man knew what
would be their hap or lot.

The heart of Mansoul begins to fail.

When the good Prince Emmanuel had thus beleaguered Mansoul, in the first place he hangs out the
white flag, which he caused to be set up among the
golden slings that were planted upon Mount Gracious.
And this he did for two reasons: 1. To give notice to
Mansoul that he could and would yet be gracious if
they turned to him. 2. And that he might leave them
the more without excuse, should he destroy them,
they continuing in their rebellion.

The white flag hung out.

So the white flag, with the three golden doves in
it, was hanged out for two days together, to give them
time and space to consider. But they, as was hinted
before, as if they were unconcerned, made no reply to
the favourable signal of the Prince.

Then he commanded, and they set the red flag,
upon that mount called Mount Justice. 'Twas the red
flag of Captain Judgment, whose scutcheon was the
burning fiery furnace. And this also stood waving before them in the wind, for several days together. But
look, how they carried it under the white flag, when
that was hanged out, so did they also when the red
one was; and yet he took no advantage of them.

The red flag hung out.

Then he commanded again that his servants would
hang out the black flag of defiance against them,
whose scutcheon was the three burning thunderbolts.
But as unconcerned was Mansoul at this, as at those
that went before. But when the Prince saw that
neither mercy nor judgment, nor execution of judgment, would or could come near the heart of Mansoul,
he was touched with much compunction, and said,

The black flag hung out.

10

20

30

29   *carried it:* behaved.

'Surely this strange carriage of the town of Mansoul, doth rather arise from ignorance of the manner and feats of war, than from a secret defiance of us, and abhorrence of their own lives. Or if they know the manner of the war of their own, yet not the rites and ceremonies of the wars in which we are concerned, when I make wars upon mine enemy Diabolus.'

Christ makes not war as the world does.

Therefore he sent to the town of Mansoul, to let them know what he meant by those signs, and cere-
10 monies of the flag; and also to know of them which of the things they will choose, whether grace and mercy, or judgment and the execution of judgment? All this while they kept their gates shut with locks, bolts and bars, as fast as they could. Their guards also were doubled, and their watch made as strong as they could. Diabolus also did pluck up what heart he could, to encourage the town to make resistance.

He sends to know if they would have mercy or justice.

The townsmen also made answer to the Prince's messenger, in substance, according to that which fol-
20 lows:

'Great Sir: As to what, by your messenger you have signified to us, whether we will accept of your mercy, or fall by your justice, we are bound by the law and custom of this place, and can give you no positive answer. For it is against the law, government,

The townsfolk's answer.

8ff. Such protocol, with Emmanuel's comments thereon, should alert us to the fact that Bunyan is here writing within the framework of accepted conventions of war. The ostentatious display of significant flags, for instance, accords with late medieval military practice, which adopted this procedure as a recognisable sign of war. The custom bore "considerable legal significance, because deeds done in those circumstances were performed *in actu belli* . . ." (M. H. Keen, *The Laws of War in the Late Middle Ages* [London, 1965], p. 107. Mr. Keen's fascinating discussion deserves to be read in full: the chapters "Signs of War" and "Sieges" are especially important for an understanding of *The Holy War*.) Notice that the Prince takes all the necessary legal steps: he first hangs out a white flag, the universal symbol of truce, to give his enemies time to think things over; next, a red flag, the heraldic token of ferocity, as a threat of war to the death; and finally, a black flag, his personal standard as Christian prince and executor of judgment, that irrevocably proclaims a state of war legally existing. That Emmanuel does not thereafter visit the obdurate Diabolonians with immediate disaster, preferring instead to excuse these unchivalrous ones on grounds of their ignorance of the law of arms, is merely another indication of his all-embracing loving-kindness. So justice is, initially at least, nicely tempered with mercy.

82

and the prerogative royal of our king, to make either peace or war without him. But this we will do: we will petition that our prince will come down to the wall, and there give you such treatment as he shall think fit and profitable for us.'

When the good Prince Emmanuel heard this answer, and saw the slavery and bondage of the people, and how much content they were to abide in the chains of the tyrant Diabolus, it grieved him at the heart. And indeed, when at any time he perceived that any were contented under the slavery of the giant, he would be affected with it.

Emmanuel grieved at the folly of Mansoul.

10

But to return again to our purpose. After the town had carried this news to Diabolus, and had told him, moreover, that the Prince that lay in the leaguer, without the wall, waited upon them for an answer, he refused, and huffed as well as he could; but in heart he was afraid.

Diabolus afraid.

Then said he, 'I will go down to the gates myself, and give him such an answer as I think fit.' So he went down to Mouthgate, and there addressed himself to speak to Emmanuel (but in such language as the town understood not), the contents whereof were as follow:

20

'O thou great Emmanuel, Lord of all the world, I know thee, that thou art the Son of the great Shaddai! Wherefore art thou come to torment me, and to cast me out of my possession? This town of Mansoul, as thou very well knowest, is mine, and that by a twofold right. 1. It is mine by right of conquest; I won it in the open field. And shall the prey be taken from the mighty, or the lawful captive be delivered? 2. This town of Mansoul is mine also by their subjection. They have opened the gates of their town unto me. They have sworn fidelity to me, and have openly chosen me to be their king. They have also given their

His speech to the Prince.

30

Heart.

15   *leaguer*: the camp of the besieging army.
17   *huffed*: blustered.
30   In view of his proven indifference to the laws of just war, it is ironic that Diabolus should now take his stand on the legality of right of conquest.
31f. See Isa. 49:24.

castle into my hands; yea, they have put the whole strength of Mansoul under me.

'Moreover, this town of Mansoul hath disavowed thee. Yea, they have cast thy law, thy name, thy image and all that is thine, behind their back, and have accepted, and set up in their room my law, my name, mine image and all that ever is mine. Ask else thy captains, and they will tell thee that Mansoul hath, in answer to all their summons, shown love, and loyalty to me; but always disdain, despite, contempt, and scorn to thee, and thine. Now thou art the just one, and the holy, and shouldest do no iniquity. Depart then, I pray thee, therefore from me, and leave me to my just inheritance, peaceably.'

This oration was made in the language of Diabolus himself. For although he can, to every man, speak in their own language (else he could not tempt them all as he does), yet he has a language proper to himself, and it is the language of the infernal cave, or black pit.

Wherefore the town of Mansoul (poor hearts!) understood him not, nor did they see how he crouched, and cringed, while he stood before Emmanuel their Prince.

Yea, they all this while took him to be one of that power and force that by no means could be resisted. Wherefore, while he was thus entreating that he might have yet his residence there, and that Emmanuel would not take it from him by force, the inhabitants boasted even of his valour, saying, 'Who is able to make war with him?'

Well, when this pretended king had made an end of what he would say, Emmanuel, the golden Prince, stood up and spake; the contents of whose words follow.

'Thou deceiving one,' said he, 'I have in my Father's name, in mine own name, and on the behalf and for the good of this wretched town of Mansoul, somewhat to say unto thee. Thou pretendest a right, a lawful right, to the deplorable town of Mansoul, when it is most apparent to all my Father's court that the entrance which thou hast obtained in at the gates of Mansoul was through thy lie and falsehood. Thou beliedst my Father, thou beliedst his law, and so deceivedst the people of Mansoul. Thou pretendest that the people have accepted thee for their king, their captain, and right liege-lord; but that also was by the exercise of deceit and guile. Now if lying, wiliness, sinful craft and all manner of horrible hypocrisy, will go in my Father's court (in which court thou must be tried) for equity and right, then will I confess unto thee that thou hast made a lawful conquest. But alas! What thief, what tyrant, what devil is there that may not conquer after this sort? But I can make it appear, O Diabolus, that thou in all thy pretences to a conquest of Mansoul, hast nothing of truth to say. Thinkest thou this to be right, that thou didst put the lie upon my Father and madest him (to Mansoul) the greatest deluder in the world? And what sayest thou to thy perverting knowingly the right purport and intent of the law? Was it good also that thou madest a prey of the innocency and simplicity of the now miserable town of Mansoul? Yea, thou didst overcome Mansoul by promising to them happiness in their transgressions against my Father's law, when thou knewest, and couldest not but know, hadst thou consulted nothing but thine own experience, that that was the way to undo them. Thou hast also thyself—O thou master of enmity!—of spite defaced my Father's image in Mansoul, and set up thy own in its place, to the great contempt of my Father, the heightening of thy sin, and to the intolerable damage of the perishing town of Mansoul.

'Thou hast, moreover (as if all these were but little things with thee), not only deluded and undone this place, but by thy lies and fraudulent carriage, hast set them against their own deliverance. How hast thou stirred them up against my Father's captains, and made them to fight against those that were sent of him to deliver them from their bondage! All these things and very many more thou hast done against thy light, and in contempt of my Father, and of his law; yea, and with design to bring under his displeasure for ever the miserable town of Mansoul. I am therefore come to avenge the wrong that thou hast done to my Father, and to deal with thee for the blasphemies wherewith thou hast made poor Mansoul blaspheme his name. Yea, upon thy head, thou prince of the infernal cave, will I requite it.

'As for myself, O Diabolus, I am come against thee by lawful power, and to take by strength of hand, this town of Mansoul out of thy burning fingers. For this town of Mansoul is mine, O Diabolus, and that by undoubted right, as all shall see that will diligently search the most ancient, and most authentic records; and I will plead my title to it, to the confusion of thy face.

'First, for the town of Mansoul, my Father built and did fashion it with his hand. The palace also that is in the midst of that town, he built it for his own delight. This town of Mansoul therefore is my Father's, and that by the best of titles; and he that gainsays the truth of this, must lie against his soul.

'Secondly, O thou master of the lie, this town of Mansoul is mine.

1. 'For that I am my Father's heir, his first-born, and the only delight of his heart. I am therefore come up against thee in mine own right, even to recover mine own inheritance out of thine hand. [Heb. 1:2. John 16:15.]

2. 'But further, as I have a right and title to Mansoul, by being my Father's heir, so I have also by my Father's donation. His it was, and he gave it me; nor have I at any time offended my Father that he should take it from me and give it to thee. Nor have I been forced by playing the bankrupt to sell, or set to sale to thee, my beloved town of Mansoul. Mansoul is my desire, my delight, and the joy of my heart. But, [John 17. Isa. 50:1.]

3. 'Mansoul is mine by right of purchase. I have bought it, O Diabolus, I have bought it to myself. Now, since it was my Father's and mine, as I was his heir, and since also I have made it mine by virtue of a great purchase, it followeth, that by all lawful right the town of Mansoul is mine, and that thou art an

usurper, a tyrant and traitor in thy holding possession thereof. Now the cause of my purchasing of it was this. Mansoul had trespassed against my Father: now my Father had said that in the day that they broke his law, they should die. Now it is more possible for heaven and earth to pass away, than for my Father to break his word. Wherefore, when Mansoul had sinned indeed by hearkening to thy lie, I put in and became a surety to my Father, body for body, and soul for soul, that I would make amends for Mansoul's transgressions; and my Father did accept thereof. So when the time appointed was come, I gave body for body, soul for soul, life for life, blood for blood, and so redeemed my beloved Mansoul.

Matt. 5:18.

O sweet Prince Emmanuel!

4. 'Nor did I do this to the halves. My Father's law and justice that were both concerned in the threat'-ning upon transgression, are both now satisfied, and very well content that Mansoul should be delivered.

5. 'Nor am I come out this day against thee, but by commandment of my Father; 'twas he that said unto me, 'Go down and deliver Mansoul.'

'Wherefore be it known unto thee, O thou fountain of deceit, and be it also known to the foolish town of Mansoul that I am not come against thee this day without my Father.

'And now,' said the golden-headed Prince, 'I have a word to the town of Mansoul.' But so soon as mention was made that he had a word to speak to the besotted town of Mansoul, the gates were double-guarded, and all men commanded not to give him audience. So he proceeded, and said, 'O unhappy town of Mansoul, I cannot but be touched with pity and compassion for thee. Thou hast accepted of Diabolus for thy King, and art become a nurse and minister of Diabolonians against thy sovereign Lord. Thy gates thou hast opened to him, but hast shut them fast against me; thou hast given him a hearing, but hast

---

8f. *I put in and became a surety:* I intervened and took upon myself responsibility for all debts and obligations.

15   *to the halves:* by halves.

stopped thine ears at my cry; he brought to thee thy destruction, and thou didst receive both him and it. I am come to thee bringing salvation, but thou regardest me not. Besides, thou hast as with sacrilegious hands taken thyself with all that was mine in thee, and hast given all to my foe, and to the greatest enemy my Father has. You have bowed and subjected yourselves to him; you have vowed and sworn yourselves to be his. Poor Mansoul! What shall I do unto thee? Shall I save thee? Shall I destroy thee? What shall I do unto thee? Shall I fall upon thee and grind thee to powder, or make thee a monument of the richest grace? What shall I do unto thee? Hearken, therefore, thou town of Mansoul, hearken to my word, and thou shalt live. I am merciful, Mansoul, and thou shalt find me so; shut me not out at thy gates. Cant. 5:2.

'O Mansoul, neither is my commission nor inclination at all to do thee hurt. Why fliest thou so fast from thy friend, and stickest so close to thine enemy? Indeed, I would have thee, because it becomes thee, to be sorry for thy sin. But do not despair of life. This great force is not to hurt thee, but to deliver thee from thy bondage, and to reduce thee to thy obedience. John 12:47. Luke 9:56.

'My commission indeed is to make a war upon Diabolus thy King, and upon all Diabolonians with him. For he is the strong man armed that keeps the house, and I will have him out. His spoils I must divide, his armour I must take from him, his hold I must cast him out of, and must make it an habitation for myself. And this, O Mansoul, shall Diabolus know, when he shall be made to follow me in chains, and when Mansoul shall rejoice to see it so.

'I could, would I now put forth my might, cause that forthwith he should leave you and depart. But I have it in my heart so to deal with him, as that the justice of the war that I shall make upon him, may be seen and acknowledged by all. He hath taken Mansoul by fraud, and keeps it by violence and deceit,

26ff. See Luke 11:21-22.

and I will make him bare and naked in the eyes of all observers.

'All my words are true. I am mighty to save, and will deliver my Mansoul out of his hand.'

This speech was intended chiefly for Mansoul, but Mansoul would not have the hearing of it. They shut up Eargate, they barricaded it up, they kept it locked and bolted, they set a guard thereat, and commanded that no Mansoulian should go out to him, nor that any from the camp should be admitted into the town. All this they did, so horribly had Diabolus enchanted them to do, and seek to do for him, against their rightful Lord and Prince. Wherefore no man, nor voice, nor sound of man that belonged to the glorious host, was to come into the town.

Emmanuel prepares to make war upon Mansoul.

So when Emmanuel saw that Mansoul was thus involved in sin, he calls his army together—since now also his words were despised—and gave out a commandment throughout all his host to be ready against the time appointed. Now, forasmuch as there was no way lawfully to take the town of Mansoul, but to get in by the gates, and at Eargate as the chief, therefore he commanded his captains and commanders to bring their rams, their slings, and their men, and place them at Eyegate and Eargate, in order to his taking the town.

Diabolus sends by the hand of his servant Mr. Loth-to-stoop, and by him he propounds conditions of peace.

When Emmanuel had put all things in a readiness to bid Diabolus battle, he sent again to know of the town of Mansoul, if in peaceable manner they would yield themselves? Or whether they were yet resolved to put him to try the utmost extremity? They then together with Diabolus their king called a council of war, and resolved upon certain propositions that should be offered to Emmanuel, if he will accept thereof. So they agree; and then the next was, who should be sent on this errand. Now there was in the town of

10

20

30

28ff. A curious paradox is involved. Although Emmanuel summons Mansoul to surrender, he must actually take the town by assault, else abrogate his claim to lawful spoil by right of conquest. Yet the call to surrender must be made, as a mere formality or courtesy, if nothing else. On this chivalric aspect of siege-warfare in medieval times, consult Keen, *Laws of War*, esp. pp. 119-20.

Mansoul an old man, a Diabolonian, and his name was Mr. Loth-to-stoop, a stiff man in his way, and a great doer for Diabolus; him, therefore, they sent, and put into his mouth what he should say. So he went and came to the camp to Emmanuel, and when he was come, a time was appointed to give him audience. So at the time he came, and after a Diabolonian ceremony or two, he thus began and said: 'Great Sir, that it may be known unto all men how good-natured a prince my master is, he hath sent me to tell your Lordship that he is very willing, rather than to go to war, to deliver up into your hands one half of the town of Mansoul. I am therefore to know if your Mightiness will accept of this proposition.'

Titus 1:16.

Mark this.

Then said Emmanuel, 'The whole is mine by gift and purchase, wherefore I will never lose one half.'

Then said Mr. Loth-to-stoop, 'Sir, my master hath said that he will be content that you shall be the nominal and titular Lord of all, if he may possess but a part.'

Mark this.
Luke 13:25.

Then Emmanuel answered, 'The whole is mine really, not in name and word only; wherefore I will be the sole Lord and possessor of all, or of none at all of Mansoul.'

Then Mr. Loth-to-stoop said again, 'Sir, behold the condescension of my master! He says that he will be content, if he may but have assigned to him some place in Mansoul as a place to live privately in, and you shall be Lord of all the rest.'

Mark this.
Acts 5:1-5.

Then said the golden Prince, 'All that the Father giveth me shall come to me; and of all that he hath given me I will lose nothing—no, not a hoof, nor a hair. I will not therefore grant him—no, not the least corner in Mansoul to dwell in. I will have all to myself.'

Then Loth-to-stoop said again, 'But, Sir, suppose that my Lord should resign the whole town to you, only with this proviso, that he sometimes when he comes into this country, may for old acquaintance'

Mark this.

30ff. See John 6:37, 17:12.

sake be entertained as a wayfaring man for two days, or ten days, or a month, or so. May not this small matter be granted?'

Then said Emmanuel, 'No. He came as a wayfaring man to David, nor did he stay long with him, and yet it had like to have cost David his soul. I will not consent that he ever should have any harbour more there.'

II Sam. 12:1-5.

Then said Mr. Loth-to-stoop, 'Sir, you seem to be very hard. Suppose my master should yield to all that your Lordship hath said, provided that his friends and kindred in Mansoul may have liberty to trade in the town, and to enjoy their present dwellings. May not that be granted, Sir?'

Sins and carnal lusts.

Then said Emmanuel, 'No; that is contrary to my Father's will. For all, and all manner of Diabolonians that now are, or that at any time shall be found in Mansoul, shall not only lose their lands and liberties, but also their lives.'

Rom. 6:13.
Col. 3:5.
Gal. 5:24.

Then said Mr. Loth-to-stoop again, 'But, Sir, may not my master, and great lord, by letters, by passengers, by accidental opportunities, and the like, maintain, if he shall deliver up all unto thee, some kind of old friendship with Mansoul?'

Mark this.
John 10:8.

Emmanuel answered, 'No, by no means; for as much as any such fellowship, friendship, intimacy or acquaintance in what way, sort or mode soever maintained, will tend to the corrupting of Mansoul, the alienating of their affections from me, and the endangering of their peace with my Father.'

Mr. Loth-to-stoop yet added further, saying, 'But great Sir, since my master hath many friends, and those that are dear to him in Mansoul, may he not, if he shall depart from them, even of his bounty and good nature, bestow upon them, as he sees fit, some tokens of his love and kindness that he had for them, to the end that Mansoul, when he is gone, may look upon such tokens of kindness once received from their old friend, and remember him who was once their king, and the merry times that they sometimes en-

Mark this.
Rom. 6:12,13.

10

20

30

40

joyed one with another, while he and they lived in peace together?'

Then said Emmanuel, 'No; for if Mansoul come to be mine, I shall not admit of nor consent that there should be the least scrap, shred, or dust of Diabolus left behind, as tokens or gifts bestowed upon any in Mansoul, thereby to call to remembrance the horrible communion that was betwixt them and him.'

'Well, Sir,' said Mr. Loth-to-stoop, 'I have one thing more to propound, and then I am got to the end of my commission. Suppose that when my master is gone from Mansoul, any that yet shall live in the town, should have such business of high concerns to do, that if they be neglected the party shall be undone; and suppose, Sir, that nobody can help in that case so well as my master and lord; may not now my master be sent for upon so urgent an occasion as this? Or if he may not be admitted into the town, may not he and the person concerned, meet in some of the villages near Mansoul, and there lay their heads together, and there consult of matters?'

Mark this.
II Kings 1:3, 6, 7.

This was the last of those ensnaring propositions that Mr. Loth-to-stoop had to propound to Emmanuel on behalf of his master Diabolus, but Emmanuel would not grant it; for he said, 'There can be no case, or thing, or matter fall out in Mansoul, when thy master shall be gone, that may not be salved by my Father; besides, 'twill be a great disparagement to my Father's wisdom and skill to admit any from Mansoul to go out to Diabolus for advice, when they are bid before, in everything by prayer and supplication to let their requests be made known to my Father. Further, this, should it be granted, would be to grant that a door should be set open for Diabolus, and the Diabolonians in Mansoul to hatch and plot and bring to pass treasonable designs to the grief of my Father and me, and to the utter destruction of Mansoul.'

I Sam. 28:15.

II Kings 1:2,3.

When Mr. Loth-to-stoop had heard this answer,

Loth-to-stoop departs.

27   *salved*: remedied, solved.

he took his leave of Emmanuel and departed, saying that he would do word to his master concerning this whole affair. So he departed and came to Diabolus to Mansoul, and told him the whole of the matter, and how Emmanuel would not admit—no, not by any means—that he when he was once gone out, should for ever have anything more to do either in or with any that are of the town of Mansoul. When Mansoul and Diabolus had heard this relation of things, they with one consent concluded to use their best endeavour to keep Emmanuel out of Mansoul, and sent old Ill-pause, of whom you have heard before, to tell the Prince and his captains so. So the old gentleman came up to the top of Eargate, and called to the camp for a hearing; who, when they gave audience, he said, 'I have in commandment from my high lord to bid you to tell it to your Prince Emmanuel that Mansoul and their king are resolved to stand and fall together, and that it is in vain for your Prince to think of ever having of Mansoul in his hand, unless he can take it by force.' So some went and told to Emmanuel what old Ill-pause, a Diabolonian in Mansoul, had said. Then said the Prince, 'I must try the power of my sword, for I will not, for all the rebellions and repulses that Mansoul has made against me, raise my siege and depart, but will assuredly take my Mansoul and deliver it from the hand of her enemy.' And with that he gave out a commandment that Captain Boanerges, Captain Conviction, Captain Judgment, and Captain Execution should forthwith march up to Eargate with trumpets sounding, colours flying, and with shouting for the battle. Also he would that Captain Credence should join himself with them. Emmanuel, moreover, gave order that Captain Goodhope, and Captain Charity should draw themselves up before Eyegate. He bid also that the rest of his captains and their men should place themselves for the best of their advantage against the enemy round about the town; and all was done as he had commanded. Then he bid that the word should be given forth, and the word was at that time,

A speech of old Ill-pause to the camp.

Eph. 6:17.

They must fight.

Preparations to the battle.

10

20

30

40

Emmanuel. Then was an alarm sounded, and the battering-rams were played, and the slings did whirl stones into the town amain, and thus the battle began. Now Diabolus himself did manage the townsmen in the war, and that at every gate; wherefore their resistance was the more forcible, hellish, and offensive to Emmanuel. Thus was the good Prince engaged and entertained by Diabolus and Mansoul for several days together. And a sight worth seeing it was to behold how the captains of Shaddai behaved themselves in this war.

And first for Captain Boanerges (not to undervalue the rest): he made three most fierce assaults, one after another, upon Eargate, to the shaking of the posts thereof. Captain Conviction, he also made up as fast with Boanerges as possibly he could, and both discerning that the gate began to yield, they commanded that the rams should still be played against it. Now Captain Conviction, going up very near to the gate, was with great force driven back, and received three wounds in the mouth. And those that rode reformades, they went about to encourage the captains.

For the valour of the two captains made mention of before, the Prince sent for them to his pavilion, and commanded that a while they should rest themselves, and that with somewhat they should be refreshed. Care also was taken for Captain Conviction, that he should be healed of his wounds. The Prince also gave to each of them a chain of gold, and bid them yet be of good courage.

Nor did Captain Goodhope, nor Captain Charity come behind in this most desperate fight; for they so well did behave themselves at Eyegate, that they had almost broken it quite open. These also had a reward from their Prince, as also had the rest of the captains, because they did valiantly round about the town.

Boanerges plays the man.

Conviction wounded.

Angels.

Goodhope and Charity play the men at Eyegate.

---

1   *Emmanuel*: the battle-cry, commonly used to denote allegiance in the field or as a signal to advance.
3   *amain*: strongly.
8   *entertained*: occupied.

94

In this engagement several of the officers of Diabolus were slain, and some of the townsmen wounded. For the officers, there was one Captain Boasting slain. This Boasting thought that nobody could have shaken the posts of Eargate, nor have shaken the heart of Diabolus. Next to him there was one Captain Secure slain—this Secure used to say that the blind and lame in Mansoul were able to keep the gates of the town against Emmanuel's army. This Captain Secure did Captain Conviction cleave down the head with a two-handed sword, when he received himself three wounds in his mouth.

Besides these there was one Captain Bragman, a very desperate fellow, and he was captain over a band of those that threw fire-brands, arrows and death. He also received by the hand of Captain Goodhope, at Eyegate, a mortal wound in the breast.

There was, moreover, one Mr. Feeling; but he was no captain, but a great stickler to encourage Mansoul to rebellion. He received a wound in the eye by the hand of one of Boanerges' soldiers, and had by the captain himself been slain, but that he made a sudden retreat.

But I never saw Willbewill so daunted in all my life. He was not able to do as he was wont, and some say that he also received a wound in the leg, and that some of the men in the Prince's army have certainly seen him limp as he afterwards walked on the wall.

I shall not give you a particular account of the names of the soldiers that were slain in the town, for many were maimed and wounded, and slain; for when they saw that the posts of Eargate did shake, and Eyegate was well nigh broken quite open, and also that their captains were slain, this took away the hearts of many of the Diabolonians. They fell also by the force of the shot that were sent by the golden slings into the midst of the town of Mansoul.

Of the townsmen there was one Love-no-good; he was a townsman, but a Diabolonian. He also received

Captain Boasting slain.

II Sam. 5:6.

Captain Secure slain.

10

Captain Bragman slain.

Mr. Feeling hurt.

20

Willbewill hurt.

30

Many of the soldiers in Mansoul slain.

19   *stickler*: persistent advocate.

his mortal wound in Mansoul, but he died not very soon.

Love-no-good wounded.

Mr. Ill-pause also, who was the man that came along with Diabolus when at first he attempted the taking of Mansoul, he also received a grievous wound in the head; some say that his brain-pan was cracked. This I have taken notice of that he was never after this able to do that mischief to Mansoul as he had done in times past. Also old Prejudice and Mr. Anything fled.

Ill-pause wounded.

Now when the battle was over, the Prince commanded that yet once more the white flag should be set upon Mount Gracious in sight of the town of Mansoul, to show that yet Emmanuel had grace for the wretched town of Mansoul.

The white flag hung out again.

When Diabolus saw the white flag hanged out again, and knowing that it was not for him but Mansoul, he cast in his mind to play another prank, to wit, to see if Emmanuel would raise his siege and be gone upon promise of a reformation. So he comes down to the gate one evening, a good while after the sun was gone down, and calls to speak with Emmanuel, who presently came down to the gate, and Diabolus saith unto him:

Diabolus's new prank.

'For as much as thou makest it appear by thy white flag that thou art wholly given to peace and quiet, I thought meet to acquaint thee that we are ready to accept thereof upon terms which thou mayest admit.

His speech to Emmanuel.

'I know that thou art given to devotion, and that holiness pleases thee; yea, that thy great end in making a war upon Mansoul is that it may be an holy habitation. Well, draw off thy forces from the town, and I will bend Mansoul to thy bow.

'First, I will lay down all acts of hostility against thee, and will be willing to become thy deputy, and will as I have formerly been against thee, now serve thee in the town of Mansoul. And more particularly,

Diabolus would be Emmanuel's deputy, and he would turn reformer.

1. 'I will persuade Mansoul to receive thee for their Lord, and I know that they will do it the

sooner when they shall understand that I am thy deputy.

2. 'I will show them wherein they have erred, and that transgression stands in the way to life.

3. 'I will show them the holy law unto which they must conform, even that which they have broken.

4. 'I will press upon them the necessity of a reformation according to thy law. 10

5. 'And moreover, that none of these things may fail, I myself at my own proper cost and charge will set up and maintain a sufficient ministry, besides lecturers, in Mansoul.

6. 'Thou shalt receive as a token of our subjection to thee continually year by year what thou shalt think fit to lay and levy upon us, in token of our subjection to thee.'

The answer. Then said Emmanuel to him, 'O full of deceit, how movable are thy ways! How often hast thou 20 changed and rechanged, if so be thou mightest still keep possession of my Mansoul, though as has been plainly declared before, I am the right heir thereof! Often hast thou made thy proposals already, nor is this last a whit better than they. And failing to

II Cor. 11:14. deceive when thou showedst thyself in thy black, thou hast now transformed thyself into an angel of light, and wouldest, to deceive, be now as a minister of righteousness.

'But know thou, O Diabolus, that nothing must 30

14 *lecturers*: special ministers, common in Puritan England, whose responsibility lay in preaching alone, rather than in both preaching and pastoral care. "The lecturer was not as a rule, though he might be, designated or approved by the patron of the parish, nor did he enjoy the revenue from tithes vested in the regular incumbent . . . His duty was to lecture upon the Bible, that is to preach, on Sundays at times other than those of the usual services and in most instances upon weekdays as well." (William Haller, *The Rise of Puritanism* [New York, 1958], p. 53.) In 1629, Archbishop Laud found it necessary to restrict the activities of these Puritan lecturers, particularly in the towns, because of the grave threat they constituted to the power of the Established Church. How grimly humorous that the system Diabolus proposes should be so attractively Nonconformist!

be regarded that thou canst propound, for nothing is done by thee but to deceive. Thou neither hast conscience to God, nor love to the town of Mansoul; whence then should these thy sayings arise but from sinful craft and deceit? He that can of list and will propound what he pleases, and that wherewith he may destroy them that believe him, is to be abandoned with all that he shall say. But if righteousness be such a beauty-spot in thine eyes now, how is it that wickedness was so closely stuck to by thee before? But this is by-the-by.

Diabolus has no conscience to God, nor love to Mansoul.

'Thou talkest now of a reformation in Mansoul, and that thou thyself, if I will please, will be at the head of that reformation, all the while knowing that the greatest proficiency that man can make in the law, and the righteousness thereof, will amount to no more for the taking away of the curse from Mansoul than *just nothing at all*. For a law being broken by Mansoul, that had before, upon a supposition of the breach thereof, a curse pronounced against him for it of God, can never, by his obeying of the law, deliver himself therefrom—to say nothing of what a reformation is like to be set up in Mansoul, when the Devil is become the corrector of vice. Thou know'st that all that thou hast now said in this matter is nothing but guile and deceit; and is, as it was the first, so is it the last card that thou hast to play. Many there be that do soon discern thee when thou showest them thy cloven foot; but in thy white, thy light, and in thy transformation, thou art seen but of a few. But thou shalt not do thus with my Mansoul, O Diabolus, for I do still love my Mansoul.

He knows that that will do no good which yet he propounds for the health of Mansoul.

'Besides, I am not come to put Mansoul upon works to live thereby—should I do so, I should be like unto thee— but I am come that by me, and by what

---

5   *of list and will*: of his own inclination and accord.
20   *a curse pronounced against him*: see Gal. 3:10.
27   The metaphor from card-playing is not inappropriately used by Emmanuel in reference to the Devil.
33ff. See Gal. 2:16, 3:11-13. Emmanuel's reply contains the sum of the Puritan creed.

I have and shall do for Mansoul, they may to my Father be reconciled, though by their sin they have provoked him to anger, and though by the law they cannot obtain mercy.

'Thou talkest of subjecting of this town to good, when none desireth it at thy hands. I am sent by my Father to possess it myself, and to guide it by the skilfulness of my hands into such a conformity to him as shall be pleasing in his sight. I will therefore possess it myself; I will dispossess and cast thee out; I will set up mine own standard in the midst of them; I will also govern them by new laws, new officers, new motives, and new ways. Yea, I will pull down this town, and build it again, and it shall be as though it had not been, and it shall then be the glory of the whole Universe.'

When Diabolus heard this, and perceived that he was discovered in all his deceits, he was confounded and utterly put to a nonplus; but having in himself the fountain of iniquity, rage, and malice against both Shaddai and his Son, and the beloved town of Mansoul, what doth he but strengthen himself what he could to give fresh battle to the noble Prince Emmanuel? So then, now we must have another fight before the town of Mansoul is taken. Come up then to the mountains you that love to see military actions, and behold by both sides how the fatal blow is given, while one seeks to hold, and the other seeks to make himself master of the famous town of Mansoul.

Diabolus, therefore, having withdrawn himself from the wall to his force that was in the heart of the town of Mansoul, Emmanuel also returned to the camp; and both of them after their divers ways, put themselves into a posture fit to bid battle one to another.

Diabolus, as filled with despair of retaining in his

marginal notes:

All things must be new in Mansoul.

Diabolus confounded.

New preparations for to fight.

line numbers: 10, 20, 30

1   The meaning here is uncertain: either "by what I have, and shall do" or "by what I have done, and shall do."

3f.   The second edition makes nonsense of the passage by reading "by the law they can obtain mercy." See Rom. 3:20.

19   *put to a nonplus*: bewildered, brought to a halt.

hands the famous town of Mansoul, resolved to do what mischief he could (if indeed he could do any) to the army of the Prince and to the famous town of Mansoul; for, alas! it was not the happiness of the silly town of Mansoul that was designed by Diabolus, but the utter ruin and overthrow thereof, as now is enough in view. Wherefore he commands his officers that they should then, when they see that they could hold the town no longer, do it what harm and mis-
10 chief they could, renting and tearing of men, women and children. 'For,' said he, 'we had better quite demolish the place, and leave it like a ruinous heap, than so leave it that it may be an habitation for Emmanuel.'

Emmanuel again, knowing that the next battle would issue in his being made master of the place, gave out a Royal Commandment to all his officers, high captains, and the men of war, to be sure to show themselves men of war against Diabolus, and all
20 Diabolonians; but favourable, merciful, and meek to all the old inhabitants of Mansoul. 'Bend, therefore,' said the noble Prince, 'the hottest front of the battle against Diabolus and his men.'

So the day being come, the command was given, and the Prince's men did bravely stand to their arms, and did as before bend their main force against Eargate and Eyegate. The word was then, *Mansoul is won!* So they made their assault upon the town. Diabolus also, as fast as he could with the main of his
30 power, made resistance from within and his high lords, and chief captains for a time fought very cruelly against the Prince's army.

But after three or four notable charges by the Prince and his noble captains, Eargate was broken open, and the bars and bolts wherewith it was used to be fast shut up against the Prince, was broken into a thousand pieces. Then did the Prince's trumpets

Side notes:

Diabolus despairs of holding of Mansoul, and therefore contrives to do it what mischief he can.

Mark 9:26,27.

The battle joined, and they fight on both sides fiercely.

Eargate broken open.

21ff. See II Sam. 10:9. This echo of the Old Testament and of ancient Israelite warfare serves as a useful reminder that the origin of Bunyan's account is Biblical as well as personal.

sound, the captains shout, the town shake, and Diabolus retreat to his hold. Well, when the Prince's forces had broken open the gate, himself came up and did set his throne in it; also he set his standard thereby, upon a mount that before by his men was cast up to place the mighty slings thereon. The mount was called Mount Hear-well. There, therefore, the Prince abode, to wit, hard by the going in at the gate. He commanded also that the golden slings should yet be played upon the town, especially against the castle, because for shelter thither was Diabolus retreated. Now from Eargate the street was straight even to the house of Mr. Recorder that so was before Diabolus took the town; and hard by his house stood the castle, which Diabolus for a long time had made his irksome den. The captains, therefore, did quickly clear that street by the use of their slings, so that way was made up to the heart of the town. Then did the Prince command that Captain Boanerges, Captain Conviction, and Captain Judgment, should forthwith march up the town to the old gentleman's* gate. Then did the captains in most warlike manner enter into the town of Mansoul, and marching in with flying colours, they came up to the Recorder's house, and that was almost as strong as was the castle. Battering-rams they took also with them to plant against the castle-gates. When they were come to the house of Mr. Conscience, they knocked and demanded entrance. Now the old gentleman, not knowing as yet fully their design, kept his gates shut all the time of this fight. Wherefore Boanerges demanded entrance at his gates, and no man making answer, he gave it one stroke with the head of a ram, and this made the old gentleman shake, and his house to tremble and totter. Then came Mr. Recorder down to the gate, and as he could with quivering lips, he asked who was there? Boanerges answered, 'We are the captains and commanders of the great Shaddai, and of the blessed Emmanuel his Son, and we demand pos-

The Prince's standard set up, and the slings are played still at the castle.

*Conscience

They go up to the Recorder's house.

They demand entrance.

10

20

30

---

15 *irksome*: something stronger than the usual meaning of "wearisome, tedious" is surely warranted. The OED records sixteenth-century usage in the sense of "loathsome."

session of your house for the use of our noble Prince.' And with that the battering-ram gave the gate another shake. This made the old gentleman tremble the more, yet durst he not but open the gate: then the King's forces marched in, namely the three brave captains mentioned before. Now the Recorder's house was a place of much convenience for Emmanuel, not only because it was near to the castle, and strong, but also because it was large, and fronted the castle, the den where now Diabolus was; for he was now afraid to come out of his hold. As for Mr. Recorder, the captains carried it very reservedly to him; as yet he knew nothing of the great designs of Emmanuel, so that he did not know what judgment to make, nor what would be the end of such thund'ring beginnings. It was also presently noised in the town, how the Recorder's house was possessed, his rooms taken up, and his palace made the seat of war; and no sooner was it noised abroad, but they took the alarm as warmly, and gave it out to others of his friends; and you know as a snowball loses nothing by rolling, so in little time the whole town was possessed that they must expect nothing from the Prince but destruction; and the ground of the business was this: the Recorder was afraid, the Recorder trembled, and the captains carried it strangely to the Recorder. So many came to see. But when they with their own eyes did behold the captains in the palace, and their battering-rams ever playing at the castle-gates to beat them down, they were riveted in their fears, and it made them as in amaze. And, as I said, the man of the house would increase all this, for whoever came to him, or discoursed with him, nothing would he talk of, tell them, or hear, but that death and destruction now attended Mansoul.

'For,' quoth the old gentleman, 'you are all of you sensible that we all have been traitors to that once despised, but now famously victorious and glorious Prince Emmanuel. For he now, as you see, doth not

They go in.

They do keep themselves reserved from the Recorder.

His house the seat of war.

The office of Conscience when he is awakened.

31   *amaze*: amazement, state of mental stupefaction.

only lie in close siege about us, but hath forced his entrance in at our gates. Moreover, Diabolus flees before him; and he hath, as you behold, made of my house a garrison against the castle, where he is. I, for my part, have transgressed greatly—and he that is clean, 'tis well for him. But, I say, I have transgressed greatly in keeping of silence when I should have spoken, and in perverting of justice when I should have executed the same. True, I have suffered something at the hand of Diabolus for taking part with the laws of King Shaddai; but that, alas! what will that do? Will that make compensation for the rebellions and treasons that I have done, and have suffered without gainsaying, to be committed in the town of Mansoul? O I tremble to think what will be the end of this so dreadful and so ireful a beginning.'

Now while these brave captains were thus busy in the house of the old Recorder, Captain Execution was as busy in other parts of the town, in securing the back-streets and the walls. He also hunted the Lord Willbewill sorely; he suffered him not to rest in any corner. He pursued him so hard that he drove his men from him, and made him glad to thrust his head into a hole. Also this mighty warrior did cut three of the Lord Willbewill's officers down to the ground; one was old Mr. Prejudice, he that had his crown cracked in the mutiny. This man was made by Lord Willbewill keeper of Eargate, and fell by the hand of Captain Execution. There was also one Mr. Backward-to-all-but-naught, and he also was one of Lord Willbewill's officers, and was the captain of the two guns that once were mounted on the top of Eargate. He also was cut down to the ground by the hands of Captain Execution. Besides these two, there was another, a third, and his name was Captain Treacherous, a vile man this was, but one that Willbewill did put a great deal of confidence in; but him also did this Captain Execution cut down to the ground with the rest.

He also made a very great slaughter among my Lord Willbewill's soldiers, killing many that were stout and sturdy, and wounding of many that for

The brave exploits of the Captain Execution.

Old Prejudice slain.

Backward-to-all-but-naught slain.

Treacherous slain.

Diabolus were nimble and active. But all these were Diabolonians; there was not a man, a native of Mansoul hurt.

Other feats of war were also likewise performed by other of the captains, as at Eyegate, where Captain Goodhope, and Captain Charity had a charge, was great execution done; for the Captain Goodhope with his own hands slew one Captain Blindfold, the keeper of the gate. This Blindfold was captain of a thousand men, and they were they that fought with mauls. He also pursued his men, slew many, and wounded more, and made the rest hide their heads in corners.

Captain Good-hope doth slay Captain Blind-fold.

There was also at that gate Mr. Ill-pause, of whom you have heard before. He was an old man, and had a beard that reached down to his girdle: the same was he that was orator to Diabolus. He did much mischief in the town of Mansoul, and fell by the hand of Captain Goodhope.

And old Ill-pause.

What shall I say? The Diabolonians in these days lay dead in every corner, though too many yet were alive in Mansoul.

Now the old Recorder, and my Lord Understanding, with some others of the chief of the town, to wit, such as knew they must stand and fall with the famous town of Mansoul, came together upon a day, and after consultation had, did jointly agree to draw up a petition, and to send it to Emmanuel, now while he sat in the gate of Mansoul. So they drew up their petition to Emmanuel, the contents whereof were this: *that they the old inhabitants of the now deplorable town of Mansoul, confessed their sin, and were sorry that they had offended his Princely Majesty, and prayed that he would spare their lives.*

The old townsmen meet and consult.

The town does petition, and are answered with silence.

Unto this petition he gave no answer at all, and that did trouble them yet so much the more. Now all this while the captains that were in the Recorder's house were playing with the battering-rams at the gates of the castle to beat them down. So after some time, labour and travel, the gate of the castle that was called Impregnable, was beaten open, and broken into several splinters; and so a way was made to go up to

The castle-gates broke open.

the hold in which Diabolus had hid himself. Then was tidings sent down to Eargate, for Emmanuel still abode there, to let him know that a way was made in at the gates of the castle of Mansoul. But, oh! how the trumpets at the tidings sounded throughout the Prince's camp, for that now the war was so near an end, and Mansoul itself of being set free.

Then the Prince arose from the place where he was, and took with him such of his men of war as were fittest for that expedition, and marched up the street of Mansoul to the old Recorder's house.

Emmanuel marches into Mansoul.

Now the Prince himself was clad all in armour of gold, and so he marched up the town with his standard borne before him; but he kept his countenance much reserved all the way as he went, so that the people could not tell how to gather to themselves love or hatred by his looks. Now as he marched up the street, the townsfolk came out at every door to see, and could not but be taken with his person, and the glory thereof, but wond'red at the reservedness of his countenance; for as yet he spake more to them by his actions and works, than he did by words or smiles. But also poor Mansoul (as in such cases all are apt to do), they interpreted the carriages of Emmanuel to them, as did Joseph's brethren his to them, even all the quite contrary way. 'For,' thought they, 'if Emmanuel loved us, he would show it to us by word or carriage, but none of these he doth; therefore Emmanuel hates us. Now if Emmanuel hates us, then Mansoul shall be slain, then Mansoul shall become a dunghill.' They knew that they had transgressed his Father's law, and that against him they had been in with Diabolus his enemy. They also knew that the Prince Emmanuel knew all this; for they were convinced that he was as an angel of God, to know all things that are done in the earth. And this made them think that their condition was miserable, and that the good Prince would make them desolate.

How they interpret Emmanuel's carriages.

25   See Gen. 44.
35   See II Sam. 14:20.

'And,' thought they, 'what time so fit to do this in as now, when he has the bridle of Mansoul in his hand?' And this I took special notice of, that the inhabitants, notwithstanding all this, could not—no, they could not, when they see him march through the town, but cringe, bow, bend, and were ready to lick the dust of his feet. They also wished a thousand times over, that he would become their Prince and Captain, and would become their protection. They would also one to another talk of the comeliness of his person, and how much for glory and valour he outstripped the great ones of the world. But, poor hearts! as to themselves, their thoughts would change, and go upon all manner of extremes. Yea, through the working of them backward and forward, Mansoul became as a ball tossed, and as a rolling thing before the whirlwind.

Now, when he was come to the castle gates, he commanded Diabolus to appear and to surrender himself into his hands. But, oh! how loth was the beast to appear! How he stuck at it! How he shrunk! Ay, how he cringed! Yet out he came to the Prince. Then Emmanuel commanded, and they took Diabolus and bound him fast in chains, the better to reserve him to the judgment that he had appointed for him. But Diabolus stood up to entreat for himself that Emmanuel would not send him into the deep, but suffer him to depart out of Mansoul in peace. *He comes up to the castle, and commands Diabolus to surrender himself.*

When Emmanuel had taken him and bound him in chains, he led him into the market-place, and there before Mansoul, stripped him of his armour in which he boasted so much before. This now was one of the acts of triumph of Emmanuel over his enemy; and all the while that the giant was stripping, the trumpets of the golden Prince did sound amain. The captains also shouted, and the soldiers did sing for joy. *He is taken and bound in chains.*

16 *as a ball tossed*: the analogy is from Isa. 22:18.
21f. *Ay, how he cringed*: first edition, "I how he cringed!"
25 See Jude 6.
27 See Luke 8:31.
31 See Luke 11:22.

Then was Mansoul called upon to behold the beginning of Emmanuel's triumph over him in whom they so much had trusted, and of whom they so much had boasted in the days when he flattered them.

Thus having made Diabolus naked in the eyes of Mansoul, and before the commanders of the Prince, in the next place he commands that Diabolus should be bound with chains to his chariot-wheels. Then leaving of some of his forces, to wit, Captain Boanerges, and Captain Conviction, as a guard for the castle-gates, that resistance might be made on his behalf (if any that heretofore followed Diabolus should make an attempt to possess it), he did ride in triumph over him quite through the town of Mansoul, and so out at, and before the gate called Eyegate, to the plain where his camp did lie.

But you cannot think unless you had been there —as I was—what a shout there was in Emmanuel's camp when they saw the tyrant bound by the hand of their noble Prince, and tied to his chariot-wheels!

And they said, 'He hath led captivity captive, he hath spoiled principalities and powers. Diabolus is subjected to the power of his sword, and made the object of all derision.'

Those also that rode reformades, and that came down to see the battle, they shouted with that greatness of voice, and sung with such melodious notes, that they caused them that dwell in the highest orbs to open their windows, put out their heads, and look down to see the cause of that glory.

The townsmen also, so many of them as saw this sight, were, as it were, while they looked, betwixt the earth and the Heavens. True, they could not tell what would be the issue of things as to them, but all things were done in such excellent methods; and I cannot tell how, but things in the management of them seemed to cast a smile towards the town, so that their eyes, their heads, their hearts, and their minds, and all that they had were taken and held while they observed Emmanuel's order.

Mansoul must behold it.

Eph. 4.
He is bound to his chariot-wheels.

The Prince rides in triumph over him, in the sight of Mansoul.

They sing.

The reformades joy.

Luke 15:7,10.

The men of Mansoul taken with Emmanuel.

10

20

30

21   See Eph. 4:8; Col. 2:15.

So when the brave Prince had finished this part of his triumph over Diabolus his foe, he turned him up in the midst of his contempt and shame, having given him a charge no more to be a possessor of Mansoul. Then went he from Emmanuel, and out of the midst of his camp to inherit the parched places in a salt land, seeking rest but finding none.

Matt. 12:43.

Now Captain Boanerges and Captain Conviction were both of them men of very great majesty; their faces were like the faces of lions, and their words like the roaring of the sea; and they still quartered in Mr. Conscience's house, of whom mention was made before. When therefore the high and mighty Prince had thus far finished his triumph over Diabolus, the townsmen had more leisure to view and to behold the actions of these noble captains. But the captains carried it with that terror and dread in all that they did—and you may be sure that they had private instructions so to do—that they kept the town under continual heart-aching, and caused (in their apprehension) the well-being of Mansoul for the future, to hang in doubt before them, so that for some considerable time they neither knew what rest, or ease, or peace, or hope meant.

The carriage of Boanerges, and of Captain Conviction do crush the spirit of Mansoul.

Nor did the Prince himself as yet abide in the town of Mansoul, but in his royal pavilion in the camp, and in the midst of his Father's forces. So at a time convenient, he sent special orders to Captain Boanerges to summons Mansoul, the whole of the townsmen, into the castle-yard, and then and there before their faces, to take my Lord Understanding, Mr. Conscience, and that notable one the Lord Willbewill and put them all three in ward, and that they should set a strong guard upon them there, until his pleasure concerning them were further known. The which orders, when the captains had put them in execution, made no small addition to the fears of the town of Mansoul; for now, to their thinking, were their former fears of the ruin of Mansoul confirmed. Now, what death they should die, and how long they should be in dying, was that which most perplexed their heads

The Prince commands, & the captains put the three chief of Mansoul in ward.

and hearts; yea, they were afraid that Emmanuel would command them all into the deep, the place that the Prince Diabolus was afraid of; for they knew that they had deserved it. Also, to die by the sword in the face of the town, and in the open way of disgrace, from the hand of so good and so holy a Prince—that, too, troubled them sore. The town was also greatly troubled for the men that were committed to ward, for that they were their stay and their guide, and for that they believed that if those men were cut off, their execution would be but the beginning of the ruin of the town of Mansoul. Wherefore, what do they, but together with the men in prison, draw up a petition to the Prince, and sent it to Emmanuel by the hand of Mr. Wouldlive. So he went and came to the Prince's quarters, and presented the petition; the sum of which was this—

Mansoul greatly distressed.

They send a petition to Emmanuel by the hand of Mr. Wouldlive.

Great and wonderful Potentate, Victor over Diabolus, and Conqueror of the town of Mansoul:

We, the miserable inhabitants of that most woeful corporation, do humbly beg that we may find favour in thy sight, and remember not against us former transgressions, nor yet the sins of the chief of our town, but spare us according to the greatness of thy mercy, and let us not die, but live in thy sight. So shall we be willing to be thy servants, and if thou shalt think fit, to gather our meat under thy table. Amen.

So the petitioner went, as was said, with his petition to the Prince, and the Prince took it at his hand, but sent him away with silence. This still afflicted the town of Mansoul, but yet considering that now they must either petition, or die; for now they could not do anything else; therefore they consulted again, and sent another petition, and this petition was much after the form and method of the former.

But when the petition was drawn up, By whom should they send it? was the next question; for they

They are answered with silence.

10

20

30

would not send this by him by whom they sent the first, for they thought that the Prince had taken some offence at the manner of his deportment before him. So they attempted to make Captain Conviction their messenger with it; but he said that he neither durst nor would petition Emmanuel for traitors, nor be to the Prince an advocate for rebels. 'Yet withal,' said he, 'our Prince is good, and you may adventure to send it by the hand of one of your town, provided he went with a rope about his head, and pleaded nothing but mercy.'

They petition again.

They cannot tell by whom to send it.

Well, they made through fear their delays as long as they could, and longer than delays were good; but fearing at last the dangerousness of them, they thought, but with many a fainting in their minds, to send their petition by Mr. Desires-awake. So they sent for Mr. Desires-awake. Now he dwelt in a very mean cottage in Mansoul, and he came at his neighbours' request. So they told him what they had done, and what they would do concerning petitioning, and that they did desire of him that he would go therewith to the Prince.

Then said Mr. Desires-awake, 'Why should not I do the best I can to save so famous a town as Mansoul from deserved destruction?' They therefore delivered the petition to him, and told him how he must address himself to the Prince, and wished him ten thousand good speeds. So he comes to the Prince's pavilion, as the first, and asked to speak with his Majesty. So word was carried to Emmanuel and the Prince came out to the man. When Mr. Desires-awake saw the Prince, he fell flat with his face to the ground, and cried out, 'O that Mansoul might live before thee!' And with that he presented the petition; the which, when the Prince had read, he turned away for a while and wept; but refraining himself, he turned again to the man, who all this while lay crying at his feet as at the first, and

Mr. Desires-awake goes with the petition to the Prince.

His entertainment.

10   See I Kings 20:31. The placing of a rope on one's head was a sign of abject submission. "I thought also of Benhadad's servants, who went with ropes upon their heads to their enemies for mercy." *Grace Abounding*, par. 251.

110

said to him, 'Go thy way to thy place, and I will consider of thy requests.'

Now you may think that they of Mansoul that had sent him, what with guilt, and what with fear, lest their petition should be rejected, could not but look with many a long look, and that too with strange workings of heart, to see what would become of their petition. At last they saw their messenger coming back. So when he was come, they asked him how he fared, what Emmanuel said? And what was become of the petition? But he told them that he would be silent till he came to the prison to my Lord Mayor, my Lord Willbewill, and Mr. Recorder. So he went forwards towards the prison-house, where the men of Mansoul lay bound. But, oh! what a multitude flocked after to hear what the messenger said. So when he was come and had shown himself at the grate of the prison, my Lord Mayor himself looked as white as a clout, the Recorder also did quake. But they asked and said, 'Come, good Sir, what did the great Prince say to you?' Then said Mr. Desires-awake, 'When I came to my Lord's pavilion, I called, and he came forth. So I fell prostrate at his feet, and delivered to him my petition (for the greatness of his person, and the glory of his countenance would not suffer me to stand upon my legs). Now as he received the petition, I cried, O *that Mansoul might live before thee!* So when for a while he had looked thereon, he turned him about and said to his servant, *Go thy way to thy place again, and I will consider of thy requests.*' The messenger added moreover, and said, 'The Prince to whom you sent me, is such a one for beauty and glory, that whoso sees him must both love and fear him. I, for my part, can do no less; but I know not what will be the end of these things.' At this answer they were all at a stand, both they in prison, and they that followed the messenger thither to hear the news; nor knew they what, or what manner of interpretation to put upon what

His return and answer to them that sent him.

Mansoul confounded at the answer.

10

20

30

17   *grate*: bars. There is no authority for the reading of the second edition, "gate." The word is used again, on p. 117, where both editions agree.

the Prince had said. Now when the prison was cleared of the throng, the prisoners among themselves began to comment upon Emmanuel's words. My Lord Mayor said that the answer did not look with a rugged face; but Willbewill said it betokened evil; and the Recorder, that it was a messenger of death. Now they that were left, and that stood behind, and so could not so well hear what the prisoners said, some of them catched hold of one piece of a sentence, and some on a bit of another; some took hold of what the messenger said, and some of the prisoners' judgment thereon, so none had the right understanding of things. But you cannot imagine what work these people made, and what a confusion there was in Mansoul now.

For presently they that had heard what was said, flew about the town, one crying one thing, and another the quite contrary; and both were sure enough they told true, for they did hear they said with their ears what was said, and therefore could not be deceived. One would say, 'We must all be killed'; another would say, 'We must all be saved'; and a third would say, that the Prince would not be concerned with Mansoul; and a fourth, that the prisoners must be suddenly put to death. And as I said, every one stood to it, that he told his tale the rightest; and that all others but he were out. Wherefore Mansoul had now molestation upon molestation, nor could any man know on what to rest the sole of his foot; for one would go by now, and as he went, if he heard his neighbour tell his tale, to be sure he would tell the quite contrary, and both would stand in it that he told the truth. Nay, some of them had got this story by the end, that the Prince did intend to put Mansoul to the sword. And now it begun to be dark, wherefore poor Mansoul was in sad perplexity all that night until the morning.

The prisoners' judgment upon the Prince's answer.

Misgiving thoughts breed confusion in Mansoul.

Mansoul in perplexity.

4   *did not look with a rugged face*: i.e., it was a soft answer.
32f.   *by the end*: an allusion to the process of spinning, in which an end of fibre is drawn out from the distaff and twisted into thread. It perhaps suggests how some of the Mansoulians in their anxiety could quickly fasten on a story and elaborate it as truth.

But so far as I could gather by the best information that I could get, all this hubbub came through the words that the Recorder said, when he told them that in his judgment the Prince's answer was a messenger of death. 'Twas this that fired the town, and that began the fright in Mansoul; for Mansoul in former times did use to count that Mr. Recorder was a seer, and that his sentence was equal to the best of oracles; and thus was Mansoul a terror to itself.

What will guilt do.

And now did they begin to feel what was the effects of stubborn rebellion, and unlawful resistance against their Prince. I say they now began to feel the effects thereof by guilt and fear that now had swallowed them up; and who more involved in the one but they that were most in the other—to wit, the chief of the town of Mansoul?

To be brief, when the fame of the fright was out of the town, and the prisoners had a little recovered themselves, they take to themselves some heart, and think to petition the Prince for life again. So they did draw up a third petition, the contents whereof was this—

They resolve to petition again.

Prince Emmanuel the Great, Lord of all Worlds, and Master of Mercy:

Their petition.

We thy poor wretched, miserable, dying town of Mansoul, do confess unto thy great and glorious Majesty, that we have sinned against thy Father and thee, and are no more worthy to be called thy Mansoul, but rather to be cast into the pit. If thou wilt slay us, we have deserved it. If thou wilt condemn us to the deep, we cannot but say thou art righteous. We cannot complain whatever thou dost, or however thou carriest it towards us. But oh! let mercy reign! and let it be extended to us! O let mercy take hold upon us, and free us from our transgressions, and we will sing of thy mercy, and of thy judgment. Amen.

This petition when drawn up was designed to be sent to the Prince as the first; but who should carry it?—that was the question. Some said, 'Let him do it that went with the first;' but others thought not good to do that, and that because he sped no better. Now, there was an old man in the town, and his name was Mr. Good-deed, a man that bare only the name, but had nothing of the nature of the thing. Now, some were for sending of him, but the Recorder was by no means for that. 'For,' said he, 'we now stand in need of, and are pleading for mercy; wherefore, to send our petition by a man of this name will seem to cross the petition itself. Should we make Mr. Good-deed our messenger, when our petition cries for mercy?

'Besides,' quoth the old gentleman, 'should the Prince now as he receives the petition, ask him, and say, *What is thy name?* as nobody knows but he will; and he should say, *Old Good-deed*; what, think you, would Emmanuel say but this—*Ay, is old Good-deed yet alive in Mansoul? Then let old Good-deed save you from your distresses.* And if he says so, I am sure we are lost, nor can a thousand of old Good-deeds save Mansoul.'

After the Recorder had given in his reasons why old Good-deed should not go with this petition to Emmanuel, the rest of the prisoners and chief of Mansoul opposed it also, and so old Good-deed was laid aside, and they agreed to send Mr. Desires-awake again. So they sent for him, and desired him that he would a second time go with their petition to the Prince, and he readily told them he would. But they bid him that in any wise he should take heed that in no word or carriage he gave offence to the Prince. 'For by doing so, for ought we can tell, you may bring Mansoul into utter destruction,' said they.

Now Mr. Desires-awake, when he saw that he must go of this errand, besought that they would grant that Mr. Wet-eyes might go with him. Now this Wet-eyes was a near neighbour of Mr. Desires, a poor man, a man of a broken spirit, yet one that could speak well to a petition. So they granted that he should go with him. Wherefore they address themselves to their business. Mr. Desires put a rope upon

Prayer attended with difficulty.

Old Good-deed propounded as a fit person to carry the petition; the old Recorder opposes it, and he is rejected.

Mr. Desires-awake goes again and takes one Wet-eyes with him.

his head, and Mr. Wet-eyes went with hands wringing together. Thus they went to the Prince's pavilion.

Now when they went to petition this third time, they were not without thoughts that by often coming they might be a burden to the Prince. Wherefore, when they were come to the door of his pavilion, they first made their apology for themselves, and for their coming to trouble Emmanuel so often; and they said, *that they came not hither today, for that they delighted in being troublesome, or for that they delighted to hear themselves talk, but for that necessity caused them to come to his Majesty. They could, they said, have no rest day nor night, because of their transgressions against Shaddai, and against Emmanuel his Son.* They also thought *that some misbehaviour of Mr. Desires-awake the last time might give distaste to his Highness, and so cause that he returned from so merciful a Prince empty, and without countenance.* So when they had made this apology, Mr. Desiresawake cast himself prostrate upon the ground as at the first, at the feet of the mighty Prince, saying, 'Oh! that Mansoul might live before thee!' And so he delivered his petition. The Prince, then, having read the petition, turned aside a while as before, and coming again to the place where the petitioner lay on the ground, he demanded what his name was, and of what esteem in the account of Mansoul, for that he above all the multitude in Mansoul should be sent to him upon such an errand. Then said the man to the Prince, 'O let not my Lord be angry; and why enquirest thou after the name of such a dead dog as I am? Pass by, I pray thee, and take not notice of who I am, because there is, as thou very well knowest, so great a disproportion between me and thee. Why the townsmen chose to send me on this errand to my Lord, is best known to themselves, but it could not be, for that they thought that I had favour with my Lord. For my part I am out of charity with myself; who, then, should be in love with me? Yet live I would, and so would I that my townsmen should; and because both they and myself are guilty of great

Their apology for their coming again.

The Prince talketh with them.

Mr. Desires' free speech to his Prince.

10

20

30

40

transgressions, therefore they have sent me, and I am
come in their names to beg of my Lord for mercy. Let
it please thee, therefore, to incline to mercy, but ask
not what thy servants are.'

Then said the Prince, 'And what is he that is
become thy companion in this so weighty a matter?'
So Mr. Desires-awake told Emmanuel that he was a
poor neighbour of his, and one of his most intimate
associates. 'And his name,' said he, 'may it please your
most excellent Majesty, is Wet-eyes of the town of
Mansoul. I know that there are many of that name
that are naught; but I hope 'twill be no offence to my
Lord that I have brought my poor neighbour with me.'

Then Mr. Wet-eyes fell on his face to the ground,
and made this apology for his coming with his neighbour to his Lord—

'O my Lord,' quoth he, 'what I am, I know not
myself, nor whether my name be feigned or true,
especially when I begin to think what some have said,
namely that this name was given me because Mr.
Repentance was my father. Good men have bad children, and the sincere do oftentimes beget hypocrites.
My mother also called me by this name from my
cradle, but whether because of the moistness of my
brain, or because of the softness of my heart, I cannot
tell. I see dirt in mine own tears, and filthiness in the
bottom of my prayers. But I pray thee' (and all this
while the gentleman wept) 'that thou wouldest not
remember against us our transgressions, nor take
offence at the unqualifiedness of thy servants, but
mercifully pass by the sin of Mansoul, and refrain
from the glorifying of thy grace no longer.'

So at his bidding they arose, and both stood
trembling before him, and he spake to them to this
purpose:

'The town of Mansoul hath grievously rebelled
against my Father, in that they have rejected him
from being their King, and did choose to themselves
for their captain, a liar, a murderer, and a runagate-
slave. For this Diabolus, and your pretended prince,
though once so highly accounted of by you, made

Mr. Wet-eyes'
apology for his
coming with his
neighbour.

The Prince's
answer.

rebellion against my Father and me, even in our palace
and highest court there, thinking to become a prince
and king. But being there timely discovered and apprehended, and for his wickedness bound in chains, and
separated to the pit with those that were his companions, he offered himself to you, and you have
received him.

'Now this is, and for a long time hath been, an
high affront to my Father; wherefore my Father sent
to you a powerful army to reduce you to your obedi-   10
ence. But you know how those men, their captains
and their counsels were esteemed of you, and what
they received at your hand. You rebelled against
them, you shut your gates upon them, you bid them
battle, you fought them, and fought for Diabolus
against them. So they sent to my Father for more
power, and I with my men are come to subdue you.
But as you treated the servants, so you treated their
Lord. You stood up in hostile manner against me, you
shut up your gates against me, you turned the deaf ear   20
to me, and resisted as long as you could; but now I
have made a conquest of you. Did you cry me mercy
so long as you had hopes that you might prevail
against me? But now I have taken the town, you cry.
But why did you not cry before, when the white flag
of my mercy, the red flag of justice, and the black flag
that threatened execution, were set up to cite you to
it? Now I have conquered your Diabolus, you come
to me for favour; but why did you not help me
against the mighty? Yet I will consider your petition,   30
and will answer it so as will be for my glory.

'Go bid Captain Boanerges, and Captain Conviction, bring the prisoners out to me into the camp tomorrow, and say you to Captain Judgment, and Captain
Execution, *Stay you in the castle, and take good heed
to yourselves that you keep all quiet in Mansoul until
you shall hear further from me.*' And with that he
turned himself from them, and went into his royal
pavilion again.

22   *cry me mercy*: beg my pardon or forgiveness.

So the petitioners having received this answer from the prince, returned as at the first, to go to their companions again. But they had not gone far, but thoughts began to work in their minds, that no mercy as yet was intended by the prince to Mansoul. So they went to the place where the prisoners lay bound; but these workings of mind about what would become of Mansoul, had such strong power over them, that by that they were come unto them that sent them, they were scarce able to deliver their message.

But they came at length to the gates of the town —now the townsmen with earnestness were waiting for their return—where many met them to know what answer was made to the petition. Then they cried out to those that were sent, 'What news from the Prince, and what hath Emmanuel said?' But they said, that they must (as afore) go up to the prison, and there deliver their message. So away they went to the prison with a multitude* at their heels. Now when they were come to the grates of the prison, they told the first part of Emmanuel's speech to the prisoners, to wit, how he reflected upon their disloyalty to his Father and himself, and how they had chosen, and closed with Diabolus, had fought for him, hearkened to him, and been ruled by him, but had despised him and his men. This made the prisoners look pale, but the messengers proceeded, and said, 'He, the Prince, said, moreover, that yet he would consider your petition, and give such answer thereto as would stand with his glory.' And as these words were spoken, Mr. Wet-eyes gave a great sigh. At this they were all of them struck into their dumps, and could not tell what to say; fear also possessed them in marvellous manner, and death seem'd to sit upon some of their eyebrows. Now there was in the company a notable sharp-witted fellow, a mean man of estate, and his name was old

*Of inquisitive thoughts.

The messengers in telling their tale, fright the prisoners.

32 *struck into their dumps*: cast into a state of perplexity or extreme dejection.
34 *death seemed to sit*, etc.: apparently a folk-idiom, meaning that death seemed near to some of them. Bunyan's own religious experience testifies to the psychological truth of this passage. See *Grace Abounding*, pars. 210-12.
36 *a mean man of estate*: a man of poor standing in the community.

Old Inquisitive. Inquisitive. This man asked the petitioners if they had told out every whit of what Emmanuel said. And they answered, 'Verily, no.' Then said Inquisitive, 'I thought so, indeed. Pray what was it more that he said unto you?' Then they paused awhile; but at last they brought out all saying, 'The Prince did bid us bid Captain Boanerges and Captain Conviction bring the prisoners down to him tomorrow'—and that Captain Judgment and Captain Execution should take charge of the castle and town till they should hear further   10 from him. They said also, that when the Prince had commanded them thus to do, he immediately turned his back upon them, and went into his royal pavilion.

But, O! how this return, and specially this last clause of it, *that the prisoners must go out to the Prince into the camp,* brake all their loins in pieces! Wherefore with one voice they set up a cry that reached up to the heavens. This done, each of the *Conscience. three prepared himself to die (and the Recorder* said unto them, 'This was the thing that I feared.'), for   20 they concluded that tomorrow by that the sun went down, they should be tumbled out of the world. The whole town also counted of no other, but that in their time and order they must all drink of the same cup. Wherefore the town of Mansoul spent that night in mourning, and sackcloth, and ashes. The prisoners also, when the time was come for them to go down before the Prince, dressed themselves in mourning attire, with ropes upon their head. The whole town of Mansoul also showed themselves upon the wall, all   30 clad in mourning weeds, if perhaps the Prince with the sight thereof might be moved with compassion. But, *Vain thoughts. oh! how the busy-bodies* that were in the town of Mansoul did now concern themselves! They did run here and there through the streets of the town by companies, crying out as they ran in tumultuous wise, one after one manner, and another the quite contrary, to the almost utter distraction of Mansoul.

Well, the time is come that the prisoners must

31   *weeds*: clothes.

go down to the camp, and appear before the Prince. And thus was the manner of their going down: Captain Boanerges went with a guard before them, and Captain Conviction came behind, and the prisoners went down bound in chains in the midst. So, I say, the prisoners went in the midst, and the guard went with flying colours behind and before, but the prisoners went with drooping spirits.

Or more particularly thus: The prisoners went down all in mourning; they put ropes upon themselves; they went on smiting of themselves on the breasts, but durst not lift up their eyes to Heaven. Thus they went out at the gate of Mansoul, till they came into the midst of the Prince's army, the sight and glory of which did greatly heighten their affliction. Nor could they now longer forbear, but cry out aloud, 'O unhappy men! O wretched men of Mansoul!' Their chains, still mixing their dolorous notes with the cries of the prisoners, made the noise more lamentable.

So when they were come to the door of the Prince's pavilion, they cast themselves prostrate upon the place; then one went in and told his Lord that the prisoners were come down. The Prince then ascended a Throne of State, and sent for the prisoners in; who, when they came, did tremble before him, also they covered their faces with shame. Now, as they drew near to the place where he sat, they threw themselves down before him. Then said the Prince to the Captain Boanerges, 'Bid the prisoners stand upon their feet.' Then they stood trembling before him, and he said, 'Are you the men that heretofore were the servants of Shaddai?' And they said, 'Yes, Lord, yes.' Then said the Prince again, 'Are you the men that did suffer yourselves to be corrupted and defiled by that abominable one, Diabolus?' And they said, 'We did more than suffer it, Lord; for we chose it of our own mind.' The Prince asked further, saying, 'Could you have been content that your slavery should have continued under his tyranny as long as you had lived?' Then said the prisoners, 'Yes, Lord, yes; for his ways were

The prisoners had to trial.

How they went.

They fall down prostrate before him.

They are upon their trial.

pleasing to our flesh, and we were grown aliens to a better state.' 'And did you,' said he, 'when I came up against this town of Mansoul, heartily wish that I might not have the victory over you?' 'Yes, Lord, yes,' said they. Then said the Prince, 'And what punishment is it, think you, that you deserve at my hand for these and other your high and mighty sins?' And they said, 'Both death and the deep, Lord; for we have deserved no less.' He asked again if they had aught to say for themselves, why the sentence that they confessed that they had deserved, should not be passed upon them? And they said, 'We can say nothing, Lord; thou art just, for we have sinned.' Then said the Prince, 'And for what are those ropes on your heads?' The prisoners answered, 'These ropes* are to bind us withal to the place of execution, if mercy be not pleasing in thy sight.' So he further asked if all the men in the town of Mansoul were in this confession, as they? And they answered, 'All the natives,* Lord; but for the Diabolonians* that came into our town when the tyrant got possession of us, we can say nothing for them.'

Then the Prince commanded that an herald* should be called, and that he should in the midst, and throughout the camp of Emmanuel proclaim, and that with sound of trumpet, that the Prince, the Son of Shaddai, had in his Father's name, and for his Father's glory, gotten a perfect conquest and victory over Mansoul, and that the prisoners should follow him and say, 'Amen.' So this was done as he had commanded. And presently the music* that was in the upper region sounded melodiously. The captains that were in the camp shouted, and the soldiers did sing songs of triumph to the Prince, the colours waved in the wind, and great joy was everywhere, only it was wanting as yet in the hearts of the men of Mansoul.

Then the Prince called for the prisoners to come and to stand again before him, and they came and stood trembling. And he said unto them, 'The sins, trespasses, iniquities that you with the whole town of Mansoul, have from time to time committed against

They condemn themselves.

*Sins. Prov. 5:22.

*Powers of the soul. *Corruptions and lusts.

*A victory proclaimed.

*Joy for the victory.

They are pardoned, and are commanded to proclaim it tomorrow in Mansoul.

10

20

30

40

my Father and me, I have power and commandment
from my Father to forgive to the town of Mansoul;
and do forgive you accordingly.' And having so said,
he gave them written in parchment, and sealed with
seven seals, a large and general pardon, commanding
both my Lord Mayor, my Lord Willbewill, and Mr.
Recorder, to proclaim, and cause it to be proclaimed
tomorrow by that the sun is up, throughout the whole
town of Mansoul.

Moreover the Prince stripped the prisoners of
their mourning weeds, and gave them beauty for
ashes, the oil of joy for mourning, and the garment
of praise for the spirit of heaviness.

Their rags are taken from them. Isa. 61:3.

Then he gave to each of the three, jewels of gold,
and precious stones, and took away their ropes, and
put chains of gold about their necks, and ear-rings in
their ears. Now the prisoners when they did hear the
gracious words of Prince Emmanuel, and had beheld
all that was done unto them, fainted almost quite
away; for the grace, the benefit, the pardon, was
sudden, glorious, and so big, that they were not able
without staggering to stand up under it. Yea, my Lord
Willbewill swooned outright, but the Prince stepped
to him, put his everlasting arms under him, embraced
him, kissed him, and bid him be of good cheer, for all
should be performed according to his word. He also
did kiss and embrace, and smile upon the other two
that were Willbewill's companions, saying, 'Take
these as further tokens of my love, favour and compassions to you; and I charge you that you, Mr. Recorder, tell in the town of Mansoul what you have
heard and seen.'

A strange al-teration.

Then were their fetters broken to pieces before
their faces, and cast into the air, and their steps were
enlarged under them. Then they fell down at the feet
of the Prince, and kissed his feet, and wetted them
with tears: also they cried out with a mighty strong
voice, saying, 'Blessed be the glory of the Lord from

Their guilt.

33ff. See II Sam. 22:37.

his place.' So they were bid rise up, and go to the town, and tell to Mansoul what the Prince had done. He commanded also that one with a pipe and tabor

They are sent home with pipe and tabor.

should go and play before them all the way into the town of Mansoul. Then was fulfilled what they never looked for, and they were made to possess that which they never dreamt of. The Prince also called for the

Captain Credence guards them home.

noble Captain Credence, and commanded that he and some of his officers should march before the noble men of Mansoul with flying colours into the town. He gave also unto Captain Credence a charge that about

When faith and pardon meet together, judgment and execution depart from the heart.

that time that the Recorder did read the general pardon in the town of Mansoul, that at that very time he should with flying colours march in at Eyegate with his ten thousands at his feet, and that he should so go until he came by the high street of the town, up to the castle-gates, and that himself should take possession thereof against his Lord came thither. He commanded, moreover, that he should bid Captain Judgment, and Captain Execution to leave the stronghold to him, and to withdraw from Mansoul, and to return into the camp with speed unto the Prince.

And now was the town of Mansoul also delivered from the terror of the first four captains and their men.

Well, I told you before how the prisoners were entertained by the noble Prince Emmanuel, and how they behaved themselves before him, and how he sent them away to their home with pipe and tabor going before them. And now you must think that those of the town that had all this while waited to hear of their death, could not but be exercised with sadness of mind, and with thoughts that pricked like thorns. Nor could their thoughts be kept to any one point; the wind blew with them all this while at great uncertainties; yea, their hearts were like a balance that had been disquieted with shaking hand. But at last as they with many a long look looked over the wall of Mansoul, they thought that they saw some returning to

1   *his place*: first edition, "this place." See Ezek. 3:12.
3   *tabor*: small drum, chiefly used as accompaniment to the pipe.

the town; and thought again, 'Who should they be,
too? Who should they be?' At last they discerned that
they were the prisoners; but can you imagine how
their hearts were surprised with wonder—especially
when they perceived also in what equipage, and with
what honour they were sent home! They went down
to the camp in black, but they came back to the town
in white; they went down to the camp in ropes, they
came back in chains of gold; they went down to the
camp with their feet in fetters, but came back with
their steps enlarged under them, they went also to the
camp looking for death, but they came back from
thence with assurance of life; they went down to the
camp with heavy hearts, but came back again with
pipe and tabor playing before them. So, so soon as they
were come to Eyegate, the poor and tottering town of
Mansoul adventured to give a shout; and they gave
such a shout as made the captains in the Prince's army
leap at the sound thereof. Alas! for them, poor hearts,
who could blame them, since their dead friends were
come to life again? For 'twas to them as life from
the dead, to see the ancients of the town of Mansoul
to shine in such splendour. They looked for nothing
but the axe and the block; but behold! joy and gladness, comfort and consolation, and such melodious
notes attending of them, that was sufficient to make
a sick man well.

A strange alter-
ation.

Isa. 33:24.

So when they came up, they saluted each other
with 'Welcome, welcome!' and 'Blessed be he that has
spared you!' They added also, 'We see it is well with
you; but how must it go with the town of Mansoul?
And will it go well with the town of Mansoul?' said
they. Then answered them the Recorder, and my Lord
Mayor, 'Oh! tidings! glad tidings! good tidings of good,
and of great joy to poor Mansoul!' Then they gave
another shout that made the earth to ring again. After
this they enquired yet more particularly how things
went in the camp, and what message they had from

Conscience.

The Under-
standing.

5   *equipage*: outfit or retinue.
8   *in white*: see Rev. 19:8.

124

Emmanuel to the town. So they told them all passages
that had happened to them at the camp, and everything that the Prince did to them. This made Mansoul
wonder at the wisdom and grace of the Prince Emmanuel. Then they told them what they had received
at his hands for the whole town of Mansoul, and the
Recorder delivered it in these words, 'PARDON,
PARDON, PARDON for Mansoul! And this shall
Mansoul know tomorrow.' Then he commanded, and
they went and summoned Mansoul to meet together
in the market-place tomorrow, there to hear their
general pardon read.

O the joy of pardon of sin!

But who can think what a turn, what a change,
what an alteration this hint of things did make in
the countenance of the town of Mansoul! No man
of Mansoul could sleep that night for joy; in every
house there was joy and music, singing and making
merry—telling and hearing of Mansoul's happiness,
was then all that Mansoul had to do. And this was
the burden of all their song: 'Oh! more of this at the
rising of the sun! more of this tomorrow! Who
thought yesterday, would one say, that this day would
have been *such* a day to us? And who thought, that
saw our prisoners go down in irons, that they would
have returned in chains of gold! Yea, they that judged
themselves as they went to be judged of their Judge,
were by his mouth acquitted, not for that they were
innocent, but of the Prince's mercy, and sent home
with pipe and tabor.

Town-talk of the King's mercy.

'But is this the common custom of Princes? Do
they use to show such kind of favours to traitors?
No! This is only peculiar to Shaddai, and unto Emmanuel, his Son.'

Now morning drew on apace; wherefore the Lord
Mayor, the Lord Willbewill, and Mr. Recorder came
down to the market-place at the time that the Prince
had appointed, where the townsfolk were waiting for
them. And when they came, they came in that attire,
and in that glory that the Prince had put them into

23 *And who thought*: first edition, "And who though."

the day before, and the street was lightened with their glory. So the Mayor, Recorder, and my Lord Willbe-will, drew down to Mouthgate, which was at the lower end of the market-place, because that of old time was the place where they used to read public matters. Thither therefore they came in their robes, and their tabret went before them. Now the eagerness of the people to know the full of the matter was great.

Then the Recorder stood up upon his feet, and first beckoning with his hand for a silence, he read out with loud voice the pardon. But when he came to these words, *the Lord, the Lord God merciful and gracious, pardoning iniquity, transgressions and sins; and to them, all manner of sin and blasphemy shall be forgiven, etc.,* they could not forbear but leap for joy. For this, you must know, that there was conjoined herewith every man's name in Mansoul; also the seals of the pardon made a brave show.

The manner of reading the pardon.

Exod. 34. Mark 3.

When the Recorder had made an end of reading the pardon, the townsmen ran up upon the walls of the town, and leaped and skipped thereon for joy, and bowed themselves seven times with their faces towards Emmanuel's pavilion, and shouted out aloud for joy, and said, 'Let Emmanuel live forever!' Then order was given to the young men in Mansoul, that they should ring the bells for joy. So the bells did ring, and the people sing, and the music go in every house in Mansoul.

Now they tread upon the flesh.

Lively and warm thoughts.

When the Prince had sent home the three prisoners of Mansoul with joy, and pipe and tabor, he commanded his captains with all the field-officers and soldiers throughout his army to be ready, in that morning that the Recorder should read the pardon in Mansoul, to do his further pleasure. So the morning, as I have showed, being come, just as the Recorder had made an end of reading the pardon, Emmanuel commanded that all the trumpets in the camp should sound, that the colours should be displayed, half of them upon Mount Gracious, and half of them upon

The carriage of the camp.

7   *tabret*: timbrel, small tabor.

126

Mount Justice. He commanded also that all the captains should show themselves in all their harness, and that the soldiers should shout for joy. Nor was Captain Credence, though in the castle, silent in such a day, but he from the top of the hold showed himself with sound of trumpet to Mansoul, and to the Prince's camp.

Faith will not be silent when Mansoul is saved.

Thus have I showed you the manner and way that Emmanuel took to recover the town of Mansoul from under the hand and power of the tyrant Diabolus.

Now when the Prince had completed these, the outward ceremonies of his joy, he again commanded that his captains and soldiers should show unto Mansoul some feats of war. So they presently addressed themselves to this work. But oh! with what agility, nimbleness, dexterity and bravery did these military-men discover their skill in feats of war to the now gazing town of Mansoul!

The Prince displays his graces before Mansoul.

They marched, they counter-marched; they opened to the right and left; they divided, and subdivided; they closed, they wheeled, made good their front and rear with their right and left wings, and twenty things more, with that aptness, and then were all as they were again, that they took, yea, ravished the hearts that were in Mansoul to behold it. But add to this, the handling of their arms, the managing of their weapons of war, were marvellous taking to Mansoul and me.

They are ravished at the sight of them.

When this action was over, the whole town of Mansoul came out as one man to the Prince in the camp to thank him, and praise him for his abundant favour, and to beg that it would please his Grace to come unto Mansoul with his men, and there to take up their quarters for ever. And this they did in most humble manner, bowing themselves seven times to the ground before him. Then said he, 'All peace be to you.' So the town came nigh and touched with the hand the top of his golden scepter; and they said, Oh! that the Prince Emmanuel with his captains and men of

They beg that the Prince and his men will dwell with them for ever.

10

20

30

27   taking: captivating, attractive.

war would dwell in Mansoul forever; and that his
battering-rams and slings might be lodged in her for
the use and service of the Prince, and for the help and
strength of Mansoul. 'For,' said they, 'we have room
for thee, we have room for thy men, we have also room
for thy weapons of war, and a place to make a maga-
zine for thy carriages. Do it, Emmanuel, and thou
shalt be King and Captain in Mansoul for ever. Yea,
govern thou also according to all the desire of thy soul,
and make thou governors and princes under thee of
thy captains and men of war, and we will become
thy servants, and thy laws shall be our direction.'

> Say and hold to
> it Mansoul.

    They added, moreover, and prayed his Majesty
to consider thereof. 'For,' said they, 'if now after all
this grace bestowed upon us thy miserable town of
Mansoul, thou shouldest withdraw, thou, and thy
captains from us, the town of Mansoul will die. Yea,'
said they, 'our blessed Emmanuel, if thou shouldest
depart from us now, now thou hast done so much
good for us, and showed so much mercy unto us,
what will follow but that our joy will be as if it had
not been, and our enemies will a second time come
upon us with more rage than at the first! Wherefore
we beseech thee—O thou the desire of our eyes, and
the strength and life of our poor town—accept of
this motion that now we have made unto our Lord,
and come and dwell in the midst of us, and let us be
thy people. Besides, Lord, we do not know but that to
this day many Diabolonians may be yet lurking in
the town of Mansoul, and they will betray us, when
thou shalt leave us, into the hand of Diabolus again;
and who knows what designs, plots, or contrivances
have passed betwixt them about these things already?
Loth we are to fall again into his horrible hands.
Wherefore, let it please thee to accept of our palace
for thy place of residence, and of the houses of the
best men in our town for the reception of thy soldiers,
and their furniture.'

> Their fears.

    Then said the Prince, 'If I come to your town,

38   *furniture*: equipment.

128

will you suffer me further to prosecute that which is
in mine heart against mine enemies and yours? Yea,
will you help me in such undertaking?'

They answered, 'We know not what we shall do;
we did not think once that we should have been such
traitors to Shaddai, as we have proved to be. What
then shall we say to our Lord? Let him put no trust
in his saints; let the Prince dwell in our castle, and
make of our town a garrison; let him set his noble
captains, and his warlike soldiers over us. Yea, let him   10
conquer us with his love, and overcome us with his
grace, and then surely shall he be but with us, and
help us, as he was and did that morning that our
pardon was read unto us. We shall comply with this
our Lord, and with his ways, and fall in with his word
against the mighty.

'One word more, and thy servants have done, and
in this will trouble our Lord no more. We know not
the depth of the wisdom of thee, our Prince. Who
could have thought that had been ruled by his reason,   20
that so much sweet as we do now enjoy, should have
come out of those bitter trials wherewith we were
tried at the first? But, Lord, let light go before, and
let love come after: yea, take us by the hand, and
lead us by the counsels, and let this always abide upon
us, that all things shall be for the best for thy servants; and come to our Mansoul, and do as it pleaseth
thee. Or, Lord, come to our Mansoul, do what thou
wilt, so thou keepest us from sinning, and makest us
serviceable to thy Majesty.'   30

Then said the Prince to the town of Mansoul
again, 'Go return to your houses in peace. I will willingly in this comply with your desires. I will remove
my royal pavilion, I will draw up my forces before
Eyegate tomorrow, and so will march forwards into
the town of Mansoul. I will possess myself of your
castle of Mansoul, and will set my soldiers over you;
yea, I will yet do things in Mansoul that cannot be
parallel'd in any nation, country or kingdom under
Heaven.'

He consenteth
to dwell in
Mansoul, and
promiseth to
come in to-
morrow.

7f. Cf. Job 4:18.

Then did the men of Mansoul give a shout, and returned unto their houses in peace; they also told to their kindred and friends the good that Emmanuel had promised to Mansoul. 'And tomorrow,' said they, 'he will march into our town, and take up his dwelling, he and his men in Mansoul.'

Then went out the inhabitants of the town of Mansoul with haste to the green trees, and to the meadows to gather boughs and flowers, therewith to strew the streets against their Prince, the son of Shaddai, should come. They also made garlands, and other fine works to betoken how joyful they were, and should be to receive their Emmanuel into Mansoul; yea, they strewed the street quite from Eyegate to the castle-gate, the place where the Prince should be. They also prepared for his coming what music the town of Mansoul would afford, that they might play before him to the palace, his habitation.

So at the time appointed he makes his approach to Mansoul, and the gates were set open for him; there also the ancients and elders of Mansoul met him to salute him with a thousand welcomes. Then he arose and ent'red Mansoul, he and all his servants. The elders of Mansoul did also go dancing before him till he came to the castle-gates. And this was the manner of his going up thither. He was clad in his golden armour, he rode in his royal chariot, the trumpets sounded about him, the colours were displayed, his ten thousands went up at his feet, and the elders of Mansoul danced before him. And now were the walls of the famous town of Mansoul filled with tramplings of the inhabitants thereof, who went up thither to view the approach of the blessed Prince, and his royal army. Also the casements, windows, balconies and tops of the houses were all now filled with persons of all sorts to behold how their town was to be filled with good.

Now, when he was come so far into the town as to the Recorder's house, he commanded that one should go to Captain Credence, to know whether the castle of Mansoul was prepared to entertain his royal

Mansoul's preparation for his reception.

He enters the town of Mansoul and how.

Acts 15:9.

presence (for the preparation of that was left to that captain), and word was brought that it was. Then was Captain Credence commanded also to come forth with his power to meet the Prince, the which was, as he had commanded, done; and he conducted him into the castle. This done, the Prince that night did lodge in the castle with his mighty captains and men of war, to the joy of the town of Mansoul.

Eph. 3:17.

Now, the next care of the townsfolk was how the captains and soldiers of the Prince's army should be quartered among them. And the care was not how they should shut their hands of them, but how they should fill their houses with them; for every man in Mansoul now had that esteem of Emmanuel and his men, that nothing grieved them more, than because they were not enlarged enough, every one of them to receive the whole army of the Prince; yea, they counted it their glory to be waiting upon them, and would in those days run at their bidding like lacqueys. At last they came to this result:

The townsmen covet who shall have most of the soldiers that belong to the Prince.

1. That Captain Innocency should quarter at Mr. Reason's.

2. That Captain Patience should quarter at Mr. Mind's. This Mr. Mind was formerly the Lord Willbewill's clerk in time of the late rebellion.

3. It was ordered that Captain Charity should quarter at Mr. Affection's house.

4. That Captain Goodhope should quarter at my Lord Mayor's. Now for the house of the Recorder, himself desired, because his house was next to the castle, and because from him it was ordered by the Prince, that if need be, the alarm should be given to Mansoul—it was, I say, desired by him that Captain Boanerges and Captain Conviction should take up their quarters with him, even they and all their men.

How they were quartered in the town of Mansoul.

5. As for Captain Judgment, and Captain Execution, my Lord Willbewill took them and their

---

12   *shut their hands of them:* get rid of them.

men to him, because he was to rule under the Prince for the good of the town of Mansoul now, as he had before under the tyrant Diabolus for the hurt and damage thereof.

Rom. 6:19.
Eph. 3:17.

6. And throughout the rest of the town were quartered Emmanuel's forces; but Captain Credence with his men abode still in the castle. So the Prince, his captains, and his soldiers were lodged in the town of Mansoul.

Now the ancients and elders of the town of Mansoul thought that they never should have enough of the Prince Emmanuel—his person, his actions, his words and behaviour, were so pleasing, so taking, so desirable to them. Wherefore they prayed him, that though the castle of Mansoul was his place of residence—and they desired that he might dwell there for ever—yet that he would often visit the streets, houses, and people of Mansoul. 'For,' said they, 'dread sovereign, thy presence, thy looks, thy smiles, thy words, are the life, and strength, and sinews of the town of Mansoul.'

Mansoul inflamed with their Prince Emmanuel.

Besides this, they craved that they might have, without difficulty or interruption, continual access unto him (so for that very purpose he commanded that the gates should stand open), that they might there see the manner of his doings, the fortifications of the place, and the royal mansion-house of the Prince.

They have access unto him.

When he spoke, they all stopped their mouths, and gave audience; and when he walked, it was their delight to imitate him in his goings.

They learn of him.

Now upon a time Emmanuel made a feast for the town of Mansoul, and upon the feasting-day the townsfolk were come to the castle to partake of his banquet. And he feasted them with all manner of outlandish food, food that grew not in the fields of Mansoul, nor in all the whole kingdom of Universe. It was food that came from his Father's court. And so there was dish after dish set before them, and they

Promise after promise.

36   *outlandish*: exotic.

were commanded freely to eat. But still when a fresh dish was set before them, they would whisperingly say to each other, 'What is it?' for they wist not what to call it. They drank also of the water that was made wine, and were very merry with him. There was music also all the while at the table; and man did eat angels' food, and had honey given him out of the rock. So Mansoul did eat the food that was peculiar to the court; yea, they had now thereof to the full.

Exod. 16:15.
Brave entertainment.

Ps. 78:24,25.

I must not forget to tell you, that as at this table there were musicians, so they were not those of the country, nor yet of the town of Mansoul; but they were the masters of the songs that were sung at the court of Shaddai. 10

Now after the feast was over, Emmanuel was for entertaining the town of Mansoul with some curious riddles of secrets drawn up by his Father's secretary, by the skill and wisdom of Shaddai: the like to these there is not in any kingdom. These riddles were made upon the King Shaddai himself and upon Emmanuel his Son, and upon his wars and doings with Mansoul. 20

Riddles.

The Holy Scriptures.

Emmanuel also expounded unto them some of those riddles himself; but oh! how they were light'ned! They saw what they never saw; they could not have thought that such rarities could have been couched in so few and such ordinary words. I told you before whom these riddles did concern; and as they were opened, the people did evidently see 'twas so. Yea, they did gather that the things themselves were a kind of a portraiture, and that of Emmanuel himself; for when they read in the scheme where the riddles were writ, and looked in the face of the Prince, things looked so like the one to the other, that Mansoul could not forbear but say, 'This is the *Lamb*! This is the *Sacrifice*! 30

23 *light'ned*: enlightened. For Bunyan these riddles offer not merely entertainment but also a spiritual test, since the ability to explain them is a measure of the wisdom received through grace. In the Second Part of *The Pilgrim's Progress*, old Honest propounds a seemingly insoluble riddle, only to have it answered by the faithful Gaius, who has learned the secret through his own spiritual experience.

28 *opened*: expounded.

34ff. See John 1:29; Matt. 20:28; I Cor. 10:4; Heb. 9:12-14; Num. 19:2-17;

This is the Rock! This is the Red-Cow! This is the Door! And this is the Way!'—with a great many other things more.

And thus he dismissed the town of Mansoul. But can you imagine how the people of the corporation were taken with this entertainment? Oh, they were transported with joy, they were drowned with wonderment, while they saw and understood, and considered what their Emmanuel entertained them withal, and what mysteries he opened to them. And when they were at home in their houses, and in their most retired places, they could not but sing of him and of his actions. Yea, so taken were the townsmen now with their Prince, that they would sing of him in their sleep.

The end of that banquet.

Now it was in the heart of the Prince Emmanuel to new-model the town of Mansoul, and to put it into such a condition as might be most pleasing to him, and that might best stand with the profit and security of the now flourishing town of Mansoul. He provided also against insurrections at home, and invasions from abroad, such love had he for the famous town of Mansoul.

Mansoul must be new-model-led.

Wherefore he first of all commanded that the great slings that were brought from his Father's court when he came to the war of Mansoul, should be mounted, some upon the battlements of the castle, some upon the towers—for there were towers in the town of Mansoul—towers new built by Emmanuel since he came thither. There was also an instrument invented by Emmanuel, that was to throw stones from the castle of Mansoul out at Mouthgate; an instrument that could not be resisted, nor that would miss of execution; wherefore, for the wonderful exploits that it did when used, it went without a name, and

The instruments of war mounted.

A nameless terrible instrument in Mansoul.

John 10:9, 14:6.
30ff. A more explicit definition of this "nameless terrible instrument" might have been helpful, but Bunyan apparently wanted to retain the mystery. Perhaps, as George Offor suggested, it is meant to represent prayer, the irresistible offspring of grace that can move mountains.

134

it was committed to the care of, and to be managed by the brave captain, the Captain Credence, in case of war.

Willbewill promoted.

This done, Emmanuel called the Lord Willbewill to him, and gave him in commandment to take care of the gates, the wall and towers in Mansoul; also the Prince gave him the militia into his hand, and a special charge to withstand all insurrections and tumults that might be made in Mansoul against the peace of our Lord the King, and the peace and tranquillity of the town of Mansoul. He also gave him in commission, that if he found any of the Diabolonians lurking in any corner in the famous town of Mansoul, he should forthwith apprehend them, and stay them, or commit them to safe custody, that they may be proceeded against according to law.

My Lord Mayor put into place.

Then he called unto him the Lord Understanding, who was the old Lord Mayor, he that was put out of place when Diabolus took the town, and put him into his former office again, and it became his place for his life-time. He bid him also that he should build him a palace near Eyegate, and that he should build it in fashion like a tower for defence. He bid him also that he should read in the *Revelation of Mysteries* all the days of his life, that he might know how to perform his office aright.

Mr. Knowledge made Recorder.

He also made Mr. Knowledge the Recorder, not of contempt to old Mr. Conscience, who had been Recorder before, but for that it was in his princely mind to confer upon Mr. Conscience another employ, of which he told the old gentleman he should know more hereafter.

The image of the Prince and his Father set up again in Mansoul. Rev. 22:4.

Then he commanded that the image of Diabolus should be taken down from the place where it was set up, and that they should destroy it utterly, beating of it into powder, and casting it into the wind, without the town wall; and that the image of Shaddai, his Father, should be set up again with his own, upon the castle-gates; and that it should be more fairly drawn than ever, for as much as both his Father and himself were come to Mansoul in more grace and mercy than heretofore. He would also that his name should be fairly engraven upon the front of the town, and that it should be done in the best of gold for the honour of the town of Mansoul.

After this was done, Emmanuel gave out a commandment that those three great Diabolonians should be apprehended, namely, the two late Lord Mayors, to wit, Mr. Incredulity, Mr. Lustings, and Mr. Forgetgood, the Recorder. Besides these, there were some of them that Diabolus made burgesses and aldermen in Mansoul, that were committed to ward by the hand of the now valiant, and now right noble, the brave Lord Willbewill.

Some Diabolonians commited to prison under the hand of Mr. Trueman, the Keeper.

And these were their names: Alderman Atheism, Alderman Hard-heart, and Alderman False-peace. The burgesses were Mr. No-truth, Mr. Pitiless, Mr. Haughty, with the like. These were committed to close custody; and the gaoler's name was Mr. Trueman. This Trueman was one of those that Emmanuel brought with him from his Father's court, when at the first he made a war upon Diabolus in the town of Mansoul.

After this, the Prince gave a charge that the three strongholds that at the command of Diabolus the Diabolonians built in Mansoul, should be demolished and utterly pulled down; of which holds and their names, with their captains and governors, you read a little before. But his was long in doing, because of the largeness of the places, and because the stones, the timber, the iron, and all rubbish, was to be carried without the town.

Diabolus's strongholds pull'd down.

When this was done, the Prince gave order that the Lord Mayor and aldermen of Mansoul should call a Court of Judicature for the trial and execution of the Diabolonians in the corporation now under the charge of Mr. Trueman, the gaoler.

A court to be called to try the Diabolonians.

Now when the time was come, and the court set, commandment was sent to Mr. Trueman, the gaoler, to bring the prisoners down to the bar. Then were the

The prisoners brought to the bar.

1   *his name*, etc.: see Rev. 3:12.
33   *a Court of Judicature*: i.e., a court concerned with the administration of justice.

136

prisoners brought down, pinioned, and chained to-
gether, as the custom of the town of Mansoul was.
So when they were presented before the Lord Mayor,
the Recorder, and the rest of the Honourable Bench,
The jury em- first, the jury was empanelled, and then the witnesses
panelled, and sworn. The names of the jury were these: Mr. Belief,
witnesses sworn. Mr. True-heart, Mr. Upright, Mr. Hate-bad, Mr. Love-
God, Mr. See-truth, Mr. Heavenly-mind, Mr. Moderate,
Mr. Thankful, Mr. Good-work, Mr. Zeal-for-God, and
Mr. Humble.   10

The names of the witnesses were Mr. Know-all,
Mr. Tell-true, Mr. Hate-lies, with my Lord Willbewill
and his man, if need were.

So the prisoners were set to the bar. Then said
Do-right the Mr. Do-right (for he was the town-clerk), 'Set Athe-
clerk. ism to the bar, gaoler.' So he was set to the bar. Then
Atheism set to said the clerk, 'Atheism, hold up thy hand. Thou art
the bar. His here indicted by the name of Atheism (an intruder
indictment. upon the town of Mansoul), for that thou hast per-
niciously and doltishly taught and maintained that   20
there is no God, and so no heed to be taken to religion.
This thou hast done against the being, honour, and
glory of the King, and against the peace and safety of
the town of Mansoul. What sayest thou? Art thou
guilty of this indictment, or not?'
His plea.   ATHEISM. 'Not guilty.'

CRIER. 'Call Mr. Know-all, Mr. Tell-true, and Mr.
Hate-lies into the court.'

So they were called, and they appeared.

CLERK. Then said the clerk, 'You, the witnesses for   30
the King, look upon the prisoner at the bar. Do you
know him?'

KNOW. Then said Mr. Know-all, 'Yes, my Lord, we
know him. His name is Atheism; he has been a very
pestilent fellow for many years in the miserable town
of Mansoul.'

35   *pestilent fellow*: a term of abuse, popular in the seventeenth century and
taken from Acts 24:5. In this and his other court scenes, Bunyan clearly
draws upon his own intimate knowledge of the legal process, and in relating
his imprisonment, he records that Justice Chester called him "a pestilent
fellow."

CLERK. 'You are sure you know him?'

KNOW. 'Know him! Yes, my Lord; I have heretofore too often been in his company, to be at this time ignorant of him. He is a Diabolonian, the son of a Diabolonian: I knew his grandfather, and his father.'

CLERK. 'Well said. He standeth here indicted by the name of Atheism, etc., and is charged that he hath maintained and taught that there is no God, and so no heed need be taken to any religion. What say you the King's witnesses, to this? Is he guilty or not?'

KNOW. 'My Lord, I and he were once in Villains' Lane together, and he at that time did briskly talk of divers opinions; and then and there I heard him say that for his part he did believe that there was no God. *But, said he, I can profess one, and be as religious too, if the company I am in, and circumstances of other things, said he, shall put me upon it.*'

CLERK. 'You are sure you heard him say thus?'

KNOW. 'Upon mine oath, I heard him say thus.'

Then said the clerk, 'Mr. Tell-true, what say you to the King's judges, touching the prisoner at the bar?'

TELL. 'My Lord, I formerly was a great companion of his, for the which I now repent me; and I have often heard him say, and that with very great stomachfulness, that he believed there was neither God, angel, nor spirit.'

CLERK. 'Where did you hear him say so?'

TELL. 'In Blackmouth Lane, and in Blasphemer's Row, and in many other places besides.'

CLERK. 'Have you much knowledge of him?'

TELL. 'I know him to be a Diabolonian, the son of a Diabolonian, and an horrible man to deny a deity. His Father's name was Never-be-good, and he had more children than this Atheism. I have no more to say.'

CLERK. 'Mr. Hate-lies look upon the prisoner at the bar. Do you know him?'

HATE. 'My Lord, this Atheism is one of the vilest wretches that ever I came near, or had to do with in

12   *briskly*: flashily.
24   *stomachfulness*: obstinacy.

my life. I have heard him say that there is no God; I have heard him say that there is no world to come, no sin, nor punishment hereafter; and moreover, I have heard him say that 'twas as good to go to a whorehouse as to go to hear a sermon.'

CLERK. 'Where did you hear him say these things?'

HATE. 'In Drunkards' Row, just at Rascal-Lane's-End, at a house in which Mr. Impiety lived.'

CLERK. 'Set him by, gaoler, and set Mr. Lustings to the bar. Mr. Lustings, thou art here indicted by the name of Lustings (an intruder upon the town of Mansoul), for that thou hast devilishly and traitorously taught by practice and filthy words, that it is lawful and profitable to man to give way to his carnal desires, and that thou for thy part hast not, nor never wilt, deny thyself of any sinful delight as long as thy name is Lustings. How sayest thou, art thou guilty of this indictment, or not?'

LUST. Then said Mr. Lustings, 'My Lord, I am a man of high birth, and have been used to pleasures and pastimes of greatness. I have not been wont to be snubb'd for my doings, but have been left to follow my will as if it were law. And it seems strange to me that I should this day be called into question for that, that not only I, but almost all men do either secretly or openly countenance, love, and approve of.'

CLERK. 'Sir, we concern not ourselves with your greatness (though the higher, the better you should have been), but we are concerned, and so are you now, about an indictment preferred against you. How say you? Are you guilty of it, or not?'

LUST. 'Not guilty.'

CLERK. 'Crier, call upon the witnesses to stand forth, and give their evidence.'

CRIER. 'Gentlemen, you the witnesses for the King, come in and give in your evidence for our Lord the King against the prisoner at the bar.'

CLERK. 'Come, Mr. Know-all, look upon the prisoner at the bar. Do you know him?'

Lustings set to the bar.

His indictment.

His plea.

10

20

30

---

22   *snubb'd*: reprimanded.

KNOW. 'Yes, my Lord, I know him.'

CLERK. 'What's his name?'

KNOW. 'His name is Lustings. He was the son of one Beastly, and his mother bare him in Flesh Street; she was one Evil-Concupiscence's daughter. I knew all the generation of them.'

CLERK. 'Well said. You have here heard his indictment—what say you to it? Is he guilty of the things charged against him, or not?'

KNOW. 'My Lord, he has, as he saith, been a great man indeed; and greater in wickedness than by pedigree, more than a thousandfold.'

CLERK. 'But what do you know of his particular actions, and especially with reference to his indictment?'

KNOW. 'I know him to be a swearer, a liar, a Sabbath-breaker; I know him to be a fornicator, and an unclean person; I know him to be guilty of abundance of evils. He has been to my knowledge a very filthy man.'

CLERK. 'But where did he use to commit his wickednesses— in some private corners, or more open and shamelessly?'

KNOW. 'All the town over, my Lord.'

CLERK. 'Come, Mr. Tell-true, what have you to say for our Lord the King against the prisoner at the bar?'

TELL. 'My Lord, all that the first witness has said I know to be true, and a great deal more besides.'

CLERK. 'Mr. Lustings, do you hear what these gentlemen say?'

LUST. 'I was ever of opinion that the happiest life that a man could live on earth was to keep himself back from nothing that he desired in the world. Nor have I been false at any time to this opinion of mine, but have lived in the love of my notions all my days. Nor was I ever so churlish, having found such sweetness in them myself, as to keep the commendations of them from others.'

COURT. Then said the Court, 'There hath proceeded

His second plea.

11f. *pedigree*: birth, ancestry.

140

enough from his own mouth to lay him open to condemnation, wherefore set him by, gaoler, and set Mr. Incredulity to the bar.'

Incredulity set to the bar.

CLERK. 'Mr. Incredulity, thou art here indicted by the name of Incredulity (an intruder upon the town of Mansoul), for that thou hast feloniously and wickedly, and that when thou wert an officer in the town of Mansoul, made head against the captains of the great King Shaddai, when they came and demanded posses-

sion of Mansoul; yea, thou didst bid defiance to the name, forces and cause of the King, and didst also, as did Diabolus thy captain, stir up and encourage the town of Mansoul to make head against, and resist the said force of the King. What sayest thou to this indictment? Art thou guilty of it, or not?'

Then said Incredulity, 'I know not Shaddai, I love my old prince; I thought it my duty to be true to

my trust, and to do what I could to possess the minds of the men of Mansoul to do their utmost to resist strangers and foreigners, and with might to fight against them. Nor have I, nor shall I, change mine opinion for fear of trouble, though you at present are possessed of place and power.'

COURT. Then said the Court, 'The man, as you see, is incorrigible; he is for maintaining his villainies by stoutness of words and his rebellion with impudent confidence. And therefore set him by gaoler, and set

Mr. Forget-good to the bar.'

Forget-good set to the bar.

CLERK. 'Mr. Forget-good, thou art here indicted by the name of Forget-good (an intruder upon the town

of Mansoul), for that thou when the whole affairs of the town of Mansoul were in thy hand, didst utterly forget to serve them in what was good, and didst fall in with the tyrant Diabolus against Shaddai the King, against his captains, and all his host, to the dishonour of Shaddai, the breach of his law, and the endangering of the destruction of the famous town of Mansoul. What sayest thou to this indictment? Art thou guilty, or not guilty?'

Then said Forget-good, 'Gentlemen, and at this time my judges, as to the indictment by which I stand of several crimes accused before you, pray attribute my forgetfulness to mine age, and not to my wilfulness; to the craziness of my brain, and not to the carelessness of my mind; and then I hope I may by your charity be excused from great punishment, though I be guilty.'

His plea.

Then said the Court, 'Forget-good, Forget-good, thy forgetfulness of good was not simply of frailty, but of purpose, and for that thou didst loathe to keep virtuous things in thy mind. What was bad thou couldest retain, but what was good thou couldest not abide to think of. Thy age, therefore, and thy pretended craziness, thou makest use of to blind the court withal, and as a cloak to cover thy knavery. But let us hear what the witnesses have to say for the King against the prisoner at the bar. Is he guilty of this indictment or not?'

HATE. 'My Lord, I have heard this Forget-good say that he could never abide to think of goodness—no, not for a quarter of an hour.'

CLERK. 'Where did you hear him say so?'

HATE. 'In All-base Lane, at a house next door to the Sign of the Conscience-seared-with-an-hot-iron.'

CLERK. 'Mr. Know-all, what can you say for our Lord the King against the prisoner at the bar?'

KNOW. 'My Lord, I know this man well. He is a Diabolonian, the son of a Diabolonian; his father's name was Love-naught, and for him I have often heard him say that he counted the very thoughts of goodness the most burdensome thing in the world.'

CLERK. 'Where have you heard him say these words?'

KNOW. 'In Flesh Lane, right opposite to the church.

Then said the Clerk, 'Come, Mr. Tell-true, give in your evidence concerning the prisoner at the bar about that for which he stands here, as you see, indicted before this honourable court.'

TELL. 'My Lord, I have heard him often say, he had

rather think of the vilest thing than of what is contained in the Holy Scriptures.'

CLERK. 'Where did you hear him say such grievous words?'

TELL. 'Where? In a great many places, particularly in Nauseous Street, in the house of one Shameless, and in Filth Lane, at the sign of the Reprobate, next door to the Descent-into-the-pit.'

COURT. 'Gentlemen, you have heard the indictment, his plea, and the testimony of the witnesses. Gaoler, set Mr. Hard-heart to the bar.'

He is set to the bar.

CLERK. 'Mr. Hard-heart, thou art here indicted by the name of Hard-heart (an intruder upon the town of Mansoul), for that thou didst most desperately and wickedly possess the town of Mansoul with impenitency and obdurateness, and didst keep them from remorse and sorrow for their evils, all the time of their apostasy from and rebellion against the blessed King Shaddai. What sayest thou to this indictment? Art thou guilty, or not guilty?'

HARD. 'My Lord, I never knew what remorse or sorrow meant in all my life. I am impenetrable; I care for no man; nor can I be pierced with men's griefs—their groans will not enter into my heart; whomever I mischief, whomever I wrong, to me it is music, when to others mourning.'

COURT. 'You see the man is a right Diabolonian, and has convicted himself. Set him by, gaoler, and set Mr. False-peace to the bar.'

False-peace set to the bar.

'Mr. False-peace, thou art here indicted by the name of False-peace (an intruder upon the town of Mansoul), for that thou didst most wickedly and satanically bring, hold, and keep the town of Mansoul, both in her apostasy, and in her hellish rebellion, in a false, groundless and dangerous peace, and damnable security, to the dishonour of the King, the transgression of his law, and the great damage of the town of Mansoul. What sayest thou? Art thou guilty of this indictment, or not?'

Hard-heart set to the bar.

False-peace set to the bar.

Then said Mr. False-peace, 'Gentlemen, and you now appointed to be my judges, I acknowledge that my name is Mr. Peace, but that my name is False-peace, I utterly deny. If your Honours shall please to send for any that do intimately know me, or for the midwife that laid my mother of me, or for the gossips that was at my christening, they will, any or all of them, prove that my name is not False-peace, but Peace. Wherefore I cannot plead to this indictment, for as much as my name is not inserted therein; and as is my true name, so also are my conditions. I was always a man that loved to live at quiet, and what I loved myself, that I thought others might love also. Wherefore, when I saw any of my neighbours to labour under a disquieted mind, I endeavoured to help them what I could, and instances of this good temper of mine, many I could give: as,

'First, when at the beginning our town of Mansoul did decline the ways of Shaddai, they, some of them, afterwards began to have disquieting reflections upon themselves for what they had done; but I, as one troubled to see them disquieted, presently sought out means to get them quiet again.

2. 'When the ways of the old world, and of Sodom, were in fashion, if anything happened to molest those that were for the customs of the present times, I laboured to make them quiet again, and to cause them to act without molestation.

3. 'To come nearer home: when the wars fell out between Shaddai and Diabolus, if at any time I saw any of the town of Mansoul afraid of destruction, I often used by some way, device, invention or other, to labour to bring them to peace again.

'Wherefore, since I have been always a man of so virtuous a temper, as some say a peace-maker is, and

His plea.

He denies his name.

Pleads his goodness.

6 *laid my mother of me*: helped my mother at her lying in (i.e. at my birth).
   gossips: godparents or baptismal sponsors. The word derives from OE *godsibb*, someone spiritually related through God; and from ME *gossib*. The modern pejorative sense of "tattler" is found as early as the mid-sixteenth century.
11 *conditions*: qualities.

if a peace-maker be so deserving a man as some have been bold to attest he is, then let me, gentlemen, be accounted by you, who have a great name for justice and equity in Mansoul, for a man that deserveth not this inhumane way of treatment, but liberty, and also a licence to seek damage of those that have been my accusers.'

Then said the Clerk, 'Crier, make a proclamation.'

CRIER. 'O yes! for as much as the prisoner at the bar hath denied his name to be that which is mentioned in the indictment, the Court requireth that if there be any in this place that can give information to the Court of the original and right name of the prisoner, they would come forth and give in their evidence, for the prisoner stands upon his own innocency.'

Then came two into the court and desired that they might have leave to speak what they knew concerning the prisoner at the bar: the name of the one was Search-truth, and the name of the other Vouch-truth. So the Court demanded of these men if they knew the prisoner, and what they could say concerning him; 'for he stands,' said they, 'upon his own vindication.'

Then said Mr. Search-truth, 'My Lord, I—'

COURT. 'Hold! Give him his oath.' Then they sware him. So he proceeded.

SEARCH. 'My Lord, I know, and have known this man from a child, and can attest that his name is False-peace. I knew his father—his name was Mr. Flatter; and his mother, before she was married, was called by the name of Mrs. Sooth-up; and these two when they came together, lived not long without this son, and when he was born, they called his name Falsepeace. I was his play-fellow, only I was somewhat older than he; and when his mother did use to call

New witnesses come in against him.

10

20

30

---

27   *Hold! Give him his oath*: this realistic interruption of an over-zealous witness so that he may be sworn occurs also in the trial of Christian and Faithful before Lord Hate-good in Vanity Fair.

him home from his play, she used to say, *Falsepeace, Falsepeace, come home quick, or I'll fetch you.* Yea, I knew him when he sucked; and though I was then but little, yet I can remember that when his mother did use to sit at the door with him, or did play with him in her arms, she would call him twenty times together, *My little Falsepeace! my pretty Falsepeace!* and *O my sweet rogue, Falsepeace!* and again, *O my little bird, Falsepeace!* and *How do I love my child!* The gossips also know it is thus, though he has had the face to deny it in open court.'

Then Mr. Vouch-truth was called upon to speak what he knew of him. So they sware him.

Then Mr. Vouch-truth, 'My Lord, all that the former witness hath said is true. His name is Falsepeace, the son of Mr. Flatter, and of Mrs. Sooth-up his mother. And I have in former times seen him angry with those that have called him anything else but Falsepeace, for he would say that all such did mock and nickname him; but this was in the time when Mr. Falsepeace was a great man, and when the Diabolonians were the brave men in Mansoul.'

COURT. 'Gentlemen, you have heard what these two men have sworn against the prisoner at the bar. And now, Mr. Falsepeace, to you: you have denied your name to be Falsepeace, yet you see that these honest men have sworn that this is your name. As to your plea, in that you are quite besides the matter of your indictment, you are not by it charged for evil-doing, because you are a man of peace, or a peace-maker among your neighbours; but for that you did wickedly and satanically bring, keep, and hold the town of Mansoul both under its apostasy from, and in its rebellion against, its King, in a false, lying, and damnable peace, contrary to the law of Shaddai, and to the hazard of the destruction of the then miserable town of Mansoul. All that you have pleased for yourself is, that you have denied your name, etc.; but here you see we have witnesses to prove that you are the man.

'For the peace that you so much boast of making

among your neighbours, know that peace that is not a companion of truth and holiness, but that which is without this foundation, is grounded upon a lie, and is both deceitful and damnable, as also the great Shaddai hath said. Thy plea, therefore, has not delivered thee from what by the indictment thou art charged with, but rather it doth fasten all upon thee.

'But thou shalt have very fair play. Let us call the witnesses that are to testify, as to matter of fact, and see what they have to say for our Lord the King against the prisoner at the bar.' 10

CLERK. 'Mr. Know-all, what say you for our Lord the King against the prisoner at the bar?'

KNOW. 'My Lord, this man hath of a long time made it, to my knowledge, his business to keep the town of Mansoul in a sinful quietness in the midst of all her lewdness, filthiness and turmoils, and hath said, and that in my hearing, *Come, come, let us fly from all trouble, on what ground soever it comes, and let us be for a quiet and peaceable life, though it wanteth a* 20 *good foundation.*'

CLERK. 'Come, Mr. Hate-lies, what have you to say?'

HATE. 'My Lord, I have heard him say that peace, though in a way of unrighteousness, is better than trouble with truth.'

CLERK. 'Where did you hear him say this?'

HATE. 'I heard him say it in Folly Yard, at the house of one Mr. Simple, next door to the sign of the Self-deceiver. Yea, he hath said this to my knowledge twenty times in that place.' 30

CLERK. 'We may spare further witness; this evidence is plain and full. Set him by, gaoler, and set Mr. No-truth to the bar. Mr. No-truth, thou art here indicted by the name of No-truth (an intruder upon the town of Mansoul), for that thou hast always to the dishonour of Shaddai, and the endangering of the utter ruin of the famous town of Mansoul, set thyself to deface, and utterly to spoil, all the remainders of the law and image of Shaddai that have been found in Mansoul after her deep apostasy from her King to 40 Diabolus, the envious tyrant. What sayest thou? Art thou guilty of this indictment, or not?'

NOTR. 'Not guilty, my Lord.' His plea.

Then the witnesses were called, and Mr. Know-all did first give in his evidence against him.

KNOW. 'My Lord, this man was at the pulling down Witnesses. of the image of Shaddai; yea, this is he that did it with his own hands. I myself stood by and saw him do it, and he did it at the commandment of Diabolus. Yea, this Mr. No-truth did more than this: he did also set up the horned image of the beast Diabolus in the same place. This also is he that at the bidding of Diabolus did rent and tear, and cause to be consumed all that he could of the remainders of the law of the King, even whatever he could lay his hands on in Mansoul.'

CLERK. 'Who saw him do this besides yourself?'

HATE. 'I did, my Lord, and so did many more besides; for this was not done by stealth, or in a corner, but in the open view of all; yea, he chose himself to do it publicly, for he delighted in the doing of it.'

CLERK. 'Mr. No-truth, how could you have the face to plead not guilty, when you were so manifestly the doer of all this wickedness?'

NOTR. 'Sir, I thought I must say something, and as my name is, so I speak. I have been advantaged thereby before now, and did not know but by speaking no truth, I might have reaped the same benefit now.'

CLERK. 'Set him by, gaoler, and set Mr. Pitiless to Pitiless set to the bar. Mr. Pitiless, thou art here indicted by the the bar. name of Pitiless (an intruder upon the town of Mansoul), for that thou didst most traitorously and His indictment. wickedly shut up all bowels of compassion, and wouldest not suffer poor Mansoul to condole her own

12   *rent*: rend.
33   *bowels of compassion*: sources of mercy. The bowels were once believed to be the seat of mercy, just as other qualities resulted from different organs or secretions of the human body—anger from the spleen, melancholy from black bile, love from the liver, and so on. The use of bowels to represent mercy is frequent in Bunyan.
34   *condole*: the transitive use of condole in the sense of "to lament" marks another common Bunyan idiom.

148

misery when she had apostatised from her rightful King, but didst evade, and at all times turn her mind awry from those thoughts that had in them a tendency to lead her to repentance. What sayest thou to this indictment? Guilty, or not guilty?'

His plea.

'Not guilty of pitilessness: all I did was to cheer-up according to my name, for my name is not Pitiless, but Cheer-up; and I could not abide to see Mansoul incline to melancholy.'

CLERK. 'How! Do you deny your name, and say it is not Pitiless but Cheer-up? Call for the witnesses. What say you, the witnesses, to this plea?'

10

KNOW. 'My Lord, his name is Pitiless; so he hath writ himself in all papers of concern wherein he has had to do. But these Diabolonians love to counterfeit their names. Mr. Covetousness covers himself with the name of Good-Husbandry, or the like; Mr. Pride can, when need is, call himself Mr. Neat, Mr. Handsome, or the like; and so of all the rest of them.'

CLERK. 'Mr. Tell-true what say you?'

20

TELL. 'His name is Pitiless, my Lord. I have known him from a child, and he hath done all that wickedness whereof he stands charged in the indictment; but there is a company of them that are not acquainted with the danger of damning, therefore they call all those melancholy that have serious thoughts how that state should be shunned by them.'

Haughty set to the bar.

CLERK. 'Set Mr. Haughty to the bar, gaoler. Mr. Haughty, thou art here indicted by the name of Haughty (an intruder upon the town of Mansoul), for that thou didst most traitorously and devilishly teach the town of Mansoul to carry it loftily and stoutly against the summons that was given them by the captains of the King Shaddai. Thou didst also teach the town of Mansoul to speak contemptuously and vilifyingly of their great King Shaddai; and didst moreover encourage, both by words and examples, Mansoul to take up arms both against the King and

30

His indictment.

2   *evade*: mislead through equivocation.
14   *papers of concern*: important documents.

his Son Emmanuel. How sayest thou? Art thou guilty
of this indictment, or not?'

HAUGHTY. 'Gentlemen, I have always been a man   His plea
of courage and valour, and have not used, when under
the greatest clouds, to sneak or hang down the head
like a bullrush. Nor did it at all at any time please me
to see men veil their bonnets to those that have
opposed them; yea, though their adversaries seemed
to have ten times the advantage of them.

'I did not use to consider who was my foe, nor
what the cause was in which I was engaged. 'Twas
enough to me if I carried it bravely, fought like a man,
and came off a victor.'

COURT. 'Mr. Haughty, you are not here indicted for   The Court.
that you have been a valiant man, nor for your courage and stoutness in times of distress, but for that you
have made use of this your pretended valour to draw
the town of Mansoul into acts of rebellion both
against the great King and Emmanuel his Son. This is
the crime and the thing wherewith thou art charged
in and by the indictment.' But he made no answer to
that.

Now when the Court had thus far proceeded
against the prisoners at the bar, then they put them
over to the verdict of their jury, to whom they did
apply themselves after this manner:

'Gentlemen of the jury, you have been here, and   The Court to
have seen these men; you have heard their indict-   the jury.
ments, their pleas, and what the witnesses have testified against them. Now what remains is that you do   The jury's
forthwith withdraw yourselves to some place, where   charge.
without confusion you may consider of what verdict
in a way of truth and righteousness you ought to
bring in for the King against them; and so bring it in
accordingly.'

Then the jury, to wit, Mr. Belief, Mr. True-heart,   They withdraw
Mr. Upright, Mr. Hate-bad, Mr. Love-God, Mr. See-   themselves.
truth, Mr. Heavenly-mind, Mr. Moderate, Mr. Thank-

---

7   *veil*: doff, lower. (From Fr. *avaler*, ult. f. Lat. *ad vallem*, to the valley, down-
hill.)

ful, Mr. Humble, Mr. Good-work, and Mr. Zeal-for-God, withdrew themselves in order to their work. Now when they were shut up by themselves, they fell to discourse among themselves in order to the drawing up of their verdict.

Their conference among them-selves.

And thus Mr. Belief, for he was the foreman, began: 'Gentlemen,' quoth he, 'for the men, the prisoners at the bar, for my part I believe that they all deserve death.' 'Very right,' said Mr. True-heart, 'I am wholly of your opinion.' 'O what a mercy is it,' said Mr. Hate-bad, 'that such villains as these are apprehended!' 'Ay! Ay!' said Mr. Love-God, 'this is one of the joyfullest days that ever I saw in my life.' Then said Mr. See-truth, 'I know that if we judge them to death, our verdict shall stand before Shaddai himself.' 'Nor do I at all question it,' said Mr. Heavenly-mind; he said, moreover, 'When all such beasts as these are cast out of Mansoul, what a goodly town will it be then!' Then said Mr. Moderate, 'It is not my manner to pass my judgment with rashness, but for these their crimes are so notorious, and the witness so palpable, that that man must be willfully blind who saith the prisoners ought not to die.' 'Blessed be God,' said Mr. Thankful, 'that the traitors are in safe custody.' 'And I join with you in this upon my bare knees,' said Mr. Humble. 'I am glad also,' said Mr. Good-work. Then said the warm man, and true-hearted Mr. Zeal-for-God, 'Cut them off; they have been the plague, and have sought the destruction of Mansoul.'

Thus, therefore, being all agreed in their verdict, they come instantly into the court.

They are agreed of their verdict, and bring them in guilty.

CLERK. 'Gentlemen of the jury, answer all to your names: Mr. Belief, one; Mr. True-heart, two; Mr. Upright, three; Mr. Hate-bad, four; Mr. Love-God, five; Mr. See-truth, six; Mr. Heavenly-mind, seven; Mr. Moderate, eight; Mr. Thankful, nine; Mr. Humble, ten; Mr. Good-work, eleven; and Mr. Zeal-

10

20

30

6ff. Note that the "conference" which follows involves only eleven members of the jury; Mr. Upright's opinion is not related, probably owing to a mere oversight.

for-God, twelve. Good men and true—stand together
in your verdict. Are you all agreed?'

JURY. 'Yes, my Lord.'

CLERK. 'Who shall speak for you?'

JURY. 'Our foreman.'

CLERK. 'You, the gentlemen of the jury, being empanelled for our Lord the King to serve here in a
matter of life and death, have heard the trials of each
of these men, the prisoners at the bar. What say you
—are they guilty of that, and those crimes for which
they stand here indicted, or are they not guilty?'

FOREMAN. 'Guilty, my Lord.'

CLERK. 'Look to your prisoners, gaoler.'

This was done in the morning, and in the after-
noon they received the sentence of death according to
the law.

The gaoler, therefore, having received such a
charge, put them all in the inward prison, to preserve
them there till the day of execution, which was to be
the next day in the morning.

But now to see how it happened, one of the prisoners, Incredulity by name, in the interim betwixt the
sentence and time of execution, brake prison, and
made his escape, and gets him away quite out of the
town of Mansoul, and lay lurking in such places and
holes, as he might, until he should again have opportunity to do the town of Mansoul a mischief for their
thus handling of him as they did.

Now when Mr. Trueman, the gaoler, perceived
that he had lost his prisoner, he was in a heavy taking,
because he, that prisoner, was, to speak on, the very
worst of all the gang; wherefore, first he goes and
acquaints my Lord Mayor, Mr. Recorder, and my Lord
Willbewill with the matter, and to get of them an
order to make search for him throughout the town of
Mansoul. So an order he got, and search was made,
but no such man could now be found in all the town
of Mansoul.

All that could be gathered was that he had lurked

The verdict.

Incredulity
breaks prison.

No Incredulity
found in Man-
soul.

30   *in a heavy taking*: seriously agitated.

a while about the outside of the town, and that here and there one or other had a glimpse of him as he did make his escape out of Mansoul. One or two also did affirm that they saw him without the town, going apace quite over the plain. Now when he was quite gone, it was affirmed by one Mr. Didsee, that he ranged all over dry places, till he met with Diabolus his friend; and where should they meet one another but just upon Hellgate-hill.

He is gone to Diabolus.

But oh! what a lamentable story did the old gentleman tell to Diabolus concerning what sad alteration Emmanuel had made in Mansoul!

As first, how Mansoul had, after some delays, received a general pardon at the hands of Emmanuel, and that they had invited him into the town, and that they had given him the castle for his possession. He said, moreover, that they had called his soldiers into the town, coveted who should quarter the most of them; they also entertained him with the timbrel, song and dance. 'But that,' said Incredulity, 'that is the sorest vexation to me is that he hath pulled down, O father, thy image, and set up his own; pulled down thy officers, and set up his own. Yea, and Willbewill, that rebel, who, one would have thought, should never have turned from us, he is now in as great favour with Emmanuel, as ever he was with thee. But besides all this, this Willbewill has received a special commission from his Master to search for, to apprehend, and to put to death all, and all manner of Diabolonians that he shall find in Mansoul. Yea, and this Willbewill has taken and committed to prison already eight of my lord's most trusty friends in Mansoul. Nay further, my Lord, with grief I speak it, they have all been arraigned, condemned, and, I doubt, before this executed in Mansoul. I told my lord of eight, and myself was the ninth, who should assuredly have drunk of the same cup, but that through craft, I, as thou seest, have made mine escape from them.'

He tells Diabolus what Emmanuel now is doing in Mansoul.

When Diabolus had heard this lamentable story he yelled, and snuffed up the wind like a dragon, and made the sky to look dark with his roaring. He also

Diabolus yells at this news.

10

20

30

40

sware that he would try to be revenged on Mansoul for this. So they, both he and his old friend Incredulity concluded to enter into great consultation, how they might get the town of Mansoul again.

Now before this time, the day was come in which the prisoners in Mansoul were to be executed. So they were brought to the cross, and that by Mansoul, in most solemn manner; for the Prince said that this should be done by the hand of the town of Mansoul, 'that I may see,' said he, 'the forwardness of my now redeemed Mansoul to keep my word, and to do my commandments; and that I may bless Mansoul in doing this deed. Proof of sincerity pleases me well; let Mansoul therefore first lay their hands upon these Diabolonians to destroy them.'

So the town of Mansoul slew them according to the word of their Prince. But when the prisoners were brought to the cross to die, you can hardly believe what troublesome work Mansoul had of it to put the Diabolonians to death; for the men, knowing that they must die, and every of them having implacable enmity in their heart to Mansoul, what did they but took courage at the cross, and there resisted the men of the town of Mansoul. Wherefore the men of Mansoul were forced to cry out for help to the captains and men of war. Now the great Shaddai had a secretary in the town, and he was a great lover of the men of Mansoul, and he was at the place of execution also. So he, hearing the men of Mansoul cry out against the strugglings and unruliness of the prisoners, rose up from his place, and came and put his hands upon the hands of the men of Mansoul. So they crucified the

Margin notes:
Rom. 8:13; 6:12-14.

Gal. 5:24.

The assistance of more grace.

---

7   The cross in the market-place was the traditional site of public proclamation and execution. Bunyan's allegorical point is that sins must be publicly renounced, that the Christian must be seen to mortify the flesh.

31f.   *put his hands*, etc.: an allusion to the story of how Elisha marvellously gave power to King Joash to defeat Syria in battle, by placing his hands upon the king's to shoot the arrow of deliverance (II Kings 23:14-19). Afterwards Elisha became angry, when Joash smote the ground with the arrows only three times, instead of the mysteriously proper five or six times. Hence the account not only illustrates the magic of grace working through the prophet, but also the principle that its effect is conditional upon the receiver's playing

Execution done.
Rom. 8:13.

Diabolonians that had been a plague, a grief, and an offence to the town of Mansoul.

Now when this good work was done, the Prince

The Prince comes down to congratulate them.

came down to see, to visit, and to speak comfortably to the men of Mansoul, and to strengthen their hands in such work. And he said to them, that by this act of theirs he had proved them, and found them to be lovers of his person, observers of his laws, and such as had also respect to his honour. He said, moreover, (to show them that they by this should not be losers, nor their town weakened by the loss of them), that he

He promises to make them a new captain.

would make them another captain, and that of one of themselves. And that this captain should be the ruler of a thousand, for the good and benefit of the now flourishing town of Mansoul.

So he called one to him whose name was Waiting, and bid him, 'Go quickly up to the castle-gate, and

Experience must be the new captain.

enquire there for one Mr. Experience that waiteth upon that noble captain, the Captain Credence, and bid him come hither to me.' So the messenger that waited upon the good Prince Emmanuel went and said as he was commanded. Now the young gentleman was waiting to see the captain train and muster his men in the castle-yard. Then said Mr. Waiting to him, 'Sir, the Prince would that you should come down to his Highness forthwith.' So he brought him down to Emmanuel, and he came and made obeisance before him. Now the men of the town knew Mr. Experience

The qualifications of their new captain.

well, for he was born and bred in Mansoul; they also knew him to be a man of conduct, of valour, and a person prudent in matters; he was also a comely person, well spoken, and very successful in his undertakings.

Wherefore the hearts of the townsmen were

Mansoul takes it well.

transported with joy, when they saw that the Prince himself was so taken with Mr. Experience that he would needs make him a captain over a band of men.

10

20

30

his part. Shaddai's secretary, coming as he does in response to the expressed need of the labouring Mansoulians, finely exemplifies the concept that God helps those who help themselves by asking for help.

So with one consent they bowed the knee before Emmanuel, and with a shout said, 'Let Emmanuel live forever!' Then said the Prince to the young gentleman, whose name was Mr. Experience, 'I have thought good to confer upon thee a place of trust and honour in this my town of Mansoul.' Then the young man bowed his head and worshipped. 'It is,' said Emmanuel, 'that thou shouldest be a captain, a captain over a thousand men in my beloved town of Mansoul.' Then said the captain, 'Let the King live!' So the Prince gave out orders forthwith to the King's secretary, that he should draw up for Mr. Experience a commission to make him a captain over a thousand men—'and let it be brought to me,' said he, 'that I may set to my seal.' So it was done as it was commanded. The commission was drawn up, brought to Emmanuel, and he set his seal thereto. Then by the hand of Mr. Waiting he sent it away to the captain.

The thing told to Mr. Experience.

His commission sent him.

Now so soon as the captain had received his commission, he soundeth his trumpet for volunteers, and young men come to him apace. Yea, the greatest and chiefest men in the town sent their sons to be listed under his command. Thus Captain Experience came under command to Emmanuel, for the good of the town of Mansoul. He had for his lieutenant one Mr. Skilful, and for his cornet, one Mr. Memory. His under-officers I need not name. His colours were the white colours for the town of Mansoul; and his scutcheon was the dead lion, and dead bear. So the Prince returned to his royal palace again.

His under-officers.

I Sam. 17:36,37.

Now when he was returned thither, the elders of the town of Mansoul, to wit, the Lord Mayor, the Recorder, and the Lord Willbewill, went to congratulate him, and in special way to thank him for his love, care, and the tender compassion which he showed to his ever obliged town of Mansoul. So after a while, and some sweet communion between them, the townsmen having solemnly ended their ceremony, returned to their place again.

The elders of Mansoul congratulate him.

26   *cornet*: a commissioned officer in a cavalry troop, who carried the colours.

Emmanuel also at this time appointed them a day wherein he would renew their charter; yea, wherein he would renew and enlarge it, mending several faults therein, that Mansoul's yoke might be yet more easy. And this he did without any desire of theirs, even of his own frankness and noble mind. So when he had sent for and seen their old one, he laid it by, and said, 'Now that which decayeth and waxeth old is ready to vanish away.' He said, moreover, 'The town of Mansoul shall have another, a better, a new one, more steady and firm by far.' An epitome hereof take as follows.

Emmanuel, Prince of Peace, and a great lover of the town of Mansoul, I do in the name of my Father, and of mine own clemency, give, grant, and bequeath to my beloved town of Mansoul,

First, free, full, and everlasting forgiveness of all wrongs, injuries, and offences done by them against my Father, me, their neighbour, or themselves.

Secondly, I do give them the holy law, and my testament, with all that therein is contained, for their everlasting comfort and consolation.

Thirdly, I do also give them a portion of the self-same grace and goodness that dwells in my Father's heart and mine.

Fourthly, I do give, grant and bestow upon them freely the world, and what is therein for their good, and they shall have that power over them, as shall stand with the honour of my Father, my glory, and their comfort; yea, I grant them the benefits of life and death, and of things present, and things to come. This privilege, no other city, town or corporation shall have, but my Mansoul only.

Fifthly, I do give and grant them leave, and free access to me in my palace at all seasons—to my palace above or below—there to make known their wants to me; and I give them, moreover, a promise that I will hear and redress all their grievances.

He renews their charter.
Heb. 8:13.
Matt. 11.

An epitome of their new charter.
Heb. 8:12.
John 17:8,14.
II Pet. 1:4.
II Cor. 7:1.
I John 1:16.

I Cor. 3:21,22.

Heb. 10:19,20.
Matt. 7:7.

10

20

30

6 *frankness:* generosity.

*Sixthly, I do give, grant to, and invest the town
of Mansoul with full power and authority to seek out,
take, enslave, and destroy all, and all manner of
Diabolonians that at any time from whence soever
shall be found straggling in, or about the town of
Mansoul.*

*Seventhly, I do further grant to my beloved town
of Mansoul that they shall have authority not to
suffer any foreigner or stranger, or their seed, to be
free in and of the blessed town of Mansoul, nor to
share in the excellent privileges thereof. But that all
the grants, privileges, and immunities that I bestow
upon the famous town of Mansoul shall be for those
the old natives, and true inhabitants thereof; to them
I say, and to their right seed after them.*

*But all Diabolonians, of what sort, birth, country,
or kingdom soever, shall be debarred a share therein.*

So when the town of Mansoul had received at
the hand of Emmanuel their gracious charter (which
in itself is infinitely more large than by this lean
epitome is set before you), they carried it to audience,
that is, to the market-place, and there Mr. Recorder
read it in the presence of all the people. This being
done, it was had back to the castle-gates, and there
fairly engraven upon the doors thereof, and laid in
letters of gold, to the end that the town of Mansoul,
with all the people thereof, might have it always in
their view, or might go where they might see what a
blessed freedom their Prince had bestowed upon them,
that their joy might be increased in themselves, and
their love renewed to their great and good Emmanuel.

But what joy, what comfort, what consolation,
think you, did now possess the hearts of the men of
Mansoul! The bells ringed, the minstrels played, the
people danced, the captains shouted, the colours waved
in the wind, and the silver trumpets sounded; and the
Diabolonians now were glad to hide their heads, for
they looked like them that had been long dead.

When this was over, the Prince sent again for the
elders of the town of Mansoul, and communed with

Margin notes:

No man to die for killing of sin.

No lust has any grant by Christ, or any liberty to act in the town of Mansoul. Eph. 4:22. Col. 3:5-9.

II Cor. 3:3. Jer. 31:33. Heb. 8:10. Their charter set upon their castle-gates.

Joy renewed in Mansoul.

them about a ministry that he intended to establish among them; such a ministry that might open unto them, and that might instruct them in the things that did concern their present and future state.

Jer. 10:23.
I Cor. 2:14.

'For,' said he, 'you of yourselves, without you have teachers and guides, will not be able to know, and if not to know, to be sure, not to do the will of my Father.'

The common
good thoughts.

At this news, when the elders of Mansoul brought it to the people, the whole town came running together (for it pleased them well, as whatever the Prince now did, pleased the people), and all with one consent implored his Majesty that he would forthwith establish such a ministry among them as might teach them both law and judgment, statute and commandment; that they might be documented in all good and wholesome things. So he told them that he would grant them their requests; and would establish two among them; one that was of his Father's court, and one that was a native of Mansoul. 10

II Pet. 1:21.
I Cor. 2:10.
John 1:1.
I John 5:7.

'He that is from the court,' said he, 'is a person of no less quality and dignity than is my Father and I: and he is the Lord Chief Secretary of my Father's house, for he is, and always has been the chief dictator of all my Father's laws, a person altogether well skill'd in all mysteries, and knowledge of mysteries as is my Father, or as myself is. Indeed, he is one with us in nature, and also as to loving of, and being faithful to, and in, the eternal concerns of the town of Mansoul. 20

'And this is he,' said the Prince, 'that must be your chief teacher; for 'tis he, and he only that can teach you clearly in all high and supernatural things. He and he only it is that knows the ways and methods of my Father at court, nor can any like him show how the heart of my Father is at all times, in all things, upon all occasions towards Mansoul; for as no man knows the things of a man but that spirit of a man which is in him, so the things of my Father knows no man but this high and mighty Secretary. Nor can any, 30

16   *documented*: instructed.

as he, tell Mansoul, how and what they shall do to keep themselves in the love of my Father. He also it is that can bring lost things to your remembrance, and that can tell you things to come. This teacher therefore must of necessity have the pre-eminence both in your affections and judgment, before your other teacher; his personal dignity, the excellency of his teaching, also the great dexterity that he hath to help you to make and draw up petitions to my Father for your help, and to his pleasing, must lay obligations upon you to love him, fear him, and to take heed that you grieve him not.

'This person can put life and vigor into all he says—yea, and can also put it into your heart. This person can make seers of you, and can make you tell what shall be hereafter. By this person you must frame all your petitions to my Father and me; and without his advice and counsel first obtained, let nothing enter into the town or castle of Mansoul, for that may disgust and grieve this noble person.

'Take heed, I say, that you do not grieve this minister, for if you do, he may fight against you; and should he once be moved by you, to set himself against you, against you in battle array, that will distress you more than if twelve legions should from my Father's court be sent to make war upon you.

'But, as I said, if you shall hearken unto him, and shall love him, if you shall devote yourselves to his teaching, and shall seek to have converse, and to maintain communion with him, you shall find him ten times better than is the whole world to any. Yea, he will shed abroad the love of my Father in your hearts, and Mansoul will be the wisest, and most blessed of all people.'

Then did the Prince call unto him the old gentleman, who afore had been the Recorder of Mansoul, Mr. Conscience by name, and told him that for as much as he was well skilled in the law and government of the town of Mansoul, and was also well spoken, and could pertinently deliver to them his Master's will in all

John 14:26; 16:13.
I John 2:27.

I Thess. 1:5,6.
Acts 21:10,11.
Jude 20.
Eph. 6:18.
Rom. 8:26.
Rev. 2:7,11,17, 29.
Eph. 4:30.
Isa. 63:10.

I Cor. 13:14.
Rom. 5:5.

Conscience made a minister.

terrene and domestic matters, therefore he would also make him a Minister for, in, and to the goodly town of Mansoul, in all the laws, statutes and judgments of the famous town of Mansoul. 'And thou must,' said *His limits.* the Prince, 'confine thyself to the teaching of moral virtues, to civil and natural duties, but thou must not attempt to presume to be a revealer of those high and *His caution.* supernatural mysteries that are kept close in the bosom of Shaddai, my Father; for those things know no man, nor can any reveal them but my Father's Secretary only.

'Thou art a native of the town of Mansoul, but the Lord Secretary is a native with my Father; wherefore as thou hast knowledge of the laws and customs of the corporation, so he of the things and will of my Father.

'Wherefore, oh, Mr. Conscience, although I have made thee a minister and a preacher to the town of Mansoul, yet as to the things which the Lord Secretary knoweth, and shall teach to this people, there thou must be his scholar, and a learner, even as the rest of Mansoul are.

'Thou must therefore in all high and supernatural things, go to him for information and knowledge; for though there be a spirit in man, this person's inspiration must give him understanding. Wherefore, oh, *Job 33:8.* thou Mr. Recorder, keep low and be humble, and remember that the Diabolonians that kept not their first charge, but left their own standing, are now made prisoners in the pit. Be therefore content with thy station.

'I have made thee my Father's vice-regent on earth, in such things of which I have made mention *His power in* before: and thou, take thou power to teach them to *Mansoul.* Mansoul, yea, and to impose them with whips and chastisements, if they shall not willingly hearken to do thy commandments.

'And, Mr. Recorder, because thou art old, and

---

1 *terrene and domestic matters:* affairs of both universal and national interest.
5ff. The bailiwick of Conscience, though defined by the Spirit, is thus restricted to the sphere of nature rather than of grace.

through many abuses made feeble; therefore I give
thee leave and licence to go when thou wilt to my His liberty.
fountain, my conduit, and there to drink freely of the
blood of my grape, for my conduit doth always run
wine. Thus doing, thou shalt drive from thy heart and
stomach all foul, gross, and hurtful humours. It will Body.
also lighten thine eyes, and will strengthen thy mem- Heb. 9:14.
ory for the reception and keeping of all that the King's
most noble Secretary teacheth.'

When the Prince had thus put Mr. Recorder
(that once so was) into the place and office of a minister to Mansoul and the man had thankfully accepted
thereof, then did Emmanuel address himself in a particular speech to the townsmen themselves.

'Behold,' said the Prince to Mansoul, 'my love and
care towards you. I have added to all that is past, this The Prince's
mercy: to appoint you preachers, the most noble Secre- speech to Man-
tary to teach you in all high and sublime mysteries, soul.
and this gentleman' (pointing to Mr. Conscience) 'is
to teach you in all things humane and domestic, for
therein lieth his work. He is not by what I have said,
debarred of telling to Mansoul anything that he hath
heard, and received at the mouth of the Lord High
Secretary; only he shall not attempt to presume to
pretend to be a revealer of those high mysteries himself; for the breaking of them up, and the discovery of
them to Mansoul lieth only in the power, authority
and skill of the Lord High Secretary himself. Talk of
them he may, and so may the rest of the town of A licence to
Mansoul; yea, and may as occasion gives them oppor- Mansoul.
tunity, press them upon each other for the benefit of
the whole. These things, therefore, I would have you
observe and do, for it is for your life and the lengthen-
ing of your days.

'And one thing more to my beloved Mr. Re-
corder, and to all the town of Mansoul: You must not A world to
dwell in, nor stay upon anything of that which he come promised
to Mansoul.

---

6   *humours*: certain bodily fluids (blood, phlegm, choler, melancholy) the
     balance of which was once thought to determine a person's temperament.
26   *the breaking of them up*: the unravelling of these hidden things.

hath in commission to teach you, as to your trust and expectation of the next world—of the next world, I say, for I purpose to give another to Mansoul, when this with them is worn out—but for that you must wholly and solely have recourse to, and make stay upon his doctrine that is your teacher after the first order. Yea, Mr. Recorder himself must not look for life from that which he himself revealeth; his dependence for that must be founded in the doctrine of the other preacher. Let Mr. Recorder also take heed that he receive not any doctrine, or point of doctrine, that are not communicated to him by his superior teacher, nor yet within the precincts of his own formal knowledge.'

Now after the Prince had thus settled things in the famous town of Mansoul, he proceeded to give to the elders of the corporation a necessary caution; to wit, how they should carry it to the high and noble captains that he had, from his Father's court, sent or brought with him to the famous town of Mansoul.

'These captains,' said he, 'do love the town of Mansoul, and they are picked men, picked out of abundance, as men that best suit, and that will most faithfully serve in the wars of Shaddai against the Diabolonians for the preservation of the town of Mansoul. I charge you, therefore,' said he, 'O ye inhabitants of the now flourishing town of Mansoul, that you carry it not ruggedly, or untowardly to my captains, or their men; since, as I said, they are picked and choice men, men chosen out of many for the good of the town of Mansoul. I say, I charge you that you carry it not untowardly to them; for though they have the hearts and faces of lions, when at any time they shall be called forth to engage and fight with the King's foes, and the enemies of the town of Mansoul, yet a little discountenance cast upon them from the town of Mansoul, will deject and cast down their faces, will weaken and take away their courage. Do not therefore, oh my beloved, carry it unkindly to my valiant captains, and courageous men of war, but love them,

He gives them caution about the captains.

Graces picked from common virtues.

Satan cannot weaken our graces as we ourselves may.

10

20

30

13   *formal knowledge*: awareness of the rules.

nourish them, succour them, and lay them in your bosoms, and they will not only fight for you, but cause to fly from you all those the Diabolonians that seek, and will, if possible, be your utter destruction.

'If, therefore, any of them should at any time be sick or weak, and so not able to perform that office of love, which with all their hearts they are willing to do (and will do also when well and in health), slight them not, nor despise them, but rather strengthen them, and encourage them though weak and ready to die, for they are your fence, and your guard, your wall, your gates, your locks, and your bars. And although when they are weak, they can do but little, but rather need to be helped by you (than that you should then expect great things from them), yet when well, you know what exploits, what feats and warlike achievements they are able to do, and will perform for you.

'Besides, if they be weak, the town of Mansoul cannot be strong; if they be strong, then Mansoul cannot be weak. Your safety, therefore, doth lie in their health, and in your countenancing of them. Remember also that if they be sick, they catch that disease off the town of Mansoul itself.

'These things I have said unto you, because I love your welfare, and your honour. Observe, therefore, oh my Mansoul, to be punctual in all things that I have given in charge unto you; and that not only as a town corporate, and so to your officers and guard, and guides-in-chief, but to you as you are a people whose well-being, as single persons, depends on the observation of the orders and commandments of their Lord.

'Next, oh my Mansoul, I do warn you of that of which, notwithstanding that reformation that at present is wrought among you, you have need to be warn'd about: wherefore hearken diligently unto me. I am now sure, and you will know hereafter that there are yet of the Diabolonians remaining in the town of Mansoul; Diabolonians that are sturdy and implacable, and that do already while I am with you, and that will yet more when I am from you, study, plot, contrive,

Marginal notes:

Words.

Heb. 12:12.
Isa. 35:3.
Rev. 3:2.
I Thess. 5:14.

A caution about the Diabolonians that yet remain in Mansoul.

164

invent, and jointly attempt to bring you to desolation, and so to a state far worse than that of the Egyptian bondage; they are the avowed friends of Diabolus, therefore look about you. They used heretofore to lodge with their prince in the castle, when Incredulity was the Lord Mayor of this town, but since my coming hither, they lie more in the outsides, and walls, and have made themselves dens, and caves, and holes, and strongholds therein. Wherefore, oh Mansoul! thy work as to this, will be so much the more difficult and hard—that is, to take, mortify, and put them to death, according to the will of my Father. Nor can you utterly rid yourselves of them, unless you should pull down the walls of your town, the which I am by no means willing you should. Do you ask me, *What shall we do then?* Why, be you diligent, and quit you like men; observe their holds, find out their haunts, assault them, and make no peace with them. Where ever they haunt, lurk, or abide, and what terms of peace soever they offer you, abhor, and all shall be well betwixt you and me. And that you may the better know them from those that are the natives of Mansoul, I will give you this brief schedule of the names of the chief of them; and they are these that follow: the Lord Fornication, the Lord Adultery, the Lord Murder, the Lord Anger, the Lord Lasciviousness, the Lord Deceit, the Lord Evil-eye, Mr. Drunkenness, Mr. Reveling, Mr. Idolatry, Mr. Witchcraft, Mr. Variance, Mr. Emulation, Mr. Wrath, Mr. Strife, Mr. Sedition, and Mr. Heresy. These are some of the chief, oh Mansoul, of those that will seek to overthrow thee for ever. These, I say are the skulkers in Mansoul, but look thou well into the law of thy King, and there thou shalt find their physiognomy, and such other characteristical notes of them, by which they certainly may be known.

Mark 7:21,22.
Rom. 7:18.

Christ would not have us destroy ourselves thereby to destroy our sins.

The names of some of the Diabolonians in Mansoul.

27   *the Lord Evil-eye*: the name does not necessarily attribute magical properties to its owner, but rather describes him as a mean and covetous person. See Prov. 28:22; Mark 7:22. For an interesting account of the superstitions associated with the "evil eye," see F. T. Elworthy, *The Evil Eye* (London, 1895).

'These, O my Mansoul (and I would gladly that you should certainly know it), if they be suffered to run and range about the town as they would, will quickly like vipers eat out your bowels; yea, poison your captains, cut the sinews of your soldiers, break the bar and bolts of your gates, and turn your now most flourishing Mansoul into a barren and desolate wilderness, and ruinous heap. Wherefore, that you may take courage to yourselves to apprehend these villains where ever you find them, I give to you my Lord Mayor, my Lord Willbewill, and Mr. Recorder, with all the inhabitants of the town of Mansoul, full power and commission to seek out, to take, and to cause to be put to death by the cross, all, and all manner of Diabolonians, when and where ever you shall find them to lurk within, or to range without the walls of the town of Mansoul.

A commission to destroy the Diabolonians in Mansoul.

'I told you before, that I had placed a standing ministry among you; not that you have but these with you, for my four first captains who came against the master and lord of the Diabolonians that was in Mansoul, they can, and if need be, and if they be required, will not only privately inform, but publicly preach to the corporation both good and wholesome doctrine, and such as shall lead you in the way. Yea, they will set up a weekly—yea, if need be a daily lecture in thee, oh Mansoul, and will instruct thee in such profitable lessons, that if heeded will do thee good at the end. And take good heed that you spare not the man that you have a commission to take and crucify.

More preachers if need be for Mansoul.

'Now as I have set out before your eyes the vagrants and runagates by name, so I will tell you that among yourselves some of them shall creep in to beguile you, even such as would seem, and that in appearance are, very rife and hot for religion. And they, if you watch not, will do you a mischief, such

A caution.

20   *my four first captains*: although the second edition emends to "my first four captains," there is really no need to depart from the reading of the first edition. Bunyan's meaning, in the sense of "my four captains who first came," is clear enough, and the third edition properly reverts to the original reading.

an one as at present you cannot think of.

'These, as I said, will show themselves to you in another hue than those under description before. Wherefore, Mansoul, watch and be sober, and suffer not thyself to be betrayed.'

When the Prince had thus far new-modelled the town of Mansoul, and had instructed them in such matters as were profitable for them to know, then he appointed another day in which he intended, when the townsfolk came together, to bestow a further badge of honour upon the town of Mansoul, a badge that should distinguish them from all the people, kindreds and tongues that dwell in the Kingdom of Universe. Now it was not long before the day appointed was come, and the Prince and his people met in the King's palace, where first Emmanuel made a short speech unto them, and then did for them as he had said, and unto them as he had promised.

'My Mansoul,' said he, 'that which I now am about to do is to make you known to the world to be mine, and to distinguish you also in your own eyes, from all false traitors that may creep in among you.'

Then he commanded that those that waited upon him should go and bring forth out of his treasury those white and glistering robes, 'that I,' said he, 'have provided and laid up in store for my Mansoul.' So the white garments were fetched out of his treasury, and laid forth to the eyes of the people. Moreover, it was granted to them that they should take them and put them on, 'according,' said he, 'to your size and stature.' So the people were put into white, into fine linen, white and clean.

Then said the Prince unto them, 'This, O Mansoul, is my livery, and the badge by which mine are known from the servants of others. Yea, it is that which I grant to all that are mine, and without which no man is permitted to see my face. Wear them,

Marginal notes:
Another privilege for Mansoul.

His speech to Mansoul.

White robes. Rev. 19:8.

Line numbers: 10, 20, 30

23ff. Cf. the dressing of Christian by the three Shining Ones in *The Pilgrim's Progress*. The marginal apocalyptic reference points again the millenarian implication of the allegory.

therefore, for my sake who gave them unto you; and also if you would be known by the world to be mine.'

But now! Can you think how Mansoul shone? It was fair as the sun, clear as the moon, and terrible as an army with banners.

The Prince added further, and said, 'No prince, potentate, or mighty one of Universe, giveth this livery but myself. Behold, therefore, as I said before, you shall be known by it to be mine.

'And now,' said he, 'I have given you my livery, let me give you also in commandment concerning them; and be sure that you take good heed to my words.

'First, Wear them daily, day by day, lest you should at sometimes appear to others, as if you were none of mine.

'Secondly, Keep them always white, for if they be soiled, 'tis dishonour to me.

'Thirdly, Wherefore gird them up from the ground, and let them not lag with dust and dirt.

'Fourthly, Take heed that you lose them not, lest you walk naked, and they see your shame.

'Fifthly, But if you should sully them, if you should defile them (the which I am greatly unwilling you should, and the Prince Diabolus will be glad if you would), then speed you to do that which is written in my law, that yet you may stand, and not fall before me, and before my throne. Also this is the way to cause that I may not leave you nor forsake you, while here, but may dwell in this town of Mansoul for ever.'

And now was Mansoul, and the inhabitants of it as the signet upon Emmanuel's right hand. Where was there now a town, a city, a corporation that could compare with Mansoul? A town redeemed from the hand and from the power of Diabolus! A town that the King Shaddai loved, and that he sent Emmanuel to regain from the prince of the infernal cave: yea, a town that Emmanuel loved to dwell in,

Marginal notes:

That which distinguisheth Mansoul from other people.

Eccles. 9:8.

Rev. 3.2.

Rev. 7:15-17.

Luke 21:36.

The glorious state of Mansoul.

20   *lag*: trail carelessly.

and that he chose for his royal habitation, a town that he fortified for himself, and made strong by the force of his army. What shall I say? Mansoul has now a most excellent Prince, golden captains and men of war, weapons proved, and garments as white as snow. Nor are these benefits to be counted little but great; can the town of Mansoul esteem them so, and improve them to that end and purpose for which they are bestowed upon them?

When the Prince had thus completed the modelling of the town, to show that he had great delight in the work of his hands, and took pleasure in the good that he had wrought for the famous and flourishing Mansoul, he commanded, and they set his standard upon the battlements of the castle. And then,

First, he gave them frequent visits; not a day now but the elders of Mansoul must come to him, or he to them, into his palace. Now they must walk and talk together of all the great things that he had done, and yet further promised to do for the town of Mansoul. Thus would he often do with the Lord Mayor, my Lord Willbewill, and the honest subordinate preacher, Mr. Conscience, and Mr Recorder. But, oh, how graciously, how lovingly, how courteously and tenderly did this blessed Prince now carry it towards the town of Mansoul! In all the streets, gardens, orchards, and other places where he came, to be sure the poor should have his blessing and benediction; yea, he would kiss them, and if they were ill, he would lay hands on them, and make them well. The captains also he would daily—yea, sometimes hourly encourage with his presence and goodly words. For you must know that a smile from him upon them would put more vigor, more life and stoutness into them, than would any thing else under heaven.

The Prince would now also feast them, and with them continually: hardly a week would pass but a banquet must be had betwixt him and them. You may remember that some pages before we make mention of one feast that they had together, but now to feast them was a thing more common: every day with

II Cor. 6:16.

Understanding.
The Will.

Hungry
thoughts.

I Cor. 5:8.

10

20

30

40

Mansoul was a feast-day now. Nor did he when they returned to their places, send them empty away; either they must have a ring, a gold chain, a bracelet, a white stone, or something: so dear was Mansoul to him now, so lovely was Mansoul in his eyes.

A token of marriage.
A token of honour.
A token of beauty.
A token of pardon.

Secondly, When the elders and townsmen did not come to him, he would send in much plenty of provision unto them: meat that came from Court, wine and bread that were prepared for his Father's table. Yea, such delicates would he send unto them, and therewith would so cover their table, that whoever saw it confessed that the like could not be seen in any kingdom.

Thirdly, If Mansoul did not frequently visit him as he desired they should, he would walk out to them, knock at their doors and desire entrance, that amity might be maintained betwixt them and him. If they did hear and open to him, as commonly they would if they were at home, then would he renew his former love, and confirm it too with some new tokens, and signs of continued favour.

The danger of wandering thoughts.
Rev. 3:20.
Cant. 5:2.

And was it not now amazing to behold, that in that very place where sometimes Diabolus had his abode, and entertained his Diabolonians to the almost utter destruction of Mansoul, the Prince of Princes should sit eating and drinking with them, while all his mighty captains, men of war, trumpeters, with the singing-men and singing-women of his Father stood round about to wait upon them! Now did Mansoul's cup run over, now did her conduits run sweet wine, now did she eat the finest of the wheat, and drink milk and honey out of the rock! Now she said, 'How great is his goodness! For since I found favour in his eyes, how honourable have I been!'

Mansoul's glory.

The blessed Prince did also ordain a new officer in the town, and a goodly person he was: his name was Mr. Gods-peace. This man was set over my Lord Will-bewill, my Lord Mayor, Mr. Recorder, the Subordinate Preacher, Mr. Mind, and over all the natives of the

Col. 3:15.

10   *delicates*: delicacies.

town of Mansoul. Himself was not a native of it, but
came with the Prince Emmanuel from the Court. He

was a great acquaintance of Captain Credence, and
Captain Goodhope; some say they were kin, and I am
of that opinion too. This man, as I said, was made
governor of the town in general, specially over the
castle, and Captain Credence was to help him there.
And I made great observation of it, that so long as all
things went in Mansoul as this sweet-natured gentleman would, the town was in most happy condition.
Now there were no jars, no chiding, no interferings,
no unfaithful doings in all the town of Mansoul; every
man in Mansoul kept close to his own employment.
The gentry, the officers, the soldiers, and all in place
observed their order. And as for the women and

Holy concep-
tions.
Good thoughts.

children of the town, they followed their business
joyfully; they would work and sing, work and sing
from morning till night: so that quite through the
town of Mansoul now, nothing was to be found but
harmony, quietness, joy and health. And this lasted
all that summer.

But there was a man in the town of Mansoul,

The story of
Mr. Carnal
Security.

and his name was Mr. Carnal Security; this man did,
after all this mercy bestowed on this corporation,
bring the town of Mansoul into great and grievous
slavery and bondage. A brief account of him and of
his doings take as followeth.

When Diabolus at first took possession of the
town of Mansoul, he brought thither with himself, a
great number of Diabolonians, men of his own conditions. Now among these there was one whose name

Mr. Self-conceit.

was Mr. Self-conceit, and a notable brisk man he was,
as any that in those days did possess the town of
Mansoul. Diabolus then perceiving this man to be
active and bold, sent him upon many desperate
designs, the which he managed better, and more to
the pleasing of his lord than most that came with him

15   *observed their order*: kept to the station or rank in which they had been
placed.

from the dens could do. Wherefore, finding of him so
fit for his purpose, he preferred him, and made him
next to the great Lord Willbewill, of whom we have
written so much before. Now the Lord Willbewill
being in those days very well pleased with him, and
with his achievements, gave him his daughter, the
Lady Fear-nothing, to wife. Now of my Lady Fear-
nothing did this Mr. Self-conceit beget this gentleman
Mr. Carnal Security. Wherefore, there being then in
Mansoul those strange kind of mixtures, 'twas hard for
them in some cases to find out who were natives, who
not; for Mr. Carnal Security sprang from my Lord
Willbewill, by mother's side, though he had for his
father a Diabolonian by nature.

Carnal Security's original.

Well, this Carnal Security took much after his
father and mother. He was self-conceited, he feared
nothing, he was also a very busy man: nothing of
news, nothing of doctrine, nothing of alteration, or
talk of alteration, could at any time be on foot in
Mansoul, but be sure Mr. Carnal Security would be
at the head or tail of it; but to be sure he would
decline those that he deemed the weakest, and stood
always with them (in his way of standing), that he
supposed was the strongest side.

His qualities.

He is always for the strongest side.

Now when Shaddai the mighty, and Emmanuel
his Son, made war upon Mansoul to take it, this Mr.
Carnal Security was then in town, and was a great
doer among the people, encouraging them in their
rebellion, putting of them upon hard'ning of themselves in their resisting of the King's forces. But when
he saw that the town of Mansoul was taken and converted to the use of the glorious Prince Emmanuel,
and when he also saw what was become of Diabolus,
and how he was unroosted, and made to quit the castle
in the greatest contempt and scorn, and that the town
of Mansoul was well lined with captains, engines of
war, and men, and also provision, what doth he but
slily wheel about also; and as he had served Diabolus

18   *news*: gossip or rumour.
34   *unroosted*: dislodged, as a bird driven from its perch.

against the good Prince, so he feigned that he would serve the Prince against his foes.

And having got some little smattering of Emmanuel's things by the end, being bold, he ventures himself into the company of the townsmen, and attempts also to chat among them. Now he knew that the power and strength of the town of Mansoul was great, and that it could not but be pleasing to the people if he cried up their might and their glory. Wherefore he beginneth his tale with the power and strength of Mansoul, and affirmed that it was impregnable—now magnifying their captains, and their slings, and their rams; then crying up their fortifications, and strongholds; and lastly the assurances that they had from their Prince, that Mansoul should be happy for ever. But when he saw that some of the men of the town were tickled and taken with his discourse, he makes it his business, and walking from street to street, house to house, and man to man, he at last brought Mansoul to dance after his pipe, and to grow almost as carnally secure as himself. So from talking they went to feasting, and from feasting to sporting; and so to some other matters. (Now Emmanuel was yet in the town of Mansoul, and he wisely observed their doings.) My Lord Mayor, my Lord Willbewill, and Mr. Recorder, were also all taken with the words of this tattling Diabolonian gentleman, forgetting that their Prince had given them warning before to take heed that they were not beguiled with any Diabolonian sleight: he had further told them that the security of the now flourishing town of Mansoul did not so much lie in her present fortifications and force, as in her so using of what she had, as might oblige her Emmanuel to abide within her castle. For the right doctrine of Emmanuel was that the town of Mansoul should take heed that they forgot not his Father's love and his; also that they should so demean themselves as to continue to keep themselves therein. Now this was not

How Mr. Carnal Security begins the misery of Mansoul.

'Tis not grace received, but grace improved, that preserves the soul from temporal dangers.

10

20

30

3f. *having got some little smattering . . . by the end*: having picked up a superficial knowledge of the Prince's affairs. On this metaphor from spinning, see note on p. 111.

the way to do it, namely, to fall in love with one of the Diabolonians, and with such an one too as Mr. Carnal Security was, and to be led up and down by the nose by him. They should have heard their Prince, fear'd their Prince, loved their Prince, and have ston'd this naughty pack to death, and took care to have walked in the ways of their Prince's prescribing, for then should their peace have been as a river, when their righteousness had been like the waves of the sea.

Now when Emmanuel perceived that through the policy of Mr. Carnal Security, the hearts of the men of Mansoul were chill'd and abated in their practical love to him:

First, he bemoans them, and condoles their state with the Secretary, saying, 'Oh, that my people had hearkened unto me, and that Mansoul had walked in my ways! I would have fed them with the finest of the wheat, and with honey out of the rock would I have sustained them.' This done, he said in his heart, 'I will return to the court and go to my place till Mansoul shall consider and acknowledge their offence.' And he did so, and the cause and manner of his going away from them was thus:

The cause was for that,

First, Mansoul declined him, as is manifest in these particulars:

1. They left off their former way of visiting of him; they came not to his royal palace as afore.
2. They did not regard, nor yet take notice that he came or came not to visit them.
3. The love-feasts that had wont to be between their Prince and them, though he made them still, and called them to them, yet they neglected to come at them, or to be delighted with them.
4. They waited not for his counsels, but began to be headstrong and confident in themselves,

Emmanuel bemoans Mansoul.

The way of Mansoul's backsliding.

8   See Isa. 48:18.
15ff.   See Ps. 81:13-16.
21   *acknowledge their offence*: see Hos. 5:15.

concluding that now they were strong and invincible, and that Mansoul was secure, and beyond all reach of the foe, and that her state must needs be unalterable for ever.

Now, as was said, Emmanuel perceiving that by the craft of Mr. Carnal Security, the town of Mansoul was taken off from their dependence upon him, and upon his Father by him, and set upon what by them was bestowed upon it, he first, as I said, bemoaned their state, then he used means to make them understand that the way that they went on in was dangerous. For he sent my Lord High Secretary to them, to forbid them such ways; but twice when he came to them, he found them at dinner in Mr. Carnal Security's parlour, and perceiving also that they were not willing to reason about matters concerning their good, he took grief and went his way. The which, when he had told to the Prince Emmanuel, he took offence, and was grieved also, and so made provision to return to his Father's court.

They grieve the Holy Ghost and Christ.

Now the methods of his withdrawing, as I was saying before, were thus:

Christ withdraws not all at once.

1. Even while he was yet with them in Mansoul, he kept himself close, and more retired than formerly.

2. His speech was not now, if he came in their company, so pleasant and familiar as formerly.

3. Nor did he as in times past, send to Mansoul from his table, those dainty bits which he was wont to do.

4. Nor when they came to visit him, as now and then they would, would he be so easily spoken with as they found him to be in times past. They might now knock once, yea twice, but he would seem not at all to regard them; whereas formerly, at the sound of their feet, he would up and run, and meet them halfway, and take them too, and lay them in his bosom.

The working of their affections.

But thus Emmanuel carried it now, and by this his carriage he sought to make them bethink themselves and return to him. But, alas! they did not consider, they did not know his ways, they regarded not, they were not touched with these, now with the true remembrance of former favours. Wherefore, what does he but in private manner withdraw himself, first from his palace, then to the gate of the town, and so away from Mansoul he goes, till they should acknowledge their offence, and more earnestly seek his face. Mr. Gods-peace also laid down his commission, and would for the present act no longer in the town of Mansoul.

He is gone.
Ezek. 11:21.
Hos. 5:15.
Lev. 26:21-24.

Thus they walked contrary to him, and he again by way of retaliation, walked contrary to them. But, alas, by this time they were so hardened in their way, and had so drunk in the doctrine of Mr. Carnal Security, that the departing of their Prince touched them not, nor was he remembered by them when gone; and so of consequence his absence not condoled by them.

Jer. 2:32.

Now there was a day wherein this old gentleman Mr. Carnal Security did again make a feast for the town of Mansoul, and there was at that time in the town one Mr. Godlyfear, one now but little set by, though formerly one of great request. This man old Carnal Security had in mind, if possible, to gull and debauch, and abuse as he did the rest, and therefore he now bids him to the feast with his neighbours. So the day being come, they prepare, and he goes and appears with the rest of the guests; and being all set at the table, they did eat and drink, and were merry even all but this one man. For Mr. Godlyfear sat like a stranger, and did neither eat, nor was merry. The which, when Mr. Carnal Security perceived, he presently addressed himself in a speech thus to him:

A trick put upon Mr. Godlyfear; he goes to the feast and sits there like a stranger.

CARN. 'Mr. Godlyfear, are you not well? you seem to be ill of body or mind, or both. I have a cordial of Mr. Forget-good's making, the which, sir, if you will

Talk betwixt Mr. Carnal Security, and Mr. Godlyfear.

take a dram of, I hope it may make you bonny and blithe, and so make you more fit for we feasting companions.'

GODLY. Unto whom the good old gentleman discreetly replied, 'Sir, I thank you for all things courteous and civil, but for your cordial I have no list thereto. But a word to the natives of Mansoul. You the elders and chief of Mansoul, to me it is strange to see you so jocund and merry, when the town of Mansoul is in such woeful case.'   10

CARN. Then said Mr. Carnal Security, 'You want sleep, good sir, I doubt. If you please, lie down and take a nap, and we meanwhile will be merry.'

GODLY. Then said the good man as follows, 'Sir, if you were not destitute of an honest heart, you could not do as you have done, and do.'

CARN. Then said Mr. Carnal Security, 'Why?'

GODLY. 'Nay, pray interrupt me not. 'Tis true, the town of Mansoul was strong, and, with a proviso, impregnable; but you, the townsmen, have weak'ned   20 it, and it now lies obnoxious to its foes. Nor is it a time to flatter, or be silent. 'Tis you, Mr. Carnal Security, that have wilily stripped Mansoul, and driven her glory from her; you have broken down her gates, you have spoiled her locks and bars.

'And now to explain myself: from that time that my lords of Mansoul and you, sir, grew so great, from that time the strength of Mansoul had been offended, and now he is arisen and is gone. If any shall question the truth of my words, I will answer him by this, and   30 such like questions. Where is the Prince Emmanuel? When did a man or woman in Mansoul see him? When did you hear from him, or taste any of his dainty bits? You are now a-feasting with this Diabolonian monster, but he is not your Prince. I say, therefore, though enemies from without, had you taken heed, could not have made a prey of you, yet since you

1   *bonny and blithe*: carefree and happy.
6   *list*: desire.
21   *obnoxious*: exposed, open to harm.

have sinned against your Prince, your enemies within have been too hard for you.'

CARN. Then said Mr. Carnal Security, 'Fie! fie! Mr. Godlyfear, fie! Will you never shake off your timorousness? Are you afraid of being sparrow-blasted? Who hath hurt you? Behold I am on your side; only you are for doubting, and I am for being confident. Besides, is this a time to be sad in? A feast is made for mirth; why, then, do you now, to your shame and our trouble, break out into such passionate melancholy language when you should eat and drink, and be merry?'

GODLY. Then said Mr. Godlyfear again, 'I may well be sad, for Emmanuel is gone from Mansoul. I say again he is gone, and you, sir, are the man that has driven him away; yea, he is gone without so much as acquainting the nobles of Mansoul with his going, and if that is not a sign of his anger, I am not acquainted with the methods of godliness.

'And now, my lords and gentlemen, for my speech is still to you, your gradual declining from him did provoke him gradually to depart from you, the which he did for some time, if perhaps you would have been made sensible thereby, and have been renewed by humbling of yourselves; but when he saw that none would regard, nor lay these fearful beginnings of his anger and judgment to heart, he went away from this place, and this I saw with mine eye. Wherefore now, while you boast, your strength is gone; you are like the man that had lost his locks that before did wave about his shoulders. You may with this lord of your feast shake yourselves, and conclude to do as at other times; but since without him you can do nothing, and he is departed from you, turn your feast into a sigh, and your mirth into lamentation.'

Then the Subordinate Preacher, old Mr. Con-

His speech to the elders of Mansoul.

5　*sparrow-blasted*: struck down by some mysterious or imaginary power. The expression apparently originated in a belief that the sparrow can blight vegetation or harm humans. An instance of the latter is recorded in the apocryphal story of Tobit's blindness (The Book of Tobit, II, 10).
30　Samson; see Judg. 16.

Conscience startled. science by name, he that of old was Recorder of Man-soul, being startled at what was said, began to second it thus.

CON. 'Indeed, my brethren,' quoth he, 'I fear that Mr. Godlyfear tells us true. I, for my part, have not seen my Prince a long season. I cannot remember the day, for my part. Nor can I answer Mr. Godlyfear's question. I doubt, I am afraid that all is naught with Mansoul.'

GODLY. 'Nay, I know that you shall not find him in Mansoul, for he is departed and gone; yea, and gone for the faults of the elders, and for that they rewarded his grace with unsufferable unkindnesses.' 10

Then did the Subordinate Preacher look as if he They are all aghast. would fall down dead at the table; also all there present, except the man of the house, began to look pale and wan. But having a little recovered them-selves, and jointly agreeing to believe Mr. Godlyfear and his sayings, they began to consult what was best to be done (now Mr. Carnal Security was gone into his withdrawing-room, for he liked not such dumpish doings), both to the man of the house for drawing them into evil, and also to recover Emmanuel's love. 20

And with that, that saying of their Prince came They consult and burn their feast-master. very hot into their minds, which he had bidden them do to such as were false prophets that should arise to delude the town of Mansoul. So they took Mr. Carnal Security (concluding that he must be he), and burned his house upon him with fire, for he also was a Diabolonian by nature. 30

So when this was past and over, they bespeed themselves to look for Emmanuel their Prince, and they Cant. 5:6. sought him, but they found him not. Then were they more confirmed in the truth of Mr. Godlyfear's sayings, and began also severely to reflect upon themselves for their so vile and ungodly doings; for they concluded now that it was through them that their Prince had left them.

Then they agreed and went to my Lord Secretary

21   *dumpish*: depressing.

—him whom before they refused to hear, him whom they had grieved with their doings—to know of him, for he was a seer, and could tell where Emmanuel was, and how they might direct a petition to him. But the Lord Secretary would not admit them to a conference about this matter, nor would admit them to his royal place of abode, nor come out to them to show them his face or intelligence.

They apply themselves to the Holy Ghost, but he is grieved, etc.
Isa. 63:10.
Eph. 4:30.
I Thess. 5:19.

And now was it a day gloomy and dark, a day of clouds and of thick darkness with Mansoul. Now they saw that they had been foolish, and began to perceive what the company and prattle of Mr. Carnal Security had done, and what desperate damage his swaggering words had brought poor Mansoul into. But what further it was like to cost them, that they were ignorant of. Now Mr. Godlyfear began again to be in repute with the men of the town; yea, they were ready to look upon him as a prophet.

Well, when the Sabbath-day was come, they went to hear their Subordinate Preacher; but oh, how he did thunder and lighten this day! His text was that in the prophet Jonah, *They that observe lying vanities, forsake their own mercies.* But there was then such power and authority in that sermon, and such a dejection seen in the countenances of the people that day, that the like hath seldom been heard or seen. The people when sermon was done, were scarce able to go to their homes, or to betake themselves to their employs the week after; they were so sermon-smitten, and also so sermon-sick by being smitten, that they knew not what to do.

A thund'ring sermon.
Jonah 2:8.

Hos. 6:13.

He did not only show to Mansoul their sin, but did tremble before them, under the sense of his own, still crying out of himself, as he preached to them, 'Unhappy man that I am! That I should do so wicked a thing! That I, a preacher, whom the Prince did set up to teach to Mansoul his law, should myself live senseless, and sottishly here, and be one of the first found in transgression! This transgression also fell

The Subordinate Preacher doth acknowledge his fault, and bewails his compliance with Mr. Carnal Security.

38   *sottishly*: self-indulgently, stupidly.

within my precincts: I should have cried out against the wickedness, but I let Mansoul lie wallowing in it, until it had driven Emmanuel from its borders.' With these things he also charged all the lords and gentry of Mansoul, to the almost distracting of them.

Ps. 88.

About this time also, there was a great sickness in the town of Mansoul, and most of the inhabitants were greatly afflicted. Yea, the captains also, and men of war were brought thereby to a languishing condition, and that for a long time together; so that in case of an invasion, nothing could to purpose now have been done, either by the townsmen, or field-officers. Oh how many pale faces, weak hands, feeble knees, and staggering men were now seen to walk the streets of Mansoul! Here were groans, there pants, and yonder lay those that were ready to faint.

A great sickness in Mansoul.

Heb 12:12,13.
Rev. 3:2.
Isa. 3:24.
Sin doth cause to be weak, both body, and soul, and graces.

The garments, too, which Emmanuel had given them were but in a sorry case; some were rent, some were torn, and all in a nasty condition; some also did hang so loosely upon them that the next bush they came at was ready to pluck them off.

After some time spent in this sad and desolate condition, the Subordinate Preacher called for a day of fasting, and to humble themselves for being so wicked against the great Shaddai, and his Son. And he desired that Captain Boanerges would preach. So he consented to do it, and the day was come, and his text was this, *Cut it down; why cumb'reth it the ground?* And a very smart sermon he made upon the place. First, he showed what was the occasion of the words, to wit, *because the fig-tree was barren;* then he showed what was contained in the sentence, to wit, repent-

Boanerges doth preach to Mansoul.

10

20

30

29   *smart*: painful. A sermon on this text was liable to make any Puritan smart. See note on p. 42.

30ff. The sermon accords in structure with the form laid down by the great Elizabethan preacher, William Perkins, in his *Art of Prophecying,* and practised by many Puritan divines throughout the seventeenth century. Boanerges is therefore a most typical Puritan: he "opens" the text, states the "doctrine," gives "reasons" or "proofs," and finally offers "uses" or "applications." On the conventional technique of the Puritan sermon, see W. Fraser Mitchell, *English Pulpit Oratory from Andrewes to Tillotson* (London, 1932), esp. chap. 4.

ance, or utter desolation. He then showed also by whose authority this sentence was pronounced, and that was by Shaddai himself. And lastly, he showed the reasons of the point, and then concluded his sermon. But he was very pertinent in the application, insomuch that he made poor Mansoul tremble. For this sermon, as well as the former, wrought much upon the hearts of the men of Mansoul; yea, it greatly helped to keep awake those that were roused by the preaching that went before. So that now throughout the whole town there was little or nothing to be heard or seen but sorrow and mourning, and woe.

The men of Mansoul much affected.

Now after sermon they got together and consulted what was best to be done. 'But,' said the Subordinate Preacher, 'I will do nothing of mine own head, without advising with my neighbour, Mr. Godlyfear. For if he had afore, and understood more of the mind of our Prince than we, I do not know but he also may have it now, even now we are turning again in virtue.' So they called and sent for Mr. Godlyfear, and he forthwith appeared. Then they desired that he would further show his opinion about what they had best to do. Then said the old gentleman as followeth: 'It is my opinion that this town of Mansoul should in this day of her distress draw up and send an humble petition to their offended Prince Emmanuel, that he in his favour and grace will turn again unto you, and not keep anger for ever.'

They consult what to do.

Mr. Godlyfear's advice.

When the townsmen had heard this speech, they did with one consent agree to his advice. So they did presently draw up their request, and the next was, *But who shall carry it?* At last they did all agree to send it by my Lord Mayor. So he accepted of the service, and addressed himself to his journey; and went and came to the court of Shaddai, whither Emmanuel, the Prince of Mansoul, was gone. But the gate was shut, and a strict watch kept thereat, so that the petitioner was forced to stand without for a great while together. Then he desired that some would go into the Prince and tell him who stood at the gate, and what his business was. So one went and told to Shaddai,

They send the Lord Mayor to court.
Lam. 3:8,44.

182

and to Emmanuel his Son, that the Lord Mayor of the town of Mansoul stood without at the gate of the King's court, desiring to be admitted into the presence of the Prince, the King's Son. He also told what was the Lord Mayor's errand, both to the King and his Son Emmanuel. But the Prince would not come down nor admit that the gate should be opened to him, but sent him an answer to this effect: 'They have turned the back unto me, and not their face, but now in the time of their trouble they say to me, *Arise and save us.* But can they not now go to Mr. Carnal Security to whom they went when they turned from me, and make him their leader, their lord, and their protection now in their trouble? Why now in their trouble do they visit me, since in their prosperity they went astray?'

This answer made my Lord Mayor look black in the face; it troubled, it perplexed, it rent him sore. And now he began again to see what it was to be familiar with Diabolonians, such as Mr. Carnal Security was. When he saw that at court, as yet, there was little help to be expected, either for himself or friends in Mansoul, he smote upon his breast and returned weeping, and all the way bewailing the lamentable state of Mansoul.

Well, when he was come within sight of the town, the elders and chief of the people of Mansoul went out at the gate to meet him, and to salute him, and to know how he sped at court. But he told them his tale in so doleful a manner, that they all cried out, and mourned, and wept. Wherefore they threw ashes and dust upon their heads, and put sackcloth upon their loins, and went crying out through the town of Mansoul; the which, when the rest of the townsfolk saw, they all mourned and wept. This therefore was a day of rebuke and trouble, and of anguish to the town of Mansoul, and also of great distress.

After some time, when they had somewhat refrained themselves, they came together to consult again what by them was yet to be done; and they asked advice, as they did before, of that reverend Mr. Godlyfear, who told them that there was no way

Jer. 2:27,28.

A dreadful answer.

Lam. 4:7,8.

The Lord Mayor returns, and how.

The state of Mansoul now.

The whole town cast down.

They consult again Mr. Godlyfear's advice.

10

20

30

40

better than to do as they had done, nor would he that they should be discouraged at all with that they had met with at court; yea, though several of their petitions should be answered with nought but silence or rebuke. 'For,' said he, 'it is the way of the wise Shaddai to make men wait and to exercise patience, and it should be the way of them in want, to be willing to stay his leisure.'

Then they took courage, and sent again, and again, and again, and again; for there was not now one day, nor an hour that went over Mansoul's head, wherein a man might not have met upon the road one or other riding post, sounding the horn from Mansoul to the court of the King Shaddai; and all with letters petitionary in behalf of, and for the Prince's return to, Mansoul.

See now what's the work of a backsliding saint awakened.

Groaning desires.

The road, I say, was now full of messengers, going and returning, and meeting one another; some from the court, and some from Mansoul; and this was the work of the miserable town of Mansoul, all that long, that sharp, that cold and tedious winter.

Now, if you have not forgot, you may yet remember that I told you before, that after Emmanuel had taken Mansoul, yea, and after that he had new-modelled the town, there remained in several lurking places of the corporation many of the old Diabolonians, that either came with the tyrant when he invaded and took the town, or that had there, by reason of unlawful mixtures, their birth and breeding and bringing up. And their holes, dens and lurking places were in, under, or about the wall of the town. Some of their names are the Lord Fornication, the Lord Adultery, the Lord Murder, the Lord Anger, the Lord Lasciviousness, the Lord Deceit, the Lord Evil-eye, the Lord Blasphemy, and that horrible villain, the old and dangerous Lord Covetousness. These, as I told you, with many more, had yet their abode in the town of Mansoul, and that after that Emmanuel had driven their Prince Diabolus out of the castle.

A memento.

Against these the good Prince did grant a commission to the Lord Willbewill and others, yea, to the

184

Mansoul heeded
not her Prince's
caution, nor put
his commission
into execution.
whole town of Mansoul, to seek, take, secure, and
destroy any or all that they could lay hands of, for
that they were Diabolonians by nature, enemies to the
Prince, and those that sought to ruin the blessed town
of Mansoul. But the town of Mansoul did not pursue
this warrant, but neglected to look after, to apprehend,
to secure, and to destroy these Diabolonians. Wherefore, what do these villains but by degrees take courage to put forth their heads, and to show themselves
to the inhabitants of the town. Yea, and as I was told,   10
some of the men of Mansoul grew too familiar with
some of them, to the sorrow of the corporation, as you
yet will hear more of in time and place.

 Well, when the Diabolonian lords that were left
perceived that Mansoul had through sinning offended
Emmanuel their Prince, and that he had withdrawn

himself and was gone, what do they but plot the ruin
of the town of Mansoul. So upon a time they met
together at the hold of one Mr. Mischief, who also was
a Diabolonian, and there consulted how they might   20
deliver up Mansoul into the hands of Diabolus again.
Now some advised one way, and some another, every
man according to his own liking. At last my Lord
Lasciviousness propounded, whether it might not be
best in the first place for some of those that were
Diabolonians in Mansoul to adventure to offer themselves for servants to some of the natives of the town.
'For,' said he, 'if they so do, and Mansoul shall accept
of them, they may for us, and for Diabolus our lord,
make the taking of the town of Mansoul more easy   30
than otherwise it will be.' But then stood up the Lord
Murder, and said, 'This may not be done at this time,
for Mansoul is now in a kind of a rage, because by
our friend Mr. Carnal Security she hath been once
ensnared already and made to offend against her
Prince; and how shall she reconcile herself unto her
Lord again, but by the heads of these men? Besides, we
know that they have in commission to take and slay
us where ever they shall find us; let us therefore be
wise as foxes. When we are dead, we can do them no   40
hurt; but while we live, we may.' Thus when they had

tossed the matter to and fro, they jointly agreed that
a letter should forthwith be sent away to Diabolus in
their name by which the state of the town of Mansoul
should be showed him, and how much it is under the
frowns of their Prince. 'We may also,' said some, 'let
him know our intentions, and ask of him his advice in
the case.'

They send to
Hell for advice.

So a letter was presently framed, the contents of
which was this:

10   *To our great lord, the Prince Diabolus, dwelling below*
      in the Infernal Cave:

      O great Father, and mighty Prince Diabolus,
      we, the true Diabolonians, yet remaining in the
      rebellious town of Mansoul, having received our
      beings from thee, and our nourishment at thy hands,
      cannot with content and quiet endure to behold, as
      we do this day, how thou art dispraised, disgraced,
      and reproached among the inhabitants of this town;
      nor is thy long absence at all delightful to us,
20   *because greatly to our detriment.*

The copy of
their letter.

      The reason of this our writing unto our lord, is
      for that we are not altogether without hope that
      this town may become thy habitation again; for it is
      greatly declined from its Prince Emmanuel, and he is
      uprisen, and is departed them; yea, and though they
      send, and send, and send, and send after him to
      return to them, yet can they not prevail, nor get
      good words from him.

      There has been also of late, and is yet remaining,
30   *a very great sickness and faintings among them, and*
      that not only upon the power sort of the town, but
      upon the lords, captains, and chief gentry of the
      place (we only who are of the Diabolonians by nature
      remain well, lively, and strong); so that through their
      great transgression on the one hand, and their
      dangerous sickness on the other, we judge they lie
      open to thy hand and power. If therefore it shall
      stand with thy horrible cunning, and with the
      cunning of the rest of the princes with thee, to come

*and make an attempt to take Mansoul again, send us
word, and we shall to our utmost power be ready to
deliver it into thy hand. Or if what we have said
shall not by thy fatherhood be thought best, and
most meet to be done, send us thy mind in a few
words, and we are all ready to follow thy counsel to
the hazarding of our lives, and what else we have.*

*Given under our hands the day and date above
written, after a close consultation at the house of
Mr. Mischief, who yet is alive, and hath his place in   10
our desirable town of Mansoul.*

When Mr. Profane (for he was the carrier) was
come with his letter to Hellgate-hill, he knocked at
the brazen gates for entrance. Then did Cerberus the
porter, for he is the keeper of that gate, open to Mr.
Profane, to whom he delivered his letter, which he
had brought from the Diabolonians in Mansoul. So he
carried it in, and presented it to Diabolus his lord,
and said, 'Tidings my lord, from Mansoul, from our
trusty friends in Mansoul.'   20

Then came together from all places of the den
Beelzebub, Lucifer, Apollyon, with the rest of the
rabblement there, to hear what news from Mansoul.
So the letter was broken up and read, and Cerberus he
stood by. When the letter was openly read, and the
contents thereof spread into all the corners of the
den, command was given that without let or stop,
Dead-man's-bell should be rung for joy. So the bell was
rung, and the princes rejoiced that Mansoul was like
to come to ruin. Now the clapper of the bell went,   30
'The town of Mansoul is coming to dwell with us;
make room for the town of Mansoul.' This bell therefore they did ring, because they did hope that they
should have Mansoul again.

Now, when they had performed this their horrible
ceremony, they got together again to consult what
answer to send to their friends in Mansoul, and some

*Mr. Profane is
carrier; he
brings the letter
to Hellgate–hill,
and there pre-
sents it to Cer-
berus, the
porter.*

*Dead-man's-bell,
and how it
went.*

14   *Cerberus*: three-headed dog, keeper of the gate to the classical underworld.

advised one thing, and some another, but at length because the business required haste, they left the whole business to the Prince Diabolus, judging him the most proper lord of the place. So he drew up a letter as he thought fit, in answer to what Mr. Profane had brought, and sent it to the Diabolonians that did dwell in Mansoul, by the same hand that had brought theirs to him. And this was the contents thereof:

To our offspring the high and mighty Diabolonians,
that yet dwell in the town of Mansoul, Diabolus, the
great Prince of Mansoul, wisheth a prosperous issue
and conclusion of those many brave enterprises,
conspiracies, and designs that you of your love and
respect to our honour, have in your hearts to attempt
to do against Mansoul.

Beloved children and disciples, my Lord
Fornication, Adultery, and the rest, we have here in
our desolate den received to our highest joy and
content, your welcome letter by the hand of our
trusty Mr. Profane; and to show how acceptable your
tidings were, we rang out our bell for gladness; for
we rejoiced as much as we could, when we perceived
that yet we had friends in Mansoul, and such as
sought our honour and revenge in the ruin of the
town of Mansoul. We also rejoiced to hear that they
are in a degenerated condition, and that they have
offended their Prince, and that he is gone. Their
sickness also pleaseth us, as does also your health,
might and strength. Glad also would we be, right
horribly beloved, could we get this town into our
clutches again. Nor will we be sparing of spending our
wit, our cunning, our craft, and hellish inventions to
bring to a wished conclusion this your brave
beginning in order thereto.
And take this for your comfort (our birth, and
our offspring), that shall we again surprise it and
take it, we will attempt to put all your foes to the

35   *our birth*: you who are born of us.

sword, and will make you the great lords and captains
of the place. Nor need you fear, if ever we get it
again, that we after that shall be cast out any more;
for we will come with more strength, and so lay far
more fast hold than at the first we did. Besides, it is

Matt. 12:43-45.

the law of that Prince that now they own, that if we
get them a second time they shall be ours for ever.

Do you therefore our trusty Diabolonians, yet
more pry into, and endeavour to spy out the weakness
of the town of Mansoul. We also would that you
yourselves do attempt to weaken them more and more.
Send us word also by what means you think we had
best to attempt the regaining thereof: to wit, whether
by persuasion to a vain and loose life; or, whether
by tempting them to doubt and despair; or, whether
by blowing up of the town by the gun-powder of
pride, and self-conceit. Do you also, O ye brave
Diabolonians, and true sons of the Pit, be always
in a readiness to make a most hideous assault within,
when we shall be ready to storm it without. Now
speed you in your project, and we in our desires, the
utmost power of our gates, which is the wish of your
great Diabolus, Mansoul's enemy, and him that
trembles when he thinks of judgment to come. All
the blessings of the Pit be upon you, and so we close
up our letter.

Given at the Pit's mouth by the joint consent of all
the Princes of Darkness to be sent (to the force and
power that we have yet remaining in Mansoul)
by the hand of Mr. Profane,

By me, Diabolus.

This letter, as was said, was sent to Mansoul, to
the Diabolonians that yet remained there, and that

Flesh.

yet inhabited the wall, from the dark dungeon of
Diabolus, by the hand of Mr. Profane, by whom they
also in Mansoul sent theirs to the Pit. Now when this

Profane comes
home again.

Mr. Profane had made his return, and was come to
Mansoul again, he went and came as he was wont to
the house of Mr. Mischief, for there was the conclave,

and the place where the contrivers were met. Now when they saw that their messenger was returned safe and sound, they were greatly gladded thereat. Then he presented them with his letter which he had brought from Diabolus for them; the which, when they had read and considered, did much augment their gladness. They asked them after the welfare of their friends, as how their Lord Diabolus, Lucifer, and Beelzebub did, with the rest of those of the den. To which this Profane made answer, 'Well, well, my lords; they are well, even as well as can be in their place. They also,' said he, 'did ring for joy at the reading of your letter, as you well perceived by this when you read it.'

Now, as was said, when they had read their letter, and perceived that it encouraged them in their work, they fell to their way of contriving again—to wit, how they might complete their Diabolonian design upon Mansoul. And the first thing that they agreed upon was to keep all things from Mansoul as close as they could: 'Let it not be known, let not Mansoul be acquainted with what we design against it.' The next thing was how or by what means they should try to bring to pass the ruin and overthrow of Mansoul; and one said after this manner, and another said after that. Then stood up Mr. Deceit, and said, 'My right Diabolonian friends, our lords, and the high ones of the deep dungeon do propound unto us these three ways:

1. 'Whether we had best to seek its ruin by making of Mansoul loose and vain.
2. 'Or whether by driving them to doubt and despair.
3. 'Or whether by endeavouring to blow them up by the gun-powder of pride and self-conceit.

'Now I think if we shall tempt them to pride, that may do something; and if we tempt them to wantonness, that may help. But in my mind, if we could drive them into desperation, that would knock the nail on the head; for then we should have them in the first place question the truth of the love of the heart

Take heed Mansoul.

190

of their Prince towards them, and that will disgust
him much. This, if it works well, will make them leave
off quickly their way of sending petitions to him;
then farewell earnest solicitations for help and supply;
for then this conclusion lies naturally before them, As
good do nothing as do to no purpose.' So to Mr. Deceit
they unanimously did consent.

Take heed Man-
soul.

Then the next question was, 'But how shall we
do to bring this our project to pass?' And 'twas answered by the same gentleman—that this might be
the best way to do it: 'Even let,' quoth he, 'so many
of our friends as are willing to venture themselves for
the promoting of their Prince's cause, disguise themselves with apparel, change their names, and go into
the market like far-country-men, and proffer to let
themselves for servants to the famous town of Mansoul, and let them pretend to do their masters as
beneficially as may be; for by so doing they may, if
Mansoul shall hire them, in little time so corrupt and
defile the corporation, that her now Prince shall be
not only further offended with them, but in conclusion shall spew them out of his mouth. And when
this is done, our prince Diabolus shall prey upon them
with ease—yea, of themselves they shall fall into the
mouth of the eater.'

Take heed Man-
soul.

This project was no sooner propounded, but was
as highly accepted, and forward were all Diabolonians
now to engage in so delicate an enterprise; but it was
not thought fit that all should do thus; wherefore they
pitched upon two or three, namely, the Lord Covetousness, the Lord Lasciviousness, and the Lord Anger. The
Lord Covetousness called himself by the name of Prudent-thrifty; the Lord Lasciviousness called himself by
the name of Harmless-mirth; and the Lord Anger called
himself by the name of Good-zeal.

Take heed Man-
soul.

So upon a market-day they came into the market-
place, three lusty fellows they were to look on, and

10

20

30

32ff. Adoption of aliases by the Vices is a common device in morality plays. On
this, see Roger Sharrock, "The Trial of Vices in Puritan Fiction," *Baptist
Quarterly*, XIV (January, 1951), 3-12.

they were clothed in sheep's-russet, which was also now in a manner as white as were the white robes of the men of Mansoul. Now the men could speak the language of Mansoul well. So when they were come into the market-place, and had offered to let themselves to the townsmen, they were presently taken up, for they asked but little wages, and promised to do their master's great service.

Mr. Mind hired Prudent-thrifty, and Mr. Godly-fear hired Good-zeal. True, this fellow Harmless-mirth did hang a little in hand, and could not so soon get him a master as the other did, because the town of Mansoul was now in Lent; but after a while, because Lent was almost out, the Lord Willbewill hired Harmless-mirth to be both his waiting-man and his lacquey; and thus they got them masters.

These villains now being got thus far into the houses of the men of Mansoul, quickly began to do great mischief therein; for being filthy arch and sly, they quickly corrupted the families where they were; yea, they tainted their masters much, especially this Prudent-thrifty, and him they call Harmless-mirth. True, he that went under the vizor of Good-zeal, was not so well liked of his master, for he quickly found that he was but a counterfeit rascal; the which when the fellow perceived, with speed he made his escape from the house, or I doubt not but his master had hanged him.

Well, when these vagabonds had thus far carried on their design, and had corrupted the town as much as they could, in the next place they considered with themselves at what time their prince Diabolus without, and themselves within the town should make an attempt to seize upon Mansoul; and they all agreed upon this, that a market-day would be best for that work. 'For why? Then will the townsfolk be busy in their ways: and always take this for a rule, *When people are most busy in the world, they least fear a*

Marginal notes:

Take heed Mansoul. (line 7)

Take heed Mansoul. (line 16)

A day of worldly cumber. (line 28)

---

1 *sheep's-russet*: coarse, home-spun woollen cloth.
19 *arch*: cunning.

surprise. We also then,' said they, 'shall be able with less suspicion to gather ourselves together for the work of our friends, and lords; yea, and in such a day, if we shall attempt our work, and miss it, we may when they shall give us the rout, the better hide ourselves in the crowd and escape.'

These things being thus far agreed upon by them, they wrote another letter to Diabolus, and sent it by the hand of Mr. Profane, the contents of which was this:

The Lords of Looseness send to the great and high Diabolus from our dens, caves, holes, and strong holds, in, and about the wall of the town of Mansoul, greeting:

Our great lord, and the nourisher of our lives, Diabolus—how glad we were when we heard of your fatherhood's readiness to comply with us, and help forward our design in our attempts to ruin Mansoul! None can tell but those who as we do set themselves against all appearance of good when and wheresoever we find it.

Touching the encouragement that your greatness is pleased to give us to continue to devise, contrive, and study the utter desolation of Mansoul, that we are not solicitous about; for we know right well that it cannot but be pleasing and profitable to us, to see our enemies and them that seek our lives, to die at our feet, or fly before us. We therefore are still contriving, and that to the best of our cunning, to make this work most facile and easy to your lordships, and to us.

First we considered of that most hellishly, cunning compacted, three-fold project, that by you was propounded to us in your last; and have concluded, that though to blow them up with the gun-powder of pride would do well, and to do it by tempting them to be loose and vain will help on, yet to contrive to bring them into the gulf of desperation, we think will do best of all. Now we who are at

Take heed Mansoul.

Look to it Mansoul.

Rom. 7:21.
Gal. 5:17.

Look to it Mansoul.

10

20

30

your beck, have thought of two ways to do this: first,
we for our parts will make them as vile as we can,
and then you with us, at a time appointed, shall
be ready to fall upon them with the utmost force. And
of all the nations that are at your whistle, we
think that an army of Doubters may be the most
likely to attack and overcome the town of Mansoul.
Thus shall we overcome these enemies, else the
Pit shall open her mouth upon them, and desperation
shall thrust them down into it. We have also, to
effect this so much by us desired design, sent already
three of our trusty Diabolonians among them. They
are disguised in garb, they have changed their names,
and are now accepted of them, to wit, Covetousness,
Lasciviousness and Anger. The name of Covetousness
is changed to Prudent-thrifty; and him Mr. Mind
has hired, and is almost become as bad as our friend.
Lasciviousness has changed his name to Harmless-
mirth, and he is got to be the Lord Willbewill's
lacquey, but he has made his master very wanton.
Anger changed his name into Good-zeal, and was
entertained by Mr. Godlyfear, but the peevish old
gentleman took pepper in the nose and turned our
companion out of his house. Nay, he has informed us
since, that he ran away from him, or else his old
master had hanged him up for his labour.
　　Now these have much helped forward our work
and design upon Mansoul; for notwithstanding the
spite and quarrelsome temper of the old gentleman last
mentioned, the other two play their business well,
and are like to ripen the work apace.
　　Our next project is that it be concluded that you
come upon the town upon a market-day, and that
when they are upon the heat of their business; for
then, to be sure, they will be most secure, and least
think that an assault will be made upon them. They
will also at such a time be less able to defend themselves, and to offend you in the prosecution of our
design. And we your trusty (and we are sure your

*Take heed Man-
soul.*

*Look to it Man-
soul.*

*Take heed Man-
soul.*

23　took pepper in the nose: became vexed, took offence.

*beloved) ones shall, when you shall make your
furious assault without, be ready to second the
business within. So shall we, in all likelihood, be able
to put Mansoul to utter confusion, and to swallow
them up before they can come to themselves. If your
serpentine heads, most subtile dragons, and our
highly esteemed lords can find out a better way than
this, let us quickly know your minds.*

To the monsters of the Infernal Cave from the house
of Mr. Mischief in Mansoul, by the hand of Mr.
Profane.

10

Now all the while that the raging runagates, and
hellish Diabolonians were thus contriving the ruin of
the town of Mansoul, they—to wit, the poor town
The sad state   itself—was in a sad and woeful case, partly because
of Mansoul.   they had so grievously offended Shaddai and his Son,
and partly because that the enemies thereby got
strength within them afresh; and also because, though
they had by many petitions made suit to the Prince
Emmanuel, and to his father Shaddai by him for their   20
pardon and favour, yet hitherto obtained they not one
smile; but contrariwise, through the craft and subtlety of the domestic Diabolonians, their cloud was
made to grow blacker and blacker, and their Emmanuel
to stand at further distance.

The sickness also did still greatly rage in Mansoul, both among the captains and the inhabitants of
the town their enemies, and their enemies only were
now lively and strong, and like to become the head,
whilst Mansoul was made the tail.   30

By this time the letter last mentioned, that was
written by the Diabolonians that yet lurked in the
Profane arrives   town of Mansoul, was conveyed to Diabolus in the
at Hellgate-hill. Black-den, by the hand of Mr. Profane. He carried
the letter by Hellgate-hill as afore, and conveyed it by
Cerberus to his lord.

But when Cerberus and Mr. Profane did meet,
they were presently as great as beggars, and thus they

38   *as great as beggars*: i.e., as thick as thieves.

fell into discourse about Mansoul, and about the project against her.

CERB. 'Ah! old friend,' quoth Cerberus, 'art thou come to Hellgate-hill again! By St. Mary, I am glad to see thee!'

PROF. 'Yes, my lord, I am come again about the concerns of the town of Mansoul.'

CERB. 'Prithee, tell me what condition is that town of Mansoul in at present?'

10 PROF. 'In a brave condition, my lord, for us, and for my lords, the lords of this place, I trow; for they are greatly decayed as to godliness, and that's as well as our heart can wish; their lord is greatly out with them, and that doth also please us well. We have already also a foot in their dish, for our Diabolonian friends are laid in their bosoms, and what do we lack but to be masters of the place?

'Besides, our trusty friends in Mansoul are daily plotting to betray it to the lords of this town; also 20 the sickness rages bitterly among them, and that which makes up all, we hope at last to prevail.'

CERB. Then said the dog of Hellgate, 'No time like this to assault them. I wish that the enterprise be followed close, and that the success desired may be soon effected; yea, I wish it for the poor Diabolonians' sakes that live in the continual fear of their lives in that traitorous town of Mansoul.'

PROF. 'The contrivance is almost finished, the lords in Mansoul that are Diabolonians are at it day and 30 night, and the other are like silly doves: they want heart to be concerned with their state, and to consider that ruin is at hand. Besides, you may, yea, must think when you put all things together, that there are many reasons that prevail with Diabolus to make what haste he can.'

CERB. 'Thou hast said as it is. I am glad things are at this pass. Go in, my brave Profane, to my lords;

Talk between him and Cerberus.

---

4   *By St. Mary*: an ironic sectarian touch, for the oath fixes the pagan Cerberus as a Romanist.

15   *a foot in their dish*: a foot in their camp.

they will give thee for thy welcome as good a coranto as the whole of this kingdom will afford. I have sent thy letter in already.'

Then Mr. Profane went into the den, and his lord Diabolus met him, and saluted him with: 'Welcome, my trusty servant. I have been made glad with thy letter.' The rest of the lords of the Pit gave him also their salutations. Then Profane, after obeisance made to them all, said, 'Let Mansoul be given to my lord Diabolus, and let him be her king for ever.' And with that the hollow belly, and yawning gorge of Hell gave so loud and hideous a groan (for that is the music of that place) that it made the mountains about it totter, as if they would fall in pieces.

Now, after they had read and considered the letter, they consulted what answer to return, and the first that did speak to it was Lucifer.

LUCIF. Then said he, 'The first project of the Diabolonians in Mansoul is like to be lucky, and to take; to wit, that they will by all the ways and means they can, make Mansoul yet more vile and filthy—no way to destroy a soul like this. This is *probatum est*: our old friend Balaam went this way and prospered many years ago. Let this therefore stand with us for a maxim, and be to Diabolonians for a general rule in all ages; for nothing can make this to fail but grace, in which I would hope that this town has no share. But whether to fall upon them on a market-day, because of their cumber in business—that I would

Profane's entertainment.

10

They consult what answer to give to the letter.
Lucifer.
Num. 31:16.
Rev. 2:14.

20

Cumberments are dangerous.

1   *coranto*: lively dance employing a running or gliding step. Shakespeare refers to it in *Henry V*, III, v, 33; and *Twelfth Night*, I, iii, 120: "Why dost thou not go to church in a galliard and come home in a coranto?" (From It. or Sp., ult. f. Fr. *courante*, running [dance].)

22   *probatum est*: a thing that is proved.

23   *Balaam*: Bunyan's allusion, with its marginal gloss, tells only one side of the Balaam story. See Num. 22-24. Balaam is represented there as an almost heroic figure, who blesses Israel in response to God's will, rather than curses her as the king of Moab desires. The point is that the famous wizard is compelled to bow to the greatly superior magic of God's grace—an irresistible power, as his clear-sighted and talkative ass recognises. Perhaps Balaam's poor reputation in the New Testament is to be explained by the interweaving of different traditions within the same account. See James Black, *Rogues of the Bible* (New York, 1930), p. 65.

should be under debate. And there is more reason why this head should be debated, than why some other should, because upon this will turn the whole of what we shall attempt. If we time not our business well, our whole project may fail. Our friends the Diabolonians say that a market-day is best, for then will Mansoul be most busy, and have fewest thoughts of a surprise. But what if also they shall double their guards on those days (and methinks nature and reason should teach them to do it); and what if they should and keep such a watch on those days as the necessity of their present case doth require? Yea, what if their men should be always in arms on those days? Then you may, my lords, be disappointed in your attempts, and may bring our friends in the town to utter danger of unavoidable ruin.'

They had need do it.

BEEL. Then said the great Beelzebub, 'There is something in what my lord hath said, but his conjecture may, or may not fall out. Nor hath my lord laid it down as that which must not be receded from; for I know that he said it only to provoke to a warm debate thereabout. Therefore we must understand, if we can, whether the town of Mansoul has such sense and knowledge of her decayed state, and of the design that we have on foot against her, as doth provoke her to set watch and ward at her gates, and to double them on market-days. But if after enquiry made, it shall be found that they are asleep, then any day will do, but a market-day is best; and this is my judgment in this case.'

A lesson for Christians.

DIAB. Then quoth Diabolus, 'How should we know this?' And 'twas answered, 'Enquire about it at the mouth of Mr. Profane.' So Profane was called in and asked the question, and he made his answer as follows—

PROF. 'My lords, so far as I can gather, this is at present the condition of the town of Mansoul: they are decayed in their faith and love, Emmanuel their Prince has given them the back; they send often by petition to fetch him again, but he maketh not haste to an-

Profane's description of the present state of Mansoul.

198

swer their request, nor is there much reformation among them.'

DIAB. 'I am glad that they are backward to a reformation, but yet I am afraid of their petitioning. However, their looseness of life is a sign that there is not much heart in what they do, and without the heart things are little worth. But, go on, my masters; I will divert you, my lords, no longer.'

BEEL. 'If the case be so with Mansoul, as Mr. Profane has described it to be, 'twill be no great matter what day we assault it; not their prayers, nor their power will do them much service.'

APOLL. When Beelzebub had ended his oration, then Apollyon did begin. 'My opinion,' said he, 'concerning this matter, is that we go on fair and softly, not doing things in an hurry. Let our friends in Mansoul go on still to pollute and defile it, by seeking to draw it yet more into sin, for there is nothing like sin to devour Mansoul. If this be done, and it takes effect, Mansoul of itself will leave off to watch, to petition, or anything else that should tend to her security and safety; for she will forget her Emmanuel, she will not desire his company, and can she be gotten thus to live, her Prince will not come to her in haste. Our trusty friend, Mr. Carnal Security, with one of his tricks did drive him out of the town, and why may not my Lord Covetousness, and my Lord Lasciviousness, by what they may do, keep him out of the town? And this I will tell you (not because you know it not), that two or three Diabolonians, if entertained and countenanced by the town of Mansoul, will do more to the keeping of Emmanuel from them, and towards making of the town of Mansoul your own, than can an army of a legion that should be sent out from us to withstand him.

'Let therefore this first project that our friends in Mansoul have set on foot, be strongly and diligently carried on with all cunning and craft imaginable; and let them send continually under one guise or another, more and other of their men to play with the people of Mansoul; and then perhaps we shall not need to

Dreadful advice against Mansoul.

Dreadful advice against Mansoul.

10

20

30

40

be at the charge of making a war upon them; or if that must of necessity be done, yet the more sinful they are, the more unable, to be sure, they will be to resist us, and then the more easily we shall overcome them. And besides, suppose (and that is the worst that can be supposed) that Emmanuel should come to them again, why may not the same means (or the like) drive him from them once more? Yea, why may he not by their lapse into that sin again be driven from them for ever, for the sake of which he was at the first driven from them for a season? And if this should happen, then away go with him his rams, his slings, his captains, his soldiers, and he leaveth Mansoul naked and bare. Yea, will not this town, when she sees herself utterly forsaken of her Prince, of her own accord open her gates again unto you, and make of you as in the days of old? But this must be done by time—a few days will not effect so great a work as this.'

Dreadful advice against Mansoul.

So soon as Apollyon had made an end of speaking, Diabolus began to blow out his own malice, and to plead his own cause, and he said, 'My Lords and Powers of the Cave, my true and trusty friends, I have with much impatience, as becomes me, given ear to your long and tedious orations. But my furious gorge, and empty paunch, so lusteth after a repossession of my famous town of Mansoul, that whatever comes out I can wait no longer to see the events of lingering projects. I must, and that without further delay, seek by all means I can to fill my insatiable gulf with the soul and body of the town of Mansoul. Therefore lend me your heads, your hearts, and your help, now I am going to recover my town of Mansoul.'

Look to it Mansoul.

When the lords and princes of the Pit saw the flaming desire that was in Diabolus to devour the miserable town of Mansoul, they left off to raise any more objections, but consented to lend him what strength they could: though had Apollyon's advice been taken, they had far more fearfully distressed the town of Mansoul. But, I say, they were willing to lend him what strength they could, not knowing what need they might have of him, when they should engage for themselves, as he. Wherefore, they fell to advising about the next thing propounded, to wit, what soldiers they were, and also how many with whom Diabolus should go against the town of Mansoul to take it. And after some debate it was concluded, according as in the letter the Diabolonians had suggested, that none was more fit for that expedition than an army of terrible Doubters. They therefore concluded to send against Mansoul an army of sturdy Doubters. The number thought fit to be employed in that service, was between twenty and thirty thousand. So then the result of that great counsel of those high and mighty lords was that Diabolus should even now out of hand beat up his drum for men in the land of Doubting (which land lieth upon the confines of the place called Hellgate-hill), for men that might be employed by him against the miserable town of Mansoul. It was also concluded that these lords themselves should help him in the war, and that they would to that end head and manage his men. So they drew up a letter and sent back to the Diabolonians that lurked in Mansoul, and that waited for the backcoming of Mr. Profane, to signify to them into what method and forwardness they at present had put their design. The contents whereof now followeth.

An army of Doubters raised to go against the town of Mansoul.

The princes of the Pit go with them.

10

20

From the dark and horrible dungeon of Hell, Diabolus with all the society of the Princes of Darkness, sends to our trusty ones, in and about the walls of the town of Mansoul, now impatiently waiting for our most devilish answer to their venomous, and most poisonous design against the town of Mansoul.

Another letter from Diabolus to the Diabolonians in Mansoul.

30

Our native ones—in whom from day to day we boast, and in whose actions all the year long we do greatly delight ourselves—we received your welcome, because highly esteemed letter, at the hand of our trusty and greatly beloved, the old gentleman, Mr.

15   *beat up his drum for men:* i.e., recruit.

Profane. And do give you to understand, that when
we had broken it up, and had read the contents
thereof (to your amazing memory be it spoken) our
yawning hollow-bellied place, where we are, made
so hideous and yelling a noise for joy, that the
mountains that stand round about Hellgate-hill, had
like to have been shaken to pieces at the sound
thereof.

    We could also do no less than admire your
faithfulness to us, with the greatness of that subtlety
that now hath showed itself to be in your heads
to serve us against the town of Mansoul. For you
have invented for us so excellent a method for our
proceeding against that rebellious people, a more
effectual cannot be thought of by all the wits of Hell.
The proposals, therefore, which now at last you have
sent us, since we saw them, we have done little else
but highly approved and admired them.

    Nay, we shall to encourage you in the profundity
of your craft, let you know, that at a full assembly
and conclave of our Princes, and Principalities of this
place, your project was discoursed and tossed from
one side of our cave to the other by their Mightinesses,
but a better, and as was by themselves judged, a
more fit and proper way by all their wits could not
be invented to surprise, take, and make our own, the
rebellious town of Mansoul.

    Wherefore, in fine, all that was said that varied
from what you had in your letter propounded, fell
of itself to the ground, and yours was stuck to by
Diabolus the prince; yea, his gaping gorge, and
yawning paunch was on fire to put your invention
into execution.

    We therefore give you to understand that our
stout, furious, and unmerciful Diabolus, is raising
for your relief, and the ruin of the rebellious town of
Mansoul more than twenty thousand Doubters to
come against that people. They are all stout and

10

20

30

2   *broken it up*: opened it.
3   *memory*: fame, reputation.

sturdy men, and men that of old have been accustomed
to war, and that can therefore well endure the
drum. I say he is doing of this work of his with all
the possible speed he can; for his heart and spirit is
engaged in it. We desire, therefore, that as you have
hitherto stuck to us, and given us both advice and
encouragement thus far, that you still will prosecute
our design, nor shall you lose but be gainers thereby;
yea, we intend to make you the lords of Mansoul.

One thing may not by any means be omitted,   10
that is, those with us do desire that every one of you
that are in Mansoul would still use all your power,
cunning and skill, with delusive persuasions, yet to
draw the town of Mansoul into more sin and wickedness, even that sin may be finished and bring forth
death.

For thus it is concluded with us, that the more
vile, sinful, and debauched the town of Mansoul is,
the more backward will be their Emmanuel to come
to their help, either by presence, or other relief;   20
yea, the more sinful, the more weak, and so the more
unable will they be to make resistance when we shall
make our assault upon them to swallow them up.
Yea, that may cause that their mighty Shaddai
himself may cast them out of his protection; yea,
and send for his captains and soldiers home, with his
slings and rams, and leave them naked and bare,
Take heed Man- and then the town of Mansoul will of itself open
soul. to us, and fall as the fig into the mouth of the eater.
Yea, to be sure that we then with a great deal   30
of ease shall come upon her and overcome her.

As to the time of our coming upon Mansoul, we
as yet have not fully resolved upon that, though at
present some of us think as you, that a market-day,
or a market-day at night will certainly be the best.

2f.   *endure the drum*: stand up to the rigours of military service. Bunyan uses
the phrase elsewhere: "It is for want of hope (a sound scriptural hope,
arising from faith, and its purifying effects upon the soul), that so many
brisk professors, that have so boasted and made brags of their faith, have not
been able to endure the drum in the day of alarm and affliction." (*Israel's
Hope Encouraged*, in *Works*, ed. Offor, I, 580.)

However do you be ready, and when you shall hear   I Pet. 5:8.
our roaring drum without, do you be as busy to make
the most horrible confusion within. So shall Mansoul
certainly be distressed before and behind, and shall
not know which way to betake herself for help. My
Lord Lucifer, my Lord Beelzebub, my Lord Apollyon,
my Lord Legion, with the rest, salute you, as does
also my Lord Diabolus, and we wish both you, with all
that you do or shall possess, the very self-same
10   *fruit and success for their doing, as we ourselves at*
present enjoy for ours.

From our dreadful confines in the most fearful Pit,
we salute you, and so do those many legions here
with us, wishing you may be as hellishly prosperous
as we desire to be ourselves. By the letter-carrier,
Mr. Profane.

Then Mr. Profane addressed himself for his return to Mansoul, with his errand from the horrible
Pit to the Diabolonians that dwelt in that town. So
20   he came up the stairs from the deep to the mouth of
the cave, where Cerberus was. Now when Cerberus   More talk be-
saw him, he asked how matters did go below, about,   tween Profane
and against the town of Mansoul.   and Cerberus.
PROF. 'Things go as well as we can expect. The
letter that I carried thither was highly approved, and
well liked by all my lords, and I am returning to tell
our Diabolonians so. I have an answer to it here in
my bosom, that I am sure will make our masters that
sent me glad; for the contents thereof is to encourage
30   them to pursue their design to the utmost, and to be
ready also to fall on within, when they shall see my
lord Diabolus beleaguring of the town of Mansoul.'
CERB. 'But does he intend to go against them himself?'
PROF. 'Does he! Ay, and he will take along with
him more than twenty thousand, all sturdy Doubters,   The land from
and men of war, picked men from the land of Doubt-   the which the
ing, to serve him in the expedition.'   Doubters come.
CERB. Then was Cerberus glad, and said, 'And is

there such brave preparations a-making to go against the miserable town of Mansoul? And would I might be put at the head of a thousand of them, that I might also show my valour against the famous town of Mansoul!'

PROF. 'Your wish may come to pass. You look like one that has mettle enough, and my lord will have with him those that are valiant and stout. But my business requires haste.'

CERB. 'Ay, so it does. Speed thee to the town of Mansoul, with all the deepest mischiefs that this place can afford thee. And when thou shalt come to the house of Mr. Mischief, the place where the Diabolonians meet to plot, tell them that Cerberus doth wish them his service, and that if he may, he will with the army come up against the famous town of Mansoul.'

PROF. 'That I will. And I know that my lords that are there, will be glad to hear it, and to see you also.'

So after a few more such kind of compliments, Mr. Profane took his leave of his friend Cerberus, and Cerberus again with a thousand of their pit-wishes, bid him haste with all speed to his masters. The which when he had heard, he made obeisance, and began to gather up his heels to run.

Thus therefore he returned, and went and came to Mansoul, and going as afore to the house of Mr. Mischief, there he found the Diabolonians assembled, and waiting for his return. Now when he was come, and had presented himself, he also delivered to them his letter, and adjoined this compliment to them therewith, 'My lords from the confines of the Pit, the high and mighty principalities and powers of the den salute you here, the true Diabolonians of the town of Mansoul. Wishing you always the most proper of their benedictions, for the great service, high attempts, and brave achievements that you have put yourselves upon, for the restoring to our prince Diabolus the famous town of Mansoul.'

This was therefore the present state of the miserable town of Mansoul. She had offended her Prince, and he was gone; she had encouraged the powers of

Profane return-
ed again to
Mansoul.

10

20

30

40

Hell by her foolishness, to come against her to seek her utter destruction.

True, the town of Mansoul was somewhat made sensible of her sin, but the Diabolonians were gotten into her bowels; she cried, but Emmanuel was gone, and her cries did not fetch him as yet again. Besides, she knew not now whether ever or never, he would return and come to his Mansoul again; nor did they know the power and industry of the enemy, nor how forward they were to put in execution that plot of Hell that they had devised against her.

They did indeed still send petition after petition to the Prince, but he answered all with silence. They did neglect reformation, and that was as Diabolus would have it, for he knew, if they regarded iniquity in their heart, their King would not hear their prayer; they therefore did still grow weaker and weaker, and were as a rolling thing before the whirlwind. They cried to their King for help, and laid Diabolonians in their bosoms: what therefore should a King do to them? Yea, there seemed now to be a mixture in Mansoul: the Diabolonians and the Mansoulians would walk the streets together. Yea, they began to seek their peace, for they thought that since the sickness had been so mortal in Mansoul, 'twas in vain to go to handigripes with them. Besides, the weakness of Mansoul was the strength of their enemies; and the sins of Mansoul the advantage of the Diabolonians. The foes of Mansoul did also now begin to promise themselves the town for a possession. There was no great difference now betwixt Mansoulians and Diabolonians: both seemed to be masters of Mansoul. Yea, the Diabolonians increased and grew, but the town of Mansoul diminished greatly. There was more than eleven thousand of men, women and children that died by the sickness in Mansoul.

But now, as Shaddai would have it, there was one whose name was Mr. Prywell, a great lover of the people of Mansoul. And he, as his manner was, did

Good thoughts. Good conceptions, and good desires.

25f.   *to go to handigripes*: to engage in hand-to-hand combat.

go list'ning up and down in Mansoul to see and to
hear, if at any time he might, whether there was any
design against it or no. For he was always a jealous
man, and feared some mischief sometime would befall
it, either from the Diabolonians within, or from some
power without. Now upon a time it so happened as
Mr. Prywell went list'ning here and there, that he
lighted upon a place called Vile-hill in Mansoul, where
Diabolonians used to meet; so hearing a muttering
(you must know that it was in the night), he softly
drew near to hear. Nor had he stood long under the
house-end (for there stood a house there), but he
heard one confidently affirm that it was not or would
not be long before Diabolus should possess himself
again of Mansoul, and that then the Diabolonians did
intend to put all Mansoulians to the sword, and would
kill and destroy the King's captains, and drive all his
soldiers out of the town.

He said, moreover, that he knew there were above
twenty thousand fighting men prepared by Diabolus
for the accomplishing of this design, and that it would
not be months before they all should see it. When Mr.
Prywell had heard this story, he did quickly believe it
was true; wherefore he went forthwith to my Lord
Mayor's house, and acquainted him therewith—who,
sending for the Subordinate Preacher, brake the business to him, and he as soon gave the alarm to the
town, for he was now the chief preacher in Mansoul,
because as yet my Lord Secretary was ill at ease. And
this was the way that the Subordinate Preacher did
take to alarm the town therewith. The same hour he
caused the lecture-bell to be rung; so the people came
together; he gave them then a short exhortation to
watchfulness, and made Mr. Prywell's news the argument thereof. 'For,' said he, 'an horrible plot is con-
trived against Mansoul even to massacre us all in a
day; nor is this story to be slighted, for Mr. Prywell
is the author thereof. Mr. Prywell was always a lover

*The story of
Mr. Prywell.*

*The Diabolonian
plot discovered,
and by whom.*

*Understanding,
Conscience.*

*The Subordinate
Preacher awak-
ened.*

10

20

30

3   *jealous*: suspiciously vigilant.
26   *brake*: disclosed.

of Mansoul, a sober and judicious man, a man that is
no tattler, nor raiser of false reports, but one that loves
to look into the very bottom of matters, and talks
nothing of news but by very solid arguments. I will
call him, and you shall hear him your own selves.'

So he called him, and he came and told his tale so   Prywell tells
punctually, and affirmed its truth with such ample   his news to
grounds, that Mansoul fell presently under a convic-   Mansoul.
tion of the truth of what he said. The preacher did
10   also back him, saying, 'Sirs, it is not irrational for us
to believe it, for we have provoked Shaddai to anger,
and have sinned Emmanuel out of the town; we have
had too much correspondence with Diabolonians, and
have forsaken our former mercies; no marvel, then, if
the enemy both within and without should design and
plot our ruin; and what time like this to do it? The
sickness is now in the town, and we have been made
weak thereby. Many a good-meaning man is dead, and
the Diabolonians of late grow stronger and stronger.   Good desires.
20   'Besides,' quoth the Subordinate Preacher, 'I have
received from this good truth-teller this one inkling
further, that he understood by those that he over-   They take the
heard, that several letters have lately passed between   alarm.
the Furies and the Diabolonians in order to our destruction.' When Mansoul heard all this, and not
being able to gainsay it, they lift up their voice and
wept. Mr. Prywell did also, in the presence of the
townsmen, confirm all that their Subordinate Preacher
had said. Wherefore they now set afresh to bewail
30   their folly, and to a doubling of petitions to Shaddai
and his Son. They also brake the business to the captains, high commanders, and men of war in the town
of Mansoul, entreating of them to use the means to
be strong, and to take good courage, and that they
would look after their harness, and make themselves
ready to give Diabolus battle by night and by day,   They tell the
shall he come, as they are inform'd he will, to be-   thing to the
leaguer the town of Mansoul.   captains.

When the captains heard this, they being always

6f. *so punctually*: in such detail.

true lovers of the town of Mansoul, what do they but like so many Samsons they shake themselves, and come together to consult and contrive how to defeat those bold and hellish contrivances that were upon the wheel by the means of Diabolus and his friends against the now sickly, weakly, and much impoverished town of Mansoul; and they agreed upon these following particulars:

1. That the gates of Mansoul should be kept shut, and made fast with bars and locks, and that all persons that went out, or came in, should be very strictly examined by the captains of the guards. To the end, said they, that those that are managers of the plot amongst us, may either coming or going be taken; and that we may also find out who are the great contrivers amongst us of our ruin.

2. The next thing was that a strict search should be made for all kind of Diabolonians throughout the whole town of Mansoul; and that every man's house from top to bottom should be looked into, and that too, house by house, that if possible a further discovery might be made of all such among them as had a hand in these designs.

3. It was further concluded upon, that wheresoever or with whomsoever any of the Diabolonians were found, that even those of the town of Mansoul that had given them house and harbour should, to their shame and the warning of others, take penance in the open place.

4. It was moreover resolved by the famous town of Mansoul, that a public fast, and a day of humiliation should be kept throughout the whole corporation to the justifying of their Prince, the abasing of themselves before him for their transgressions against him, and against Shaddai his Father. It was further resolved that all such in Mansoul as did not on that day endeavour to keep that fast, and to humble themselves for their faults, but that should mind their worldly employs, or be found wand'ring up and down the

Marginal notes:

They come together to consult.

Their agreement. I Cor. 16:13.

Lam. 3:40.

Heb. 12:15,16.

Jer. 2:34; 5:26. Ezek. 16:52.

Joel 1:14; 2:15, 16.

---

4   *upon the wheel*: possibly an allusion to the wheel of Fortune.

streets, should be taken for Diabolonians, and should suffer as Diabolonians for such their wicked doings.

5. It was further concluded then that with what speed, and with what warmth of mind they could, they would renew their humiliation for sin, and their petitions to Shaddai for help; they also resolved to send tidings to the court of all that Mr. Prywell had told them.

Jer. 37:4.

6. It was also determined that thanks should be given by the town of Mansoul to Mr. Prywell for his diligent seeking of the welfare of their town; and further, that forasmuch as he was so naturally inclined to seek their good, and also to undermine their foes, they gave him a commission of Scoutmaster-General, for the good of the town of Mansoul.

Mr. Prywell is made Scout-master-General.

When the corporation with their captains had thus concluded, they did as they had said. They shut up their gates, they made for Diabolonians strict search, they made those with whom any was found to take penance in the open place. They kept their fast, and renewed their petitions to their Prince; and Mr. Prywell managed his charge and the trust that Mansoul had put in his hands with great conscience, and good fidelity; for he gave himself wholly up to his employ, and that not only within the town, but he went out to pry, to see, and to hear.

Mr. Prywell goes a-scouting.

And not many days after he provided for his journey, and went towards Hellgate-hill into the country where the Doubters were, where he heard of all that had been talked of in Mansoul, and he perceived also that Diabolus was almost ready for his march, etc.; so he came back with speed, and calling the captains and elders of Mansoul together, he told them where he had been, what he had heard, and what he had seen.

Particularly he told them that Diabolus was almost ready for his march, and that he had made old Mr. Incredulity that once brake prison in Mansoul, the general of his army; that his army consisted all of Doubters, and that their number was above twenty thousand. He told, moreover, that Diabolus did intend

He returns with great news.

to bring with him the chief Princes of the Infernal
Pit, and that he would make them chief captains over
his Doubters. He told them, moreover, that it was
certainly true that several of the Black-den would
with Diabolus ride reformades to reduce the town of
Mansoul to the obedience of Diabolus their prince.

He said, moreover, that he understood by the
Doubters among whom he had been, that the reason
why old Incredulity was made general of the whole
army, was because none truer than he to the tyrant;
and because he had an implacable spite against the
welfare of the town of Mansoul. 'Besides,' said he, 'he
remembers the affronts that Mansoul has given, and
he is resolved to be revenged of them.

'But the black princes shall be made high commanders—only Incredulity shall be over them all, because (which I had almost forgot), he can more easily,
and more dext'rously beleaguer the town of Mansoul,
than can any of the princes besides.'

Now when the captains of Mansoul with the
elders of the town, had heard the tidings that Mr.
Prywell did bring, they thought it expedient without
further delay to put into execution the laws that
against the Diabolonians, their Prince had made for
them, and given them in commandment to manage
against them. Wherefore, forthwith a diligent and
impartial search was made in all houses in Mansoul
for all and all manner of Diabolonians. Now in the
house of Mr. Mind, and in the house of the great
Lord Willbewill were two Diabolonians found. In Mr.
Mind's house was one Lord Covetousness found, but
he had changed his name to Prudent-thrifty. In my
Lord Willbewill's house, one Lasciviousness was found;
but he had changed his name to Harmless-mirth. These
two the captains and elders of the town of Mansoul
took, and committed them to custody under the hand
of Mr. Trueman, the gaoler; and this man handled
them so severely, and loaded them so well with irons,
that in time they both fell into a very deep consumption, and died in the prison-house; their masters also,
according to the agreement of the captains and elders,

Heb. 12:1.

Some Diabolon-
ians taken in
Mansoul and
committed to
prison.

10

20

30

40

were brought to take penance in the open place to their shame, and for a warning to the rest of the town of Mansoul.

The Lord Will-bewill and Mr. Mind take penance.

Now this was the manner of penance in those days. The persons offending being made sensible of the evil of their doings, were enjoined open confession of their faults, and a strict amendment of their lives.

Penance what.

After this the captains and elders of Mansoul sought yet to find out more Diabolonians, where ever they lurked, whether in dens, caves, holes, vaults, or where else they could, in, or about the wall or town of Mansoul. But though they could plainly see their footing, and so follow them by their tract and smell to their holds, even to the mouths of their caves and dens, yet take them, hold them, and do justice upon them they could not; their ways were so crooked, their holds so strong, and they so quick to take sanctuary there.

But Mansoul did now with so stiff an hand rule over the Diabolonians that were left, that they were glad to shrink into corners. Time was when they durst walk openly, and in the day, but now they were forced to embrace privacy and the night; time was when a Mansoulian was their companion, but now they counted them deadly enemies. This good change did Mr. Prywell's intelligence make in the famous town of Mansoul.

By this time Diabolus had finished his army which he intended to bring with him for the ruin of Mansoul, and had set over them captains, and other field-officers, such as liked his furious stomach best. Himself was lord paramount; Incredulity was general of his army. Their highest captains shall be named afterwards, but now for their officers, colours and scutcheons.

Diabolus's army.

1. Their first captain was Captain Rage. He was Captain over the Election-Doubters; his were the red colours, his standard-bearer was Mr. Destructive, and

---

31   *such as liked his furious stomach best*: who most appealed to his over-passionate temperament.

Rev. 12:3,4,13,
15,17.

Num. 21:6.

Matt. 22:13.
Rev. 9:1.

Prov. 27:20.

Ps. 11:6.
Rev. 14:11.

Mark 9:44,46,
48.

Rev. 4:11; 6:8.

Jer. 5:16; 2:25.

I Tim. 4:2.
Rom. 2:5.

the great red dragon he had for his scutcheon.

2. The second captain was Captain Fury. He was captain over the Vocation-Doubters; his standard-bearer was Mr. Darkness, his colours were those that were pale, and he had for his scutcheon the fiery flying serpent.

3. The third captain was Captain Damnation. He was captain over the Grace-Doubters; his were the red colours, Mr. No-life bare them, and he had for his scutcheon the black den.

4. The fourth captain was the Captain Insatiable. He was captain over the Faith-Doubters; his were the red colours, Mr. Devourer bare them, and he had for a scutcheon the yawning jaws.

5. The fifth captain was Captain Brimstone. He was captain over the Perseverance-Doubters; his also were the red colours, Mr. Burning bare them, and his scutcheon was the blue and stinking flame.

6. The sixth captain was Captain Torment. He was captain over the Resurrection-Doubters; his colours were those that were pale, Mr. Gnaw was his ancient-bearer, and he had the black worm for his scutcheon.

7. The seventh captain was Captain No-ease. He was captain over the Salvation-Doubters; his were the red colours, Mr. Restless bare them, and his scutcheon was the ghastly picture of death.

8. The eighth captain was the Captain Sepulchre. He was captain over the Glory-Doubters; his also were the pale colours, Mr. Corruption was his ancient-bearer, and he had for his scutcheon a skull, and dead men's bones.

9. The ninth captain was Captain Past-hope. He was captain of those that are called the Felicity-Doubters; his ancient-bearer was Mr. Despair; his also were the red colours, and his scutcheon was the hot iron, and the hard heart.

These were his captains, and these were their forces, these were their ancients, these were their

10

20

30

8gl. The first edition glosses "Matt. 3.22, 13," an obvious error, exacerbated by the third edition which has "Matt. 3.22, 23." We follow the sensible gloss of the second edition.

colours, and these were their scutcheons. Now over these did the great Diabolus make superior captains, and they were in number seven: as, namely, the Lord Beelzebub, the Lord Lucifer, the Lord Legion, the Lord Apollyon, the Lord Python, the Lord Cerberus, and the Lord Belial; these seven he set over the captains, and Incredulity was Lord General, and Diabolus was King.

The reformades also, such as were like themselves, were made some of them captains of hundreds, and some of them captains of more: and thus was the army of Incredulity completed.

So they set out at Hellgate-hill (for there they had their rendezvous), from whence they came with a straight course upon their march toward the town of Mansoul. Now as was hinted before, the town had, as Shaddai would have it, received from the mouth of Mr. Prywell the alarm of their coming before. Wherefore they set a strong watch at the gates, and had also doubled their guards; they also mounted their slings in good places where they might conveniently cast out their great stones to the annoyance of the furious enemy.

Nor could those Diabolonians that were in the town do that hurt as was designed they should; for Mansoul was now awake. But, alas; poor people, they were sorely affrighted at the first appearance of their foes, and at their sitting down before the town, especially when they heard the roaring of their DRUM. This, to speak truth, was amazingly hideous to hear.

Diabolus his army completed.

10

20

1   A descriptive catalogue that constitutes another satanic parody of Emmanuel's host.

6   Of the seven (the number agrees with the great and fearsome arithmetic of Revelation), two have not previously been noted. (1) *Python* is the name of a monstrous serpent hatched from the mud left by Deucalion's deluge. Living in the caves of Parnassus, it devastated the region about Delphi, until slain by Apollo, who won from his victory the title of Pythius (see Ovid, *Metamorphoses*, I, 432-51) and later the institution of the Pythian games. (2) *Belial*, a Hebrew word for "worthlessness," is used as a proper name in the O.T. of the King James Bible (following the Vulgate) to denote the wicked: see Deut. 13:13; Judg. 19:22; I Sam. 1:16, etc. In II Cor. 6:15, the name has become a synonym for the Devil: "And what concord hath Christ with Belial?" The heathen deity is nowhere incarnated so well as in *Paradise Lost*, where he appears as one of Milton's most brilliant creations.

I Pet. 5:8.

It frighted all men seven miles round if they were but awake and heard it. The streaming of their colours were also terrible, and dejecting to behold.

When Diabolus was come up against the town, first he made his approach to Eargate, and gave it a furious assault, supposing as it seems that his friends in Mansoul had been ready to do the work within; but care was taken of that before, by the vigilance of the captains. Wherefore missing of the help that he expected from them, and finding of his army warmly attended with the stones that the slingers did sling (for that I will say for the captains, that considering the weakness that yet was upon them by reason of the long sickness that had annoyed the town of Mansoul, they did gallantly behave themselves), he was forced to make some retreat from Mansoul, and to entrench himself and his men in the field without the reach of the slings of the town.

He makes an assault upon Eargate, and is repelled.

Jas. 4:7.
He retreats and entrenches himself.

Now having entrenched himself, he did cast up four mounts against the town: the first he called Mount Diabolus, putting his own name thereon, the more to affright the town of Mansoul; the other three he called thus, Mount Alecto, Mount Megaera, and Mount Tisiphone; for these are the names of the dreadful Furies of Hell. Thus he began to play his game with Mansoul, and to serve it as doth the lion his prey, even to make it fall before his terror. But, as I said, the captains and soldiers resisted so stoutly, and did do such execution with their stones, that they made him, though against stomach, to retreat; wherefore Mansoul began to take courage.

He casts up mounts against the town.

Now upon Mount Diabolus, which was raised on the North side of the town, there did the tyrant set up his standard, and a fearful thing it was to behold; for he had wrought in it by devilish art, after the man-

Diabolus his standard set up.

10f. *warmly attended*: under heavy attack.
22ff. Alecto and Tisiphone are thus given a double role in the action: see notes on pp. 12 and 14. The addition of Magaera here completes the vengeful trinity.
30 *against stomach*: against his wishes.
33 *the North side*: Bunyan is here invoking a long literary tradition that associates the North with the Devil and that ultimately derives from Isaiah's

ner of a scutcheon, a flaming flame fearful to behold, and the picture of Mansoul burning in it.

When Diabolus had thus done, he commanded that his drummer should every night approach the walls of the town of Mansoul, and so to beat a parley; the command was to do it a-nights, for in the day time they annoyed him with their slings; for the tyrant said that he had a mind to parley with the now trembling town of Mansoul, and he commanded that the drums should beat every night, that through weariness they might at last (if possibly, at the first they were unwilling yet), be forced to do it.

He bids his drummer to beat his drum.

So this drummer did as commanded: he arose and did beat his drum. But when his drum did go, if one looked toward the town of Mansoul, *behold, darkness and sorrow, and the light was darkened in the heaven thereof.* No noise was ever heard upon earth more terrible, except the voice of Shaddai when he speaketh. But how did Mansoul tremble! It now looked for nothing but forthwith to be swallowed up.

Mansoul trembles at the noise of his drum. Isa. 5:30.

When this drummer had beaten for a parley, he made this speech to Mansoul: 'My master has bid me tell you that if you will willingly submit, you shall have the good of the earth; but if you shall be stubborn, he is resolved to take you by force.' But by that the fugitive had done beating of his drum, the people of Mansoul had betaken themselves to the captains that were in the castle, so that there was none to regard, nor to give this drummer an answer; so he proceeded no further that night, but returned again to his master to the camp.

Diabolus calls back his drum.

When Diabolus saw that by drumming he could not work out Mansoul to his will, the next night he sendeth his drummer without his drum still to let the townsmen know that he had a mind to parley with them. But when all came to all, his parley was turned

---

account of how Lucifer aspired to exalt himself "above the stars of God" by sitting "upon the mount of the congregation, in the sides of the north" (14:13).

26 *fugitive*: one who moves from place to place; a vagabond.
36 *when all came to all*: when all was done.

into a summons to the town to deliver up themselves; but they gave him neither heed nor hearing, for they rememb'red what at first it cost them to hear him a few words.

The next night he sends again, and then who should be his messenger to Mansoul but the terrible Captain Sepulchre? So Captain Sepulchre came up to the walls of Mansoul, and made this oration to the town:

Mansoul summoned by Captain Sepulchre.

'O ye inhabitants of the rebellious town of Mansoul! I summon you in the name of the prince Diabolus, that without any more ado, you set open the gates of your town, and admit the great lord to come in. But if you shall still rebel, when we have taken to us the town by force, we will swallow you up as the grave; wherefore, if you will hearken to my summons, say so, and if not, then let me know.

'The reason of this my summons,' quoth he, 'is, for that my lord is your undoubted prince and lord, as you yourselves have formerly owned. Nor shall that assault that was given to my lord, when Emmanuel dealt so dishonourably by him, prevail with him to lose his right, and to forbear to attempt to recover his own. Consider then, O Mansoul, with thyself, wilt thou show thyself peaceable, or no? If thou shalt quietly yield up thyself, then our old friendship shall be renewed; but if thou shalt yet refuse and rebel, then expect nothing but fire and sword.'

When the languishing town of Mansoul had heard this summoner, and his summons, they were yet more put to their dumps, but made to the captain no answer at all; so away he went as he came.

They answer him not a word.

But after some consultation among themselves, as also with some of their captains, they applied themselves afresh to the Lord Secretary for counsel and advice from him; for this Lord Secretary was their chief preacher (as also is mentioned some pages before), only now he was ill at ease; and of him they begged favour in these two or three things:

They address themselves to their good Lord Secretary.

10

20

30

1. That he would look comfortably upon them, and not keep himself so much retired from them as formerly. Also that he would be prevailed with to give them a hearing while they should make known their miserable condition to him. But to this he told them, as before, that as yet he was but ill at ease, and therefore could not do as he had formerly done.

2. The second thing that they desired was that he would be pleased to give them his advice about their now so important affairs, for that Diabolus was come and set down before the town with no less than twenty thousand Doubters. They said, moreover, that both he and his captains were cruel men, and that they were afraid of them. But to this he said, 'You must look to the law of the Prince, and there see what is laid upon you to do.'

3. Then they desired that his Highness would help them to frame a petition to Shaddai, and unto Emmanuel his Son, and that he would set his own hand thereto as a token that he was one with them in it: 'For,' said they, 'my lord, many a one have we sent, but can get no answer of peace; but now surely one with thy hand unto it, may obtain good for Mansoul.'

But all the answer that he gave to this was that they had offended their Emmanuel, and had also grieved himself, and that therefore they must as yet partake of their own devices.

The cause of his being ill at ease.

This answer of the Lord Secretary fell like a millstone upon them; yea, it crushed them so that they could not tell what to do, yet they durst not comply with the demands of Diabolus, nor with the demands of his captain. So then here were the straits that the town of Mansoul was betwixt, when the enemy came upon her. Her foes were ready to swallow her up, and her friends did forbear to help her.

Lam. 1:3. The sad straits of Mansoul.

Then stood up my Lord Mayor, whose name was my Lord Understanding, and he began to pick and pick, until he had picked comfort out of that seem-

---

1 *look comfortably*: i.e., in a manner that would give them comfort.

ingly bitter saying of the Lord Secretary; for thus he
descanted upon it: 'First,' said he, 'this unavoidably
follows upon the saying of my Lord, that we must yet
suffer for our sins. 2. But,' quoth he, 'the words yet
sound as if at last we should be saved from our
enemies, and that after a few more sorrows Emmanuel
will come and be our help.' Now the Lord Mayor was
the more critical in his dealing with the Secretary's
words, because my lord was more than a prophet, and
because none of his words were such, but that at all
times they were most exactly significant, and the
townsmen were allowed to pry into them, and to
expound them to their best advantage.

So they took their leaves of my Lord, and returned, and went, and came to the captains, to whom
they did tell what my Lord High Secretary had said,
who, when they had heard it, were all of the same
opinion as was my Lord Mayor himself. The captains,
therefore, began to take some courage unto them, and
to prepare to make some brave attempt upon the camp
of the enemy, and to destroy all that were Diabolonians, with the roving Doubters that the tyrant had
brought with him to destroy the poor town of Mansoul.

So all betook themselves forthwith to their places
—the captains to theirs, the Lord Mayor to his, the
Subordinate Preacher to his, and my Lord Willbewill
to his. The captains longed to be at some work for
their Prince, for they delighted in warlike achievements. The next day, therefore, they came together
and consulted, and after consultation had, they resolved to give an answer to the captain of Diabolus
with slings; and so they did at the rising of the sun
on the morrow; for Diabolus had adventured to come
nearer again, but the sling-stones were to him and his
like hornets. For as there is nothing to the town of
Mansoul so terrible as the roaring of Diabolus's drum,

so there is nothing to Diabolus so terrible as the well
playing of Emmanuel's slings. Wherefore Diabolus
was forced to make another retreat, yet further off
from the famous town of Mansoul. Then did the Lord

Mayor of Mansoul cause the bells to be rung, and that thanks should be sent to the Lord High Secretary by the mouth of the Subordinate Preacher; for that by his words the captains and elders of Mansoul had been strengthened against Diabolus.

When Diabolus saw that his captains and soldiers, high lords, and renowned, were frightened and beaten down by the stones that came from the golden slings of the Prince of the town of Mansoul, he bethought himself, and said, 'I will try to catch them by fawning; I will try to flatter them into my net.'

Wherefore, after a while he came down again to the wall, not now with his drum, nor with Captain Sepulchre, but having all-to-be-sugared his lips, he seemed to be a very sweet-mouthed, peaceable prince, designing nothing for humour's sake, nor to be revenged on Mansoul for injuries by them done to him; but the welfare, and good, and advantage of the town and people therein, was now, as he said, his only design. Wherefore, after he had called for audience, and desired that the townsfolk would give it to him, he proceeded in this oration, and said:

'O! the desire of my heart, the famous town of Mansoul! How many nights have I watched, and how many weary steps have I taken, if perhaps I might do thee good! Far be it, far be it from me to desire to make a war upon you; if ye will but willingly and quietly deliver up yourselves unto me. You know that you were mine of old. Remember also, that so long as you enjoyed me for your lord, and that I enjoyed you for my subjects, you wanted for nothing of all the delights of the earth, that I your lord and prince could get for you; or that I could invent to make you bonny and blithe withal. Consider, you never had so many hard, dark, troublesome and heart-afflicting hours, while you were mine, as you have had since you revolted from me; nor shall you ever have peace

Marginal notes:

Diabolus changes his way.

I Pet. 5:8.
Rev. 12:10.

Matt. 4:8.
Luke 4:6,7.

Satan reads all backwards.

14   *all-to-be-sugared*: completely sweetened. The formation *all to*, employed as an intensive, is quite often attached to seventeenth-century verbs, particularly to those prefixed by *be*.

16   *for humour's sake*: out of capriciousness, for a mere whim.

220

Take heed Man-
soul.

Sins.

The pleasure of
sin.

No, no, no, not
upon pain of
eternal damna-
tion.

again until you and I become one as before. But be but
prevailed with to embrace me again, and I will grant,
yea enlarge your old charter with abundance of privileges; so that your licence and liberty shall be to take,
hold, enjoy, and make your own all that is pleasant
from the East to the West. Nor shall any of those
incivilities wherewith you have offended me, be ever
charged upon you by me, so long as the sun and
moon endureth. Nor shall any of those dear friends of
mine that now for the fear of you, lie lurking in dens,   10
and holes, and caves in Mansoul, be hurtful to you
any more; yea, they shall be your servants, and shall
minister unto you of their substance, and of whatever
shall come to hand. I need speak no more; you know
them, and have sometime since been much delighted
in their company. Why then should we abide at such
odds? Let us renew our old acquaintance and friendship again.

'Bear with your friend; I take the liberty at this
time to speak thus freely unto you. The love that I   20
have to you presses me to do it, as also does the zeal of
my heart for my friends with you: put me not therefore to further trouble, nor yourselves to further fears
and frights. Have you I will in a way of peace or war;
nor do you flatter yourselves with the power and force
of your captains, or that your Emmanuel will shortly
come in to your help; for such strength will do you
no pleasure.

'I am come against you with a stout and valiant
army, and all the chief princes of the den are even at   30
the head of it. Besides, my captains are swifter than
eagles, stronger than lions, and more greedy of prey
than are the evening wolves. What is Og of Bashan?
What's Goliath of Gath? And what's an hundred

33   Og, king of Bashan, was a legendary giant of Rabbinical tradition. An ante-
diluvian much too gross to embark with Noah, Og escaped the deluge only
by climbing on top of the ark, where his rations were served to him through
a hole in the roof. (See Sir James Frazer, *Folk-Lore in the Old Testament*
[London, 1919], I, 144-45.) His eventual defeat by Moses at Edrei made a
considerable imaginative impact on the Jews, and it was commemorated by
them as one of the most striking exploits in their history. See. Deut. 3:1-13;
Josh. 9:10; Neh. 9:22; Pss. 135:11, 136:20.

more of them to one of the least of my captains? How then shall Mansoul think to escape my hand and force?'

Diabolus having thus ended his flattering, fawning, deceitful and lying speech to the famous town of Mansoul, the Lord Mayor replied upon him as follows:

'O Diabolus, prince of darkness, and master of all deceit! Thy lying flatteries we have had and made sufficient probation of, and have tasted too deeply of that destructive cup already. Should we therefore again hearken unto thee, and so break the commandments of our great Shaddai, to join in affinity with thee, would not our Prince reject us, and cast us off for ever? And being cast off by him, can the place that he has prepared for thee be a place of rest for us? Besides, thou art empty and void of all truth; we are rather ready to die by thy hand than to fall in with thy flattering and lying deceits.' *The Lord Mayor's answer.*

When the tyrant saw that there was little to be got by parleying with my Lord Mayor, he fell into an hellish rage, and resolved that again with his army of Doubters he would another time assault the town of Mansoul.

So he called for his drummer, who beat up for his men (and while he did beat, Mansoul did shake) to be in a readiness to give battle to the corporation; then Diabolus drew near with his army, and thus disposed of his men. Captain Cruel, and Captain Torment, these he drew up and placed against Feelgate, and commanded them to sit down there for the war. And he also appointed, that if need were, Captain No-ease should come in to their relief. At Nosegate he placed the Captain Brimstone, and Captain Sepulchre, and bid them look well to their ward, on that side of the town of Mansoul. But at Eyegate he placed that grim-faced one, the Captain Pasthope, and there also now he did set up his terrible standard. *Feelgate.* *Nosegate.* *Eyegate.*

Now Captain Insatiable, he was to look to the carriages of Diabolus, and was also appointed to take into custody, that, or those persons and things, that should at any time as prey be taken from the enemy.

222

Now Mouthgate the inhabitants of Mansoul kept
for a sally-port; wherefore that they kept strong, for
that was it, by, and out at which the townsfolk did
send their petitions to Emmanuel, their Prince. That
also was the gate from the top of which the captains
did play their slings at the enemies; for that gate
stood somewhat ascending, so that the placing of them
there, and the letting of them fly from that place did
much execution against the tyrant's army; wherefore
for these causes with others, Diabolus sought, if pos- **10**
sible, to land up Mouthgate with dirt.

Now as Diabolus was busy and industrious in
preparing to make his assault upon the town of Mansoul without, so the captains and soldiers in the
corporation were as busy in preparing within; they
mounted their slings, they set up their banners, they
sounded their trumpets, and put themselves in such
order as was judged most for the annoyance of the
enemy, and for the advantage of Mansoul, and gave
to their soldiers orders to be ready at the sound of the **20**
trumpet for war. The Lord Willbewill also, he took the
charge of watching against the rebels within, and to
do what he could to take them while without, or to
stifle them within their caves, dens and holes in the
town-wall of Mansoul. And to speak the truth of him,
ever since he took penance for his fault, he has showed
as much honesty and bravery of spirit as any be in
Mansoul; for he took one Jolly, and his brother
Griggish, the two sons of his servant, Harmless-mirth
(for to that day, though the father was committed to **30**
ward, the sons had a dwelling in the house of my
lord)—I say he took them, and with his own hands
put them to the cross. And this was the reason why he
hanged them up. After their father was put into the
hands of Mr. Trueman, the gaoler, they his sons began
to play his pranks, and to be ticking and toying with

Mouthgate.

*The use of
Mouthgate.*

*The Lord Will-
bewill plays the
man.*

*Jolly and Grig-
gish taken and
executed.*

11 *to land up*: to silt or block up.
36 *ticking and toying*: fondling and flirting. (From ME *teck*, a pat or light
touch: whence the children's game of *tig*, or *tag*; also *tickle*. Origin of *toy*
is obscure.)

the daughters of their lord; nay, it was jealoused that they were too familiar with them, the which was brought to his lordship's ear. Now his lordship, being unwilling unadvisedly to put any man to death, did not suddenly fall upon them, but set watch and spies to see if the thing was true; of the which he was soon informed, for his two servants, whose names were Find-out and Tell-all, catched them together in uncivil manner more than once or twice, and went and told their

10 lord. So when my Lord Willbewill had sufficient ground to believe the thing was true, he takes the two young Diabolonians, for such they were (for their father was a Diabolonian born), and has them to Eyegate, where he raised a very high cross just in the face of the army of Diabolus, and of his army, and there he hanged the young villains in defiance to Captain Pasthope, and of the horrible standard of the tyrant.

> The place of their execution.

Now this Christian act of the brave Lord Willbe-will did greatly abash Captain Pasthope, discourage

20 the army of Diabolus, put fear into the Diabolonian runagates in Mansoul, and put strength and courage into the captains that belonged to Emmanuel the Prince; for they without did gather, and that by this very act of my lord, that Mansoul was resolved to fight, and that the Diabolonians within the town could not do such things as Diabolus had hopes they would. Nor was this the only proof of the brave Lord Willbewill's honesty to the town, nor of his loyalty to his Prince, as will afterwards appear.

> Mortification of sin is a sign of hope of life.

30 Now when the children of Prudent-thrifty, who dwelt with Mr. Mind, (for Thrift left children with Mr. Mind, when he was also committed to prison, and their names were Gripe and Rake-all—these he begat of Mr. Mind's bastard daughter, whose name was Mrs. Holdfastbad)—I say when his children perceived how the Lord Willbewill had served them that dwelt with him, what do they but—lest they should drink of the same cup—endeavour to make their escape. But Mr.

> Mr. Mind plays the man.

1   *jealoused*: suspected.
8   *uncivil*: improper, indecorous.

Mind being wary of it, took them and put them in hold in his house till morning (for this was done over night); and rememb'ring that by the law of Mansoul all Diabolonians were to die (and to be sure they were, at least by father's side, such, and some say by mother's side too), what does he but takes them and puts them in chains, and carries them to the self-same place where my lord hanged his two before, and there he hanged them.

The townsmen also took great encouragement at this act of Mr. Mind, and did what they could to have taken some more of these Diabolonian troublers of Mansoul; but at that time the rest lay so quat and close that they could not be apprehended; so they set against them a diligent watch, and went every man to his place.

I told you a little before that Diabolus and his army were somewhat abashed and discouraged at the sight of what my Lord Willbewill did, when he hanged up those two young Diabolonians; but his discouragement quickly turned itself into furious madness and rage against the town of Mansoul, and fight it he would. Also the townsmen, and captains within, they had their hopes and their expectations heightened, believing at last the day would be theirs, so they feared them the less. Their Subordinate Preacher, too, made a sermon about it, and he took that theme for his text, *Gad, a troop shall overcome him, but he shall overcome at the last.* Whence he showed that though Mansoul should be sorely put to it at the first, yet the victory should most certainly be Mansoul's at the last.

So Diabolus commanded that his drummer should beat a charge against the town; and the captains also that were in the town sounded a charge against them, but they had no drum; they were trumpets of silver with which they sounded against them. Then they which were of the camp of Diabolus came down to the town to take it, and the captains in the castle, with the slingers at Mouthgate played upon them amain.

Mansoul set against the Diabolonians.

Diabolus his kindness turned into furious madness.

Gen. 49:19.

10

20

30

13f.   *quat and close*: hidden and secluded. The form *quat* seems to be an abbreviation of *squat*, sitting close to the ground; hence hidden from view.

And now there was nothing heard in the camp of Diabolus but horrible rage and blasphemy; but in the town good words, prayer and singing of psalms: the enemy replied with horrible objections, and the terribleness of their drum; but the town made answer with the slapping of their slings, and the melodious noise of their trumpets. And thus the fight lasted for several days together, only now and then they had some small intermission, in which the townsmen refreshed themselves, and the captains made ready for another assault.

With heart and mouth.

The captains of Emmanuel were clad in silver armour, and the soldiers in that which was of proof; the soldiers of Diabolus were clad in iron, which was made to give place to Emmanuel's engine-shot. In the town some were hurt, and some were greatly wounded. Now the worst on't was, a surgeon was scarce in Mansoul, for that Emmanuel at present was absent. Howbeit, with the leaves of a tree the wounded were kept from dying; yet their wounds did greatly putrify, and some did grievously stink. Of the townsmen these were wounded, to wit,

Rev. 22:2.
Ps. 38:5.

My Lord Reason, he was wounded in the head.

Another that was wounded was the brave Lord Mayor: he was wounded in the eye.

Another that was wounded was Mr. Mind: he received his wound about the stomach.

Who of Mansoul were wounded.

The honest Subordinate Preacher also, he received a shot not far off the heart; but none of these were mortal.

Many also of the inferior sort, were not only wounded, but slain outright.

Hopeful thoughts.

Now the camp of Diabolus were wounded, and slain a considerable number. For instance,

Who in the camp of Diabolus were wounded and slain.

Captain Rage he was wounded, and so was Captain Cruel.

Captain Damnation was made to retreat, and to entrench himself further off of Mansoul; the

---

4   *objections*: assaults.
15   *to give place to Emmanuel's engine-shot*: to resist Emmanuel's missiles.

standard also of Diabolus was beaten down, and his standard-bearer Captain Much-hurt, had his brains beat out with a sling-stone, to the no little grief and shame of his prince Diabolus.

Many also of the Doubters were slain outright, though enough of them are left alive to make Mansoul shake and totter. Now the victory that day being turned to Mansoul, did put great valour into the townsmen and captains, and did cover Diabolus's camp with a cloud, but withal it made them far more furious. So the next day Mansoul rested, and commanded that the bells should be rung; the trumpets also joyfully sounded, and the captains shouted round the town.

My Lord Willbewill also was not idle, but did notable service within against the domestics, or the Diabolonians that were in the town, not only by keeping of them in awe, for he lighted on one at last whose name was Mr. Anything, a fellow of whom mention was made before; for 'twas he, if you remember, that brought the three fellows to Diabolus, whom the Diabolonians took out of Captain Boanerges' companies, and that persuaded them to list themselves under the tyrant, to fight against the army of Shaddai. My Lord Willbewill did also take a notable Diabolonian whose name was Loosefoot; this Loosefoot was a scout to the vagabonds in Mansoul, and that did use to carry tidings out of Mansoul to the camp, and out of the camp to those of the enemies in Mansoul; both these my lord sent away safe to Mr. Trueman, the gaoler, with a commandment to keep them in irons; for he intended then to have them out to be crucified, when 'twould be for the best to the corporation, and most for the discouragement of the camp of the enemies.

My Lord Mayor also, though he could not stir about so much as formerly, because of the wound that he lately received, yet gave he out orders to all that were the natives of Mansoul, to look to their watch, and stand upon their guard, and as occasion should offer, to prove themselves men.

The victory did turn that day to Mansoul, etc.

My Lord Willbewill taketh one Anything, and one Loosefoot, and committeth them to ward.

Mr. Conscience, the preacher, he also did his utmost to keep all his good documents alive upon the hearts of the people of Mansoul.

Well, a while after the captains and stout ones of the town of Mansoul agreed and resolved upon a time to make a sally out upon the camp of Diabolus, and this must be done in the night. And there was the folly of Mansoul, for the night is always the best for the enemy, but the worst for Mansoul to fight in; but yet they would do it, their courage was so high; their last victory also still stuck in their memories.

The captains consult to fall upon the enemy.

So the night appointed being come, the Prince's brave captains cast lots who should lead the van in this new and desperate expedition against Diabolus, and against his Diabolonian army, and the lot fell to Captain Credence, to Captain Experience, and to Captain Goodhope to lead the forlorn hope. (This Captain Experience the Prince created such when himself did reside in the town of Mansoul). So, as I said, they made their sally out upon the army that lay in the siege against them; and their hap was to fall in with the main body of their enemies. Now Diabolus and his men being expertly accustomed to night-work, took the alarm presently, and were as ready to give them battle as if they had sent them word of their coming. Wherefore to it they went amain, and blows were hard on every side; the Hell-drum also was beat most furiously, while the trumpets of the Prince most sweetly sounded. And thus the battle was joined; and Captain Insatiable looked to the enemy's carriages, and waited when he should receive some prey.

They fight in the night. Who do lead the van.

How they fall on.

The Prince's captains fought it stoutly, beyond

2   *documents*: admonitions. See note to p. 27.

17 *forlorn hope*: a picked body of men, chosen to begin the attack. The phrase is a mistranslation, doubtless caused by similarity of sound, of Dutch *verloren hoop*, the lost troop. (Cf. Fr. *les enfants perdus*, the lost ones.) Bunyan applies the phrase to himself, when, at a crucial moment of his life, contemplating civil disobedience, he sees himself as among the shock-troops of the Prince's army: "Besides, I thought, that seeing God of his mercy should choose me to go upon the forlorn hope in this country; that is, to be the first that should be opposed, for the gospel; if I should fly, it might be a discouragement to the whole body that might follow after." *A Relation of the Imprisonment of Mr. John Bunyan* (London, 1953), p. 104.

They fight
bravely.

what indeed could be expected they should; they
wounded many; they made the whole army of Diabolus to make a retreat. But I cannot tell how, but the
brave Captain Credence, Captain Goodhope, and Captain Experience, as they were upon the pursuit,
cutting down, and following hard after the enemy in

Captain Cre-
dence hurt.

the rear, Captain Credence stumbled and fell, by which
fall he caught so great a hurt that he could not rise
till Captain Experience did help him up, at which their
men were put in disorder. The captain also was so full
of pain that he could not forbear but aloud to cry out:
at this the other two captains fainted, supposing that
Captain Credence had received his mortal wound;

The rest of the
captains faint.

their men also were more disordered, and had no list
to fight. Now Diabolus being very observing, though
at this time as yet he was put to the worst, perceiving
that an halt was made among the men that were the
pursuers, what does he, but, taking it for granted
that the captains were either wounded or dead, he

Diabolus takes
courage.

therefore makes at first a stand, then faces about, and
so comes up upon the Prince's army with as much of
his fury as Hell could help him to; and his hap was to
fall in just among the three captains, Captain Credence, Captain Goodhope, and Captain Experience, and
did cut, wound, and pierce them so dreadfully, that

The Prince's
forces beaten.

what through discouragement, what through disorder, and what through the wounds that now they had
received, and also the loss of much blood, they scarce
were able, though they had for their power the three
best bands in Mansoul, to get safe into the hold again.

Now, when the body of the Prince's army saw
how these three captains were put to the worst, they

Satan sometimes
makes saints eat
their words.

thought it their wisdom to make as safe and good a
retreat as they could, and so returned by the sally-port
again, and so there was an end of this present action.
But Diabolus was so flushed with this night's work,
that he promised himself in a few days, an easy and

Diabolus
flushed.

complete conquest over the town of Mansoul. Wherefore, on the day following, he comes up to the sides

He demands the
town.

thereof with great boldness, and demands entrance,
and that forthwith they deliver themselves up to his

10

20

30

40

government. (The Diabolonians, too, that were within, they began to be somewhat brisk, as we shall show afterward.)

But the valiant Lord Mayor replied that what he got he must get by force, for as long as Emmanuel their Prince was alive (though he at present was not so with them as they wished), they should never consent to yield Mansoul up to another. The Lord Mayor's answer.

And with that the Lord Willbewill stood up and said, 'Diabolus, thou master of the den, and enemy to all that is good, we poor inhabitants of the town of Mansoul, are too well acquainted with thy rule and government, and with the end of those things that for certain will follow submitting to thee, to do it. Wherefore, though while we were without knowledge, we suffered thee to take us (as the bird that saw not the snare, fell into the hands of the fowler), yet since we have been turned from darkness to light. We have also been turned from the power of Satan to God. And though through thy subtlety and also the subtlety of the Diabolonians within, we have sustained much loss, and also plunged ourselves into much perplexity, yet give up ourselves, lay down our arms, and yield to so horrid a tyrant as thou, we shall not; die upon the place we choose rather to do. Besides, we have hopes that in time deliverance will come from court unto us, and therefore we yet will maintain a war against thee.' Brave Willbewill's speech.

This brave speech of the Lord Willbewill, with that also of the Lord Mayor, did somewhat abate the boldness of Diabolus, though it kindled the fury of his rage. It also succoured the townsmen and captains; yea, it was as a plaster to the brave Captain Credence his wound; for you must know that a brave speech now, when the captains of the town with their men of war came home routed, and when the enemy took courage and boldness at the success that he had obtained to draw up to the walls, and demand entrance, as he did, was in season, and also advantageous. The captains encouraged.

2   *brisk*: smartly active.
16   *as the bird*, etc.: see Ps. 124:7.

The Lord Willbewill also did play the man within, for while the captains and soldiers were in the field, he was in arms in the town, and where ever by him there was a Diabolonian found, they were forced to feel the weight of his heavy hand, and also the edge of his penetrating sword. Many, therefore, of the Diabolonians he wounded, as the Lord Cavil, the Lord Brisk, the Lord Pragmatic, and the Lord Murmur; several also of the meaner sort he did sorely maim, though there cannot at this time an account be given you of any that he slew outright. The cause, or rather the advantage that my Lord Willbewill had at this time to do thus, was for that the captains were gone out to fight the enemy in the field. 'For now,' thought the Diabolonians within, 'is our time to stir and make an uproar in the town.' What do they, therefore, but quickly get themselves into a body, and fall forthwith to hurricaning in Mansoul, as if now nothing but whirlwind and tempest should be there. Wherefore, as I said, he takes this opportunity to fall in among them with his men, cutting and slashing with courage that was undaunted; at which the Diabolonians with all haste dispersed themselves to their holds, and my lord to his place as before.

Willbewill's gallantry.

This brave act of my lord did somewhat revenge the wrong done by Diabolus to the captains, and also did let them know that Mansoul was not to be parted with, for the loss of a victory or two; wherefore the wing of the tyrant was clipped again, as to boasting— I mean in comparison of what he would have done if the Diabolonians had put the town to the same plight, to which he had put the captains.

Nothing like faith to crush Diabolus.

Well, Diabolus yet resolves to have the other bout with Mansoul. 'For,' thought he, 'since I beat them once, I may beat them twice.' Wherefore he commanded his men to be ready at such an hour of the night to make a fresh assault upon the town; and he gave it out in special that they should bend all their force against Feelgate, and attempt to break into the

He tries what he can do upon the sense and feeling of the Christian.

17f. *fall forthwith to hurricaning:* start at once to make a great commotion.

town through that. The word that then he did give to
his officers and soldiers was *Hellfire*. 'And,' said he, 'if
we break in upon them, as I wish we do, either with
some, or with all our force, let them that break in look
to it, that they forget not the word. And let nothing
be heard in the town of Mansoul but *Hell-fire! Hell-
fire! Hell-fire!*' The drummer was also to beat without
ceasing, and the standard-bearers were to display their
colours; the soldiers, too, were to put on what courage
they could, and to see that they played manfully their
parts against the town.

So the night was come, and all things by the
tyrant made ready for the work. He suddenly makes
his assault, upon Feelgate, and after he had a while
struggled there, he throws the gates wide open. For
the truth is, those gates were but weak, and so most
easily made to yield. When Diabolus had thus far
made his attempt, he placed his captains, to wit, Torment and No-ease, there; so he attempted to press
forward, but the Prince's captains came down upon
him and made his entrance more difficult than he
desired. And to speak truth, they made what resistance
they could; but the three of their best and most
valiant captains being wounded, and by their wounds
made much incapable of doing the town that service
they would (and all the rest having more than their
hands full of the Doubters, and their captains that did
follow Diabolus), they were overpowered with force,
nor could they keep them out of the town. Wherefore
the Prince's men and their captains betook themselves
to the castle, as to the stronghold of the town: and
this they did partly for their own security, partly for
the security of the town, and partly, or rather chiefly,
to preserve to Emmanuel the prerogative-royal of Mansoul, for so was the castle of Mansoul.

The captains therefore being fled into the castle,
the enemy, without much resistance, possess themselves of the rest of the town, and spreading themselves as they went into every corner, they cried out as
they marched, according to the command of the
tyrant, *Hell-fire! Hell-fire! Hell-fire!* so that nothing

Feelgate but weak.

When these three captains are disabled, what can the rest do for the town of Mansoul?

for a while throughout the town of Mansoul could be heard but the direful noise of *Hell-fire!* together with the roaring of Diabolus's drum. And now did the clouds hang black over Mansoul, nor to reason did anything but ruin seem to attend it. Diabolus also quartered his soldiers in the houses of the inhabitants of the town of Mansoul. Yea, the Subordinate Preacher's house was as full of these outlandish Doubters as ever it could hold; and so was my Lord Mayor's, and my Lord Willbewill's also. Yea, where was there a corner, a cottage, a barn, or a hog-sty that now were not full of these vermin? Yea, they turned the men of the town out of their houses, and would lie in their beds, and sit at their tables themselves. Ah, poor Mansoul! Now thou feelest the fruits of sin, and what venom was in the flattering words of Mr. Carnal Security! They made great havoc of what ever they laid their hands on; yea, they fired the town in several places; many young children also were by them dashed in pieces; yea, those that were yet unborn they destroyed in their mother's wombs: for you must needs think that it could not now be otherwise; for what conscience, what pity, what bowels or compassion can any expect at the hands of outlandish Doubters? Many in Mansoul that were women, both young and old, they forced, ravished, and beastlike abused, so that they swooned, miscarried, and many of them died, and so lay at the top of every street, and in all by-places of the town.

And now did Mansoul seem to be nothing but a den of dragons, an emblem of Hell, and a place of total darkness. Now did Mansoul lie almost like the barren wilderness; nothing but nettles, briars, thorns, weeds, and stinking things seemed now to cover the face of Mansoul. I told you before, how that these Diabolonian Doubters turned the men of Mansoul out of their beds, and now I will add, they wounded them, they mauled them, yea, and almost brained many of them. Many, did I say?—yea most, if not all of them. Mr. Conscience they so wounded, yea, and his wounds so fest'red, that he could have no ease day nor night, but

The sad fruits of apostasy.

Guilt.

Good and tender thoughts.

Holy conceptions of good.

Rest.

10

20

30

40

lay as if continually upon a rack. But that Shaddai rules all, certainly they had slain him outright. My Lord Mayor they so abused that they almost put out his eyes; and had not my Lord Willbewill got into the castle, they intended to have chopped him all to pieces, for they did look upon him, as his heart now stood, to be one of the very worst that was in Mansoul against Diabolus and his crew. And indeed he hath showed himself a man, and more of his exploits you will hear of afterwards.

Now a man might have walked for days together in Mansoul, and scarce have seen one in the town that looked like a religious man. Oh, the fearful state of Mansoul now! Now every corner swarmed with outlandish Doubters; red-coats and black-coats, walked the town by clusters, and filled up all the houses with hideous noises, vain songs, lying stories and blasphemous language against Shaddai and his Son. Now also those Diabolonians that lurked in the walls and dens, and holes that were in the town of Mansoul, came forth and showed themselves; yea, walked with open face in company with the Doubters that were in Mansoul. Yea, they had more boldness now to walk the streets, to haunt the houses, and to show themselves abroad, than had any of the honest inhabitants of the now woeful town of Mansoul.

But Diabolus and his outlandish men were not at peace in Mansoul, for they were not there entertained as were the captains and forces of Emmanuel; the townsmen did browbeat them what they could: nor did they partake or make stroy of any of the necessaries of Mansoul, but that which they seized on against the townsmen's will; what they could they hid from them, and what they could not, they had with an ill will. They, poor hearts, had rather have had their room than their company, but they were at present their captives, and their captives for the present they were forced to be. But, I say, they discoun-

Sad work among the townsmen.

Satan has a particular spite against a sanctified will.

Thought.

The soul full of idle thoughts and blasphemies.

Rom. 7.

15   *red-coats and black-coats*: soldiers and clerics.
31   *make stroy of*: destroy.

tenanced them as much as they were able, and showed them all the dislike that they could.

The captains also from the castle did hold them in continual play with their slings, to the chafing and fretting of the minds of the enemies. True, Diabolus made a great many attempts to have broken open the gates of the castle, but Mr. Godlyfear was made the keeper of that; and he was a man of that courage, conduct and valour, that 'twas in vain as long as life lasted within him, to think to do that work though mostly desired, wherefore all the attempts that Diabolus made against him were fruitless. (I have wished sometimes that that man had had the whole rule of the town of Mansoul.)

Well, this was the condition of the town of Mansoul for about two years and an half; the body of the town was the seat of war; the people of the town were driven into holes, and the glory of Mansoul was laid in the dust. What rest, then, could be to the inhabitants? What peace could Mansoul have, and what sun could shine upon it? Had the enemy lain so long without in the plain against the town, it had been enough to have famished them; but now when they shall be within, when the town shall be their tent, their trench, and fort against the castle that was in the town; when the town shall be against the town, and shall serve to be a defence to the enemies of her strength and life: I say, when they shall make use of the forts, and town-holds, to secure themselves in, even till they shall take, spoil, and demolish the castle— this was terrible! And yet this was now the state of the town of Mansoul.

After the town of Mansoul had been in this sad and lamentable condition for so long a time as I have told you, and no petitions that they presented their Prince with all this while could prevail, the inhabitants of the town, to wit, the elders and chief of Mansoul, gathered together, and after some time spent in condoling their miserable state, and this miserable judgment coming upon them, they agreed together to draw up yet another petition, and to send it away to

Mr. Godlyfear is made keeper of the castle-gates.

The town of Mansoul the seat of war.

Heart.

10

20

30

40

Emmanuel for relief. But Mr. Godlyfear stood up, and
answered, that he knew that his Lord the Prince never
did, nor ever would receive a petition for these matters
from the hand of any whoever, unless the Lord Secretary's hand was to it—'and this,' quoth he, 'is the
reason that you prevailed not all this while.' Then they
said they would draw up one, and get the Lord Secretary's hand unto it. But Mr. Godlyfear answered
again, that he knew also that the Lord Secretary
would not set his hand to any petition that himself
had not an hand in composing and drawing up. 'And
besides,' said he, 'the Prince doth know my Lord Secretary's hand from all the hands in the world; wherefore
he cannot be deceived by any pretence whatever.
Wherefore, my advice is that you go to my Lord, and
implore him to lend you his aid.' Now he did yet
abide in the castle where all the captains and men at
arms were.

So they heartily thanked Mr. Godlyfear, took his
counsel, and did as he had bidden them. So they went
and came to my Lord, and made known the cause of
their coming to him: to wit, that since Mansoul was in
so deplorable a condition, his Highness would be
pleased to undertake to draw up a petition for them
to Emmanuel, the Son of the mighty Shaddai, and to
their King and his Father by him.

Then said the Secretary to them, 'What petition
is it that you would have me draw up for you?' But
they said, 'Our Lord knows best the state and condition of the town of Mansoul; and how we are backslidden and degenerated from the Prince; thou also
knowest who is come up to war against us, and how
Mansoul is now the seat of war. My Lord knows,
moreover, what barbarous usages our men, women and
children have suffered at their hands, and how our
home-bred Diabolonians do walk now with more boldness than dare the townsmen in the streets of Mansoul. Let our Lord therefore, according to the wisdom
of God that is in him, draw up a petition for his poor
servants to our Prince Emmanuel.' 'Well,' said the
Lord Secretary, 'I will draw up a petition for you, and

Mr. Godlyfear's
advice about
drawing up of a
petition to the
Prince.

The Secretary
employed to
draw up a petition for Mansoul.

will also set my hand thereto.' Then said they, 'But when shall we call for it at the hands of our Lord?' But he answered, 'Yourselves must be present at the doing of it. Yea, you must put your desires to it. True, the hand and pen shall be mine, but the ink and paper must be yours; else how can you say it is your petition? Nor have I need to petition for myself, because I have not offended.'

He also added as followeth, 'No petition goes from me in my name to the Prince, and so to his Father by him, but when the people that are chiefly concerned therein do join in heart and soul in the matter, for that must be inserted therein.'

So they did heartily agree with the sentence of the Lord, and a petition was forthwith drawn up for them. But now, who should carry it?—that was next. But the Secretary advised that Captain Credence should carry it, for he was a well-spoken man. They therefore called for him, and propounded to him the business. 'Well,' said the captain, 'I gladly accept of the motion; and though I am lame, I will do this business for you, with as much speed, and as well as I can.'

The contents of the petition were to this purpose:

O our Lord, and Sovereign Prince Emmanuel, the potent, the long-suffering Prince! Grace is poured into thy lips, and to thee belongs mercy and forgiveness, though we have rebelled against thee. We, who are no more worthy to be called thy Mansoul, nor yet fit to partake of common benefits, do beseech thee, and thy Father by thee to do away our transgressions. We confess that thou mightest cast us away for them, but do it not for thy name's sake; let the Lord rather take an opportunity at our miserable condition, to let out his bowels and compassions to us; we are compassed on every side, Lord, our own back-slidings reprove us;

The petition drawn up and sent to Emmanuel by the hand of Captain Credence.

The contents of their petition.

10

20

30

5f. *the ink and paper must be yours*: a brilliant stroke. Bunyan's point is that while God takes the initiative, moving the believer by the power of His grace, man must nevertheless cooperate, since he has an essential part to play. In this way individual responsibility is assured.

14 *sentence*: opinion.

our Diabolonians within our town fright us, and the
army of the angel of the bottomless pit distresses us.
Thy grace can be our salvation, and whither to go but
to thee we know not.

Furthermore, O gracious Prince, we have
weakened our captains, and they are discouraged, sick,
and of late some of them grievously worsted and
beaten out of the field by the power and force of the
tyrant. Yea, even those of our captains in whose
valour we did formerly use to put most of our confidence, they are as wounded men. Besides, Lord, our
enemies are lively, and they are strong; they vaunt
and boast themselves, and do threaten to part us
among themselves for a booty. They are fallen also
upon us, Lord, with many thousand Doubters, such as
with whom we cannot tell what to do; they are all
grim-looked, and unmerciful ones, and they bid
defiance to us and thee.

Our wisdom is gone, our power is gone, because
thou art departed from us, nor have we what we may
call ours but sin, shame and confusion of face for sin.
Take pity upon us, O Lord, take pity upon us thy
miserable town of Mansoul, and save us out of the
hands of our enemies. Amen.

This petition as was touched afore, was handed
by the Lord Secretary, and carried to the court by the
brave and most stout Captain Credence. Now he
carried it out at Mouthgate, for that, as I said, was the
sally-port of the town; and he went and came to
Emmanuel with it. Now how it came out, I do not
know, but for certain it did, and that so far as to
reach the ears of Diabolus. Thus I conclude, because
that the tyrant had it presently by the end, and
charged the town of Mansoul with it, saying, 'Thou
rebellious and stubborn-hearted Mansoul, I will make
thee to leave off petitioning. Art thou yet for petitioning? I will make thee to leave.' Yea, he also knew who

25 *touched*: touched upon, mentioned.
33 *had it presently by the end*: knew of it at once.

238

Satan cannot abide prayer. the messenger was that carried the petition to the Prince, and it made him both to fear and rage.

Wherefore he commanded that his drum should be beat again, a thing that Mansoul could not abide to hear; but when Diabolus will have his drum beat, Mansoul must abide the noise. Well, the drum was beat, and the Diabolonians were gathered together.

Then said Diabolus, 'O ye stout Diabolonians, be it known unto you, that there is treachery hatched against us in the rebellious town of Mansoul; for albeit the town is in our possession, as you see, yet these miserable Mansoulians have attempted to dare, and have been so hardy as yet to send to the court to Emmanuel for help. This I give you to understand, that ye may yet know how to carry it to the wretched town of Mansoul. Wherefore, O my trusty Diabolonians, I command that yet more and more ye distress this town of Mansoul, and vex it with your wiles, ravish their women, deflower their virgins, slay their children, brain their ancients, fire their town, and what other mischief you can; and let this be the reward of the Mansoulians from me, for their desperate rebellions against me.'

Poor Mansoul.

This, you see, was the charge; but something stepped in betwixt that and execution, for as yet there was but little more done than to rage.

Moreover, when Diabolus had done thus, he went the next way up to the castle-gates, and demanded that upon pain of death, the gates should be opened to him, and that entrance should be given him and his men that followed after. To whom Mr. Godlyfear replied (for he it was that had the charge of that gate), that the gate should not be opened unto him, nor to the men that followed after him. He said, moreover, that Mansoul, when she had suffered a while, should be made perfect, strengthened, settled.

Then said Diabolus, 'Deliver me then the men that have petitioned against me, especially Captain Credence that carried it to your Prince. Deliver that varlet into my hands, and I will depart from the town.'

Satan cannot abide faith.

Then up starts a Diabolonian, whose name was

Mr. Fooling, and said, 'My lord offereth you fair; 'tis better for you that one man perish than that your whole Mansoul should be undone.'

But Mr. Godlyfear made him this replication, 'How long will Mansoul be kept out of the dungeon, when she hath given up her faith to Diabolus? As good lose the town as lose Captain Credence; for if one be gone, the other must follow.' But to that Mr. Fooling said nothing.

Then did my Lord Mayor reply, and said, 'O thou devouring tyrant, be it known unto thee, we shall hearken to none of thy words; we are resolved to resist thee as long as a captain, a man, a sling, and a stone to throw at thee, shall be found in the town of Mansoul.' But Diabolus answered, 'Do you hope, do you wait, do you look for help and deliverance? You have sent to Emmanuel, but your wickedness sticks too close in your skirts, to let innocent prayers come out of your lips. Think you, that you shall be prevailers and prosper in this design? You will fail in your wish, you will fail in your attempts; for 'tis not only I, but your Emmanuel is against you. Yea, it is he that hath sent me against you to subdue you; for what then do you hope, or by what means will you escape?'

Then said the Lord Mayor, 'We have sinned indeed, but that shall be no help to thee, for our Emmanuel hath said it, and that in great faithfulness, *And him that cometh to me I will in no wise cast out.* He hath also told us, our enemy, that all manner of sin and blasphemy shall be forgiven to the sons of men. Therefore we dare not despair, but will look for, wait for, and hope for deliverance still.'

Now by this time Captain Credence was returned and come from the court from Emmanuel to the castle of Mansoul, and he returned to them with a packet. So my Lord Mayor hearing that Captain Credence was come, withdrew himself from the noise of the roaring of the tyrant, and left him to yell at the wall of the

Mr. Fooling.

Diabolus rages.

The Lord Mayor's speech just at the time of the return of Captain Credence.

4   *replication*: rejoinder.
28   See John 6:37.
29f. See Matt. 12:31.

town, or against the gates of the castle. So he came up to the captains' lodgings, and saluting him, he asked him of his welfare, and what was the best news at court? But when he asked Captain Credence that, the water stood in his eyes. Then said the captain, 'Cheer up, my lord, for all will be well in time.' And with that he first produced his packet, and laid it by, but that the Lord Mayor, and the rest of the captains took for a sign of good tidings. Now a season of grace being come, he sent for all the captains and elders of the town that were here and there in their lodgings in the castle, and upon their guard, to let them know that Captain Credence was returned from the court, and that he had something in general, and something in special to communicate to them. So they all came up to him, and saluted him, and asked him concerning his journey, and what was the best news at the court? And he answered them as he had done the Lord Mayor before, that all would be well at last. Now when the captain had thus saluted them, he opened his packet, and thence did draw out his several notes for those that he had sent for. And the first note was for my Lord Mayor, wherein was signified:

That the Prince Emmanuel had taken it well that my lord Mayor had been so true and trusty in his office, and the great concerns that lay upon him for the town and people of Mansoul. Also he bid him to know *that he took it well that he had been so bold for his Prince Emmanuel, and had engaged so faithfully in his cause against Diabolus.* He also signified at the close of his letter, *that he should shortly receive his reward.*

The second note that came out was for the noble Lord Willbewill, wherein there was signified, *that his Prince Emmanuel did well understand how valiant and courageous he had been for the honour of his Lord, now in his absence, and when his name was under contempt by Diabolus.* There was signified also *that his Prince had taken it well that he had been so faithful to the town of Mansoul in his keeping of so strict a hand and eye over, and so strict a rein upon*

A sign of goodness.

The packet opened.

A note for my Lord Mayor.

A note for the Lord Willbewill.

10

20

30

40

*the necks of the Diabolonians that did still lie lurking
in their several holes in the famous town of Mansoul.*

He signified, moreover, how *that he understood
that my lord had with his own hand done great
execution upon some of the chief of the rebels there, to
the great discouragement of the adverse party, and to
the good example of the whole town of Mansoul,
and that shortly his lordship should have his reward.*

The third note came out for the Subordinate
Preacher, wherein was signified, *that his Prince took
it well from him that he had so honestly, and so
faithfully performed his office, and executed the trust
committed to him by his Lord, while he exhorted,
rebuked, and fore-warned Mansoul according to the
laws of the town.* He signified, moreover, *that he took
well at his hand that he called to fasting, to sackcloth
and ashes, when Mansoul was under her revolt. Also
that he called for the aid of the Captain Boanerges to
help in so weighty a work, and that shortly he also
should receive his reward.*

A note for the Subordinate Preacher.

The fourth note came out for Mr. Godlyfear,
wherein his Lord thus signified, *that his lordship
observed that he was the first of all the men in
Mansoul, that detected Mr. Carnal Security as the only
one that through his subtlety and cunning had
obtained for Diabolus a defection and decay of goodness in the blessed town of Mansoul.* Moreover, his
Lord gave him to understand *that he still rememb'red
his tears and mourning for the state of Mansoul.* It
was also observed by the same note *that his Lord took
notice of his detecting of this Mr. Carnal Security, at
his own table among his guests, in his own house, and
that in the midst of his jolliness, even while he was
seeking to perfect his villainies against the town of
Mansoul.* Emmanuel also took notice *that this reverend
person, Mr. Godlyfear, stood stoutly to it at the gates
of the castle against all the threats and attempts of
the tyrant, and that he had put the townsmen in a
way to make their petition to their Prince, so as that
he might accept thereof, and as that they might
obtain an answer of peace; and that therefore shortly*

A note for Mr. Godlyfear.

242

he should receive his reward.

After all this, there was yet produced a note

A note for the
town of Man-
soul.

which was written to the whole town of Mansoul, whereby they perceived *that their Lord took notice of their so often repeating of petitions to him, and that they should see more of the fruits of such their doings in time to come.* Their Prince did also therein tell them, *that he took it well, that their heart and mind, now at last, abode fixed upon him and his ways, though Diabolus had made such inroads upon them,* 10 *and that neither flatteries on the one hand, nor hardships on the other, could make them yield to serve his cruel designs.* There was also inserted at the bottom of this note, *that his Lordship had left the town of Mansoul in the hands of the Lord Secretary, and under the conduct of Captain Credence, saying,* 'Beware that you yet yield yourselves unto their governance, and in due time you shall receive your reward.'

So after the brave Captain Credence had delivered

Captain Cre-
dence retires to
the Lord Secre-
tary's lodgings.

his notes to those to whom they belonged, he retired 20 himself to my Lord Secretary's lodgings, and there spends time in conversing with him; for they two were very great one with another, and did indeed know more how things would go with Mansoul than did all the townsmen besides. The Lord Secretary also loved the Captain Credence dearly; yea, many a good bit was sent him from my Lord's table; also he might have a show of countenance when the rest of Mansoul lay under the clouds. So after some time for converse was spent, the captain betook himself to his chambers 30 to rest. But it was not long after but my Lord did send for the captain again; so the captain came to him, and they greeted one another with usual salutations. Then said the captain to the Lord Secretary, 'What

Captain Cre-
dence made the
Lord's Lieuten-
ant over all the
forces in Man-
soul.

hath my Lord to say to his servant?' So the Lord Secretary took him, and had him a to side, and after a sign or two of more favour, he said, 'I have made thee the Lord's Lieutenant over all the forces in Mansoul; so that from this day forward, all men in Man-

28   *show of countenance*: sign of grace or favour.
36   *a to side*: aside.

soul shall be at thy word, and thou shalt be he that shall lead in, and that shalt lead out Mansoul. Thou shalt therefore manage, according to thy place, the war for thy Prince, and for the town of Mansoul, against the force and power of Diabolus, and at thy command shall the rest of the captains be.'

Now the townsmen began to perceive what interest the captain had, both with the court, and also with the Lord Secretary in Mansoul; for no man before could speed when sent, nor bring such good news from Emmanuel as he. Wherefore what do they, after some lamentation, that they made no more use of him in their distresses, but send by their Subordinate Preacher to the Lord Secretary, to desire him that all that ever they were and had, might be put under the government, care, custody, and conduct of Captain Credence.

So their preacher went and did his errand, and received this answer from the mouth of his Lord, that Captain Credence should be the great doer in all the King's army, against the King's enemies, and also for the welfare of Mansoul. So he bowed to the ground, and thanked his Lordship, and returned and told his news to the townsfolk. But all this was done with all imaginable secrecy, because the foes had yet great strength in the town.

The town of Mansoul craves that she may be under the conduct of Captain Credence.

But to return to our story again. When Diabolus saw himself thus boldly confronted by the Lord Mayor, and perceived the stoutness of Mr. Godlyfear, he fell into a rage, and forthwith called a council of war that he might be revenged on Mansoul. So all the Princes of the Pit came together, and old Incredulity in the head of them, with all the captains of his army. So they consult what to do. Now the effect and conclusion of the council that day, was how they might take the castle, because they could not conclude themselves masters of the town so long as that was in the possession of their enemies. So one advised this way, and another advised that; but when they could not agree in their verdict, Apollyon, that President of the Council, stood up, and thus he began: 'My brother-

Diabolus rages.

hood,' quoth he, 'I have two things to propound unto you. And my first is this: Let us withdraw ourselves from the town into the plain again, for our presence here will do us no good, because the castle is yet in our enemies' hands; nor is it possible that we should take that so long as so many brave captains are in it, and that this bold fellow Godlyfear is made the keeper of the gates of it.

'Now when we have withdrawn ourselves into the plain, they of their own accord will be glad of some little ease, and it may be of their own accord they again may begin to be remiss, and even their so being will give them a bigger blow than we can possibly give them ourselves. But if that should fail, our going forth of the town may draw the captains out after us, and you know what it cost them when we fought them in the field before. Besides, can we but draw them out into the field, we may lay an ambush behind the town, which shall, when they are come forth abroad, rush in and take possession of the castle.'

But Beelzebub stood up and replied, saying, ''Tis impossible to draw them all off from the castle; some, you may be sure, will lie there to keep that; wherefore, it will be but in vain thus to attempt, unless we were sure that they will all come out.' He therefore concluded that what was done must be done by some other means. And the most likely means that the greatest of their heads could invent was that which Apollyon had advised to before, to wit, to get the townsmen again to sin. 'For,' said he, 'it is not our being in the town, nor in the field, nor our fighting, nor our killing of their men, that can make us the masters of Mansoul; for so long as one in the town is able to lift up his finger against us, Emmanuel will take their parts, and if he shall take their parts, we know what time a day it will be with us. Wherefore, for my part,' quoth he, 'there is in my judgment no way to bring them into bondage to us like inventing a way to make them

Look to it Mansoul.

Look to it Mansoul.

II Pet. 2:18-21.

10

20

30

35   *we know what time*, etc.: i.e., we know what the position will be or what **will** happen.

sin. Had we' (said he) 'left all our Doubters at home, we had done as well as we have done now, unless we could have made them the masters and governors of the castle; for Doubters at a distance are but like objections refell'd with arguments. Indeed, can we but get them into the hold, and make them possessors of that, the day will be our own. Let us therefore withdraw ourselves into the plain (not expecting that the captains in Mansoul should follow us); but yet, I say,

10 let us do this, and before we so do, let us advise again with our trusty Diabolonians that are yet in their holds of Mansoul, and set them to work to betray the town to us; for they indeed must do it, or it will be left undone for ever.' By these sayings of Beelzebub (for I think 'twas he that gave this counsel), the whole conclave was forced to be of his opinion—to wit, that the way to get the castle was to get the town to sin. Then they fell to inventing by what means they might do this thing.

20 Then Lucifer stood up and said, 'The counsel of Beelzebub is pertinent. Now the way to bring this to pass, in mine opinion is this: Let us withdraw our force from the town of Mansoul; let us do this, and let us terrify them no more, either with summons, or threats, or with the noise of our drum, or any other awakening means. Only let us lie in the field at a distance, and be as if we regarded them not; for frights, I see, do but awaken them, and make them more stand to their arms. I have also another strategem in my head. You

30 know Mansoul is a market-town, and a town that delights in commerce. What, therefore, if some of our Diabolonians shall feign themselves far-country men, and shall go out and bring to the market of Mansoul some of our wares to sell—and what matter at what rates they sell their wares, though it be but for half the worth? Now let those that thus shall trade in their market, be those that are witty and true to us, and I will lay my crown to pawn, it will do. There are two

Look to it Mansoul.

Look to it Mansoul.

5 *refell'd*: refuted.
37 *witty*: crafty, skilful.
38 *lay my crown to pawn*: wager my crown.

that are come to my thoughts already, that I think
will be arch at this work, and they are Mr. Pennywise-
Pound-foolish, and Mr. Get-i'th'-hundred-and-lose-i'th'-
shire; nor is this man with the long name at all
inferior to the other. What also if you join with them
Mr. Sweet-world, and Mr. Present-good? They are men
that are civil and cunning, but our true friends and
Look to it.
Rev. 3:17. helpers. Let these, with as many more, engage in this
business for us, and let Mansoul be taken up in much
business, and let them grow full and rich, and this is
the way to get ground of them. Remember ye not that
Heart. thus we prevailed upon Laodicea, and how many at
present do we hold in this snare? Now, when they
begin to grow full, they will forget their misery, and
if we shall not affright them, they may happen to fall
asleep, and so be got to neglect their town-watch, their
castle-watch, as well as their watch at the gates.

'Yea, may we not by this means, so cumber Mansoul with abundance, that they shall be forced to make
of their castle a warehouse instead of a garrison fortified against us, and a receptacle for men of war. Thus
if we get our goods and commodities thither, I reckon
that the castle is more than half ours. Besides, could
we so order it that that shall be filled with such kind of
wares, then if we made a sudden assault upon them,
it would be hard for the captains to take shelter there.
Luke 8:14; 21:34-
36. Do you not know that of the parable, *The deceitful-
ness of riches choke the word;* and again, *When the
heart is over-charged with surfeiting and drunkenness,
and the cares of this life, all mischief comes upon them
at unawares?*

'Furthermore, my lords,' (quoth he) 'you very
well know that it is not easy for a people to be filled

10
20
30

---

2 *arch*: outstanding.
3 *Mr. Get-i'th'-hundred-and-lose-i'th'-shire*: an obsolete proverb, referring to
the ancient English system of dividing counties into territorial "hundreds,"
each with its own court. The allusion means there is no profit in losing a
whole county to gain only a small part. Whoever would do so is as foolish
as he who would lose a pound to gain a penny.
7 *civil and cunning*: serious and knowledgeable.
12 *Laodicea*: city of Asia Minor, whose inhabitants (according to Rev. 3:14-
18) were "lukewarm, neither cold nor hot."

with our things, and not to have some of our Diabolonians as retainers to their houses and services. Where
is a Mansoulian that is full of this world that has not
for his servants, and waiting-men, Mr. Profuse or Mr.
Prodigality, or some other of our Diabolonian gang, as
Mr. Voluptuous, Mr. Pragmatical, Mr. Ostentation, or
the like? Now these can take the castle of Mansoul,
or blow it up, or make it unfit for a garrison for
Emmanuel, and any of these will do. Yea, these, for
aught I know, may do it for us sooner than an army
of twenty thousand men. Wherefore, to end as I began,
my advice is that we quietly withdraw ourselves, not
offering any further force, or forcible attempts upon
the castle, at least at this time, and let us set on foot
our new project, and let's see if that will not make
them destroy themselves.'

Look to it Man-
soul.

This advice was highly applauded by them all,
and was accounted the very masterpiece of Hell, to
wit, to choke Mansoul with a fullness of this world,
and to surfeit her heart with the good things thereof.
But see how things meet together! Just as this Diabolonian council was broken up, Captain Credence
received a letter from Emmanuel, the contents of
which was this, *that upon the third day he would
meet him in the field in the plains about Mansoul.*
'Meet me in the field?' quoth the captain. 'What
meaneth my Lord by this? I know not what he meaneth by meeting of me in the field.' So he took the note
in his hand, and did carry it to my Lord Secretary to
ask his thoughts thereupon; for my lord was a seer in
all matters concerning the King, and also for the
good and comfort of the town of Mansoul. So he
showed my lord the note, and desired his opinion
thereof. 'For my part,' quoth Captain Credence, 'I
know not the meaning thereof.' So my lord did take
and read it, and after a little pause he said, 'The Diabolonians have had against Mansoul a great consultation
to-day; they have, I say, this day been contriving the
utter ruin of the town; and the result of their counsel
is, to set Mansoul into such a way, which if taken,
will surely make her destroy herself. And to this end

Captain Cre-
dence receives
that from his
Prince which he
understandeth
not.

248

they are making ready for their own departure out of the town, intending to betake themselves to the field again, and there to lie till they shall see whether this their project will take or no. But be thou ready with the men of thy lord (for on the third day they will be in the plain), there to fall upon the Diabolonians; for

The riddle expounded to Captain Credence.

the Prince will by that time be in the field; yea, by that it is break of day, sun-rising, or before, and that with a mighty force against them. So he shall be before them, and thou shalt be behind them, and betwixt you both their army shall be destroyed.'

10

When Captain Credence heard this, away goes he to the rest of the captains, and tells them what a note

The captains are gladded to hear.

he had a while since received from the hand of Emmanuel. 'And,' said he, 'that which was dark therein has my lord, the Lord Secretary, expounded unto me.' He told them, moreover, what by himself and by them must be done to answer the mind of their lord. Then were the captains glad, and Captain Credence commanded that all the King's trumpeters should

20

ascend to the battlements of the castle, and there in the audience of Diabolus, and of the whole town of Mansoul, make the best music that heart could invent.

Curious music made by the trumpeters.

The trumpeters then did as they were commanded. They got themselves up to the top of the castle, and thus they began to sound. Then did Diabolus start, and said, 'What can be the meaning of this? They neither sound *boot and saddle*, nor *horse and away*, nor a *charge*. What do these mad men mean, that yet they should be so merry and glad?' Then answered him

30

one of themselves and said, 'This is for joy that their Prince Emmanuel is coming to relieve the town of Mansoul; that to this end he is at the head of an army, and that this relief is near.'

The men of Mansoul also were greatly concerned at this melodious charm of the trumpets; they said— yea, they answered one another, saying, 'This can be no harm to us; surely this can be no harm to us.' Then

28   *They neither sound boot and saddle,* etc.: they sound none of the usual trumpet-calls. (*boot and saddle* is a perversion of Fr. *boute-selle*, place saddle; a signal to cavalry to mount.)

said the Diabolonians, 'What had we best to do?' And it was answered, it was best to quit the town; and that, said one, 'Ye may do in pursuance of your last council, and by so doing also be better able to give the enemy battle, should an army from without come upon us.' So on the second day they withdrew themselves from Mansoul, and abode in the plains without; but they encamped themselves before Eyegate in what terrene and terrible manner they could. The reason why they would not abide in the town (besides the reasons that were debated in their late conclave) was for that they were not possessed of the stronghold, and because, said they, 'we shall have more convenience to fight, and also to fly, if need be, when we are encamped in the open plains.' Besides, the town would have been a pit for them rather than a place of defence, had the Prince come up and enclosed them fast therein. Therefore they betook themselves to the field, that they might also be out of the reach of the slings, by which they were much annoyed all the while that they were in the town.

Diabolus withdraws from the town, and why.

Well, the time that the captains were to fall upon the Diabolonians being come, they eagerly prepared themselves for action, for Captain Credence had told the captains over night that *they should meet their Prince in the field to-morrow.* This therefore made them yet far more desirous to be engaging the enemy: for, *you shall see the Prince in the field to-morrow,* was like oil to a flaming fire; for of a long time they had been at a distance; they therefore were for this the more earnest and desirous of the work. So, as I said, the hour being come, Captain Credence with the rest of the men of war, drew out their forces before it were day by the sally-port of the town. And being all ready, Captain Credence went up to the head of the army, and gave to the rest of the captains the word, and so they to their under-officers and soldiers: the word was *The sword of the Prince Emmanuel, and the shield of*

The time come for the captains to fight them.

They draw out into the field.

The Word.

---

9   *terrene and terrible manner*: the meaning is obscure, but the very vagueness of the phrase suggests the dreadful nature of the earth-bound encampment.

250

Captain Credence! which is, in the Mansoulian tongue, *The word of God and faith!* Then the captains fell on and began roundly to front, and flank, and rear Diabolus' camp.

Now they left Captain Experience in the town because he was yet ill of his wounds which the Diabolonians had given him in the last fight. But when he perceived that the captains were at it, what does he, but calling for his crutches with haste, gets up, and away he goes to the battle, saying, 'Shall I lie here when my brethren are in the fight, and when Emmanuel, the Prince, will show himself in the field to his servants?' But when the enemy saw the man come with his crutches, they were daunted yet the more. 'For,' thought they, 'what spirit has possessed these Mansoulians that they fight me upon their crutches?' Well, the captains, as I said, fell on, and did bravely handle their weapons, still crying out, and shouting as they laid on blows, 'The sword of the Prince Emmanuel, and the shield of Captain Credence!'

Captain Experience will fight for his Prince upon his crutches.

10

20

Now when Diabolus saw that the captains were come out, and that so valiantly they surrounded his men, he concluded that for the present nothing from them was to be looked for but blows, and the dints of their two-edged sword.

The battle joined.

Wherefore he also falls on upon the Prince's army, with all his deadly force. So the battle was joined. Now who was it that at first Diabolus met with in the fight, but Captain Credence on the one hand, and the Lord Willbewill on the other! Now Willbewill's blows were like the blows of a giant, for that man had a strong arm, and he fell in upon the Election-doubters, for they were the life-guard of Diabolus, and he kept them in play a good while, cutting and battering shrewdly. Now when Captain Credence saw my lord engaged, he did stoutly fall on, on the other hand, upon the same company also; so they put them to great disorder. Now Captain Goodhope had engaged the Vocation-doubters, and they were sturdy men; but the captain was a valiant man. Captain Experience did

Willbewill engaged.

Credence engaged.

Goodhope engaged.

30

40

also send him some aid; so he made the Vocation-
doubters to retreat. The rest of the armies were hotly
engaged, and that on every side, and the Diabolonians
did fight stoutly. Then did my Lord Secretary command that the slings from the castle should be played;
and his men could throw stones at an hair's breadth.
But after a while those that were made to fly before
the captains of the Prince, did begin to rally again,
and they came up stoutly upon the rear of the Prince's
army: wherefore the Prince's army began to faint; but
rememb'ring that they should see the face of their
Prince by and by, they took courage, and a very fierce
battle was fought. Then shouted the captains, saying,
'The sword of the Prince Emmanuel, and the shield
of Captain Credence!' And with that Diabolus gave
back, thinking that more aid had been come. But no
Emmanuel as yet appeared. Moreover, the battle did
hang in doubt; and they made a little retreat on both
sides. Now, in the time of respite, Captain Credence
bravely encouraged his men to stand to it, and Diabolus did the like as well as he could. But Captain
Credence made a brave speech to his soldiers, the
contents where of here follow:

'Gentlemen soldiers, and my brethren in this
design, it rejoiceth me much to see in the field for our
Prince this day, so stout and so valiant an army, and
such faithful lovers of Mansoul. You have hitherto,
as hath become you, shown yourselves men of truth
and courage against the Diabolonian forces, so that
for all their boast, they have not yet cause much to
boast of their gettings. Now take to yourselves your
wonted courage, and show yourselves men even this
once only; for in a few minutes after the next engagement this time, you shall see your Prince show himself
in the field; for we must make this second assault upon
this tyrant Diabolus, and then Emmanuel comes.'

No sooner had the captain made this speech to his
soldiers, but one Mr. Speedy came post to the captain
from the Prince, to tell him that Emmanuel was at
hand. This news, when the captain had received, he
communicated to the other field-officers, and they

The Lord Secretary engaged.

The battle renewed.

A fierce fight.

They both retreat, and in the time of respite Captain Credence makes a speech to his soldiers.

again to their soldiers and men of war. Wherefore, like men raised from the dead, so the captains and their men arose, made up to the enemy, and cried as before, 'The sword of the Prince Emmanuel, and the shield of Captain Credence!'

The Diabolonians also bestirred themselves, and made resistance as well as they could, but in this last engagement the Diabolonians lost their courage, and many of the Doubters fell down dead to the ground. Now when they had been in heat of battle about an hour or more, Captain Credence lift up his eyes and saw—and behold, Emmanuel came. And he came with colours flying, trumpets sounding, and the feet of his men scarce touched the ground, they hasted with that celerity towards the captains that were engaged. Then did Credence wind with his men to the townward, and gave to Diabolus the field. So Emmanuel came upon him on the one side, and the enemies' place was betwixt them both; then again they fell to it afresh, and not it was but a little while more but Emmanuel and Captain Credence met, still trampling down the slain as they came.

But when the captains saw that the Prince was come, and that he fell upon the Diabolonians on the other side, and that Captain Credence and his Highness had got them up betwixt them, they shouted— they so shouted that the ground rent again—saying, 'The sword of Emmanuel, and the shield of Captain Credence!' Now when Diabolus saw that he and his forces were so hard beset by the Prince and his princely army, what does he and the lords of the Pit that were with him, but make their escape, and forsake their army, and leave them to fall by the hand of Emmanuel, and of his noble Captain Credence. So they fell all down slain before them, before the Prince, and before his royal army; there was not left so much as one Doubter alive; they lay spread upon the ground dead men, as one would spread dung upon the land.

When the battle was over, all things came into

10

20

30

16   *wind . . . to the townward*: i.e., turned towards the town.

order in the camp. Then the captains and elders of Mansoul came together to salute Emmanuel, while without the corporation: so they saluted him, and welcomed him, and that with a thousand welcomes, for that he was come to the borders of Mansoul again. So he smiled upon them, and said, 'Peace be to you.' Then they addressed themselves to go to the town; they went then to go up to Mansoul, they, the Prince, with all the new forces that now he had brought with him to the war. Also all the gates of the town were set open for his reception, so glad were they of his blessed return. And this was the manner and order of this going of his into Mansoul.

First, as I said, all the gates of the town were set open, yea, the gates of the castle also; the elders, too, of the town of Mansoul placed themselves at the gates of the town to salute him at his entrance thither. And so they did; for as he drew near, and approached towards the gates, they said, *Lift up your heads, ye gates, and be ye lift up ye everlasting doors, and the King of Glory shall come in.* And they answered again, *Who is the King of Glory?* and they made return to themselves, *The Lord strong and mighty, the Lord mighty in battle. Lift up your heads, O ye gates, even lift them up ye everlasting doors,* etc.

Secondly, it was ordered also by those of Mansoul, that all the way from the town-gates to those of the castle his blessed Majesty should be entertained with the song, by them that could best skill in music in all the town of Mansoul; then did the elders, and the rest of the men of Mansoul answer one another as Emmanuel entered the town, till he came at the castle-gates with songs and sound of trumpets, saying, *They have seen thy goings, O God, even the goings of my God, my King in the sanctuary.* So the singers went before, the players on instruments followed after, and among them were the damsels playing on timbrels.

Cant. 8:1.
Mansoul salutes the Prince without; he addresses himself to go into the town.

The manner of his going in.

19ff. See Ps. 24:7-10.
37 See Ps. 68:24-25.

Thirdly, then the captains (for I would speak a word of them), they in their order waited on the Prince as he ent'red into the gates of Mansoul. Captain Credence went before, and Captain Goodhope with him; Captain Charity came behind with other of his companions, and Captain Patience followed after all; and the rest of the captains, some on the right hand, and some on the left, accompanied Emmanuel into Mansoul. And all the while the colours were displayed, the trumpets sounded, and continual shoutings were among the soldiers. The Prince himself rode into the town in his armour, which was all of beaten gold, and in his chariot—the pillars of it were of silver, the bottom thereof of gold, the covering of it were of purple, the midst thereof being paved with love for the daughters of the town of Mansoul.

Fourthly, when the Prince was come to the entrance of Mansoul, he found all the streets strewed with lilies and flowers, curiously decked with boughs and branches from the green trees that stood round about the town. Every door also was filled with persons who had adorned every one their forepart against their house with something of variety, and singular excellency to entertain him withal as he passed in the streets. They also themselves, as Emmanuel passed by, did welcome him with shouts and acclamations of joy, saying, 'Blessed be the Prince that cometh in the name of his Father Shaddai!'

Fifthly, at the castle-gates the elders of Mansoul, to wit, the Lord Mayor, the Lord Willbewill, the Subordinate Preacher, Mr. Knowledge, and Mr. Mind, with other of the gentry of the place, saluted Emmanuel again. They bowed before him, they kissed the dust of his feet, they thanked, they blessed, and praised his Highness for not taking advantage against them for their sins, but rather had pity upon them in their misery, and returned to them with mercies, and to build up their Mansoul for ever. Thus was he had up straightway to the castle; for that was the royal

Good and joyful thoughts.

10

20

30

---

22   *their forepart against their house*: i.e., the front of every house.

palace, and the place where his Honour was to dwell; the which was ready prepared for his Highness by the presence of the Lord Secretary, and the work of Captain Credence. So he ent'red in.

Sixthly, then the people and commonalty of the town of Mansoul came to him into the castle to mourn, and to weep, and to lament for their wickedness, by which they had forced him out of the town. So they, when they were come, bowed themselves to the ground seven times; they also wept, they wept aloud, and asked forgiveness of the Prince, and prayed that he would again, as of old, confirm his love to Mansoul.

To the which the great Prince replied, '*Weep not, but go your way, eat the fat, and drink the sweet, and send portions to them for whom nought is prepared, for the joy of your Lord is your strength.* I am returned to Mansoul with mercies, and my name shall be set up, exalted and magnified by it.' He also took these inhabitants and kissed them, and laid them in his bosom.

Moreover, he gave to the elders of Mansoul, and to each town-officer a chain of gold, and a signet. He also sent to their wives ear-rings and jewels, and bracelets, and other things. He also bestowed upon the true-born children of Mansoul, many precious things.

The holy conceptions of Mansoul. Young and tender holy thoughts.

When Emmanuel the Prince had done all these things for the famous town of Mansoul, then he said unto them, first, 'Wash your garments, then put on your ornaments, and then come to me into the castle of Mansoul.' So they went to the fountain that was set open for Judah and Jerusalem to wash in; and there they washed, and there they made their garments white; and came again to the Prince into the castle, and thus they stood before him.

Eccles. 9:8.

Zech. 13:1.
Rev. 7:14,15.

And now there was music and dancing throughout the whole town of Mansoul; and that because their Prince had again granted to them his presence, and the light of his countenance. The bells also did

13ff. See Neh. 8:9-10.

ring, and the sun shone comfortably upon them for a great while together.

The town of Mansoul did also now more thoroughly seek the destruction and ruin of all remaining Diabolonians that abode in the walls, and the dens that they had in the town of Mansoul; for there was of them that had to this day escaped with life and limb from the hand of their suppressors in the famous town of Mansoul.

But my Lord Willbewill was a greater terror to them now than ever he had been before; forasmuch as his heart was yet more fully bent to seek, contrive, and pursue them to night and day, and did put them not to sore distress, as will afterwards appear.

After things were thus far put into order in the famous town of Mansoul, care was taken, and order given by the blessed Prince Emmanuel, that the townsmen should without further delay appoint some to go forth into the plain to bury the dead that were there—

the dead that fell *by the sword of Emmanuel, and by the shield of the Captain Credence*—lest the fumes and ill savours that would arise from them, might infect the air, and so annoy the famous town of Mansoul. This also was a reason of this order, to wit, that as much as in Mansoul lay, they might cut off the name, and being, and remembrance of those enemies from the thought of the famous town of Mansoul, and its inhabitants.

So order was given out by the Lord Mayor, that wise and trusty friend of the town of Mansoul, that persons should be employed about this necessary business; and Mr. Godlyfear, and one Mr. Upright were to be overseers about this matter; so persons were put under them to work in the fields, and to bury the slain that lay dead in the plains. And these were their places of employment: some were to make the graves, some to bury the dead, and some were to go to and fro in the plains, and also round about the borders of Mansoul to see if a skull or a bone, or a piece of a bone of a Doubter, was yet to be found above ground anywhere near the corporation; and if any were found,

10

20

30

40

it was ordered that the searchers that searched should set up a mark thereby, and a sign, that those that were appointed to bury them might find it, and bury it out of sight, that the name and remembrance of a Diabolonian Doubter might be blotted out from under Heaven; and that the children, and they that were to be born in Mansoul might not know (if possible) what a skull, what a bone, or a piece of a bone of a Doubter was. So the buriers, and those that were appointed for that purpose, did as they were commanded: they buried the Doubters, and all the skulls and bones, and pieces of bones of Doubters, where ever they found them; and so they cleansed the plains. Now also Mr. Gods-peace took up his commission, and acted again as in former days.

Not a skull or a bone, or a piece of a bone of a Doubter to be left unburied.

Thus they buried in the plains about Mansoul, the Election-doubters, the Vocation-doubters, the Grace-doubters, the Perseverance-doubters, the Resurrection-doubters, the Salvation-doubters, and the Glory-doubters; whose captains were Captain Rage, Captain Cruel, Captain Damnation, Captain Insatiable, Captain Brimstone, Captain Torment, Captain No-ease, Captain Sepulchre, and Captain Pasthope; and old Incredulity was, under Diabolus, their general. There were also the seven heads of their army, and they were the Lord Beelzebub, the Lord Lucifer, the Lord Legion, the Lord Apollyon, the Lord Python, the Lord Cerberus, and the Lord Belial. But the princes, and the captains with old Incredulity their general, did all of them make their escape; so their men fell down slain by the power of the Prince's forces, and by the hands of the men of the town of Mansoul. They also were buried as is afore related, to the exceeding great joy of the now famous town of Mansoul. They that buried them, buried also with them their arms, which were cruel instruments of death (their weapons were arrows, darts, mauls, fire-brands, and the like). They buried also their armour, their colours, banners, with the standard of Diabolus, and what else soever they

Their arms and armour buried with them.

2ff. Cf. Ezek. 39:14-15.

258

could find that did smell of a Diabolonian Doubter.

Now when the tyrant was arrived at Hellgate-hill, with his old friend Incredulity, they immediately descended the Den, and having there with their fellows for a while condoled their misfortune, and great loss that they sustained against the town of Mansoul, they fell at length into a passion, and revenged they would be for the loss that they sustained before the town of Mansoul. Wherefore, they presently call a council to contrive yet further what was to be done against the famous town of Mansoul; for their yawning paunches could not wait to see the result of their Lord Lucifer's, and their Lord Apollyon's counsel that they had given before; for their raging gorge thought every day even as long as a short-for-ever, until they were filled with the body and soul, with the flesh and bones, and with all the delicates of Mansoul. They therefore resolve to make another attempt upon the town of Mansoul, and that by an army mixed, and made up partly of Doubters, and partly of Bloodmen. A more particular account now take of both.

The Doubters are such as have their name from their nature, as well as from the lord and kingdom where they are born: their nature is to put a question upon every one of the truths of Emmanuel, and their country is called the Land of Doubting, and that land lieth off, and furthest remote to the North, between the Land of Darkness, and that called the Valley of the Shadow of Death. For though the Land of Darkness, and that called the Land of the Shadow of Death, be sometimes called as if they were one and the self-same place, yet indeed they are two, lying but a little way asunder, and the Land of Doubting points in, and lieth between them. This is the Land of Doubting, and these that came with Diabolus to ruin the town of Mansoul, are the natives of that country.

The Bloodmen are a people that have their name

The tyrant resolves to have yet a bout with Mansoul.

An army of Doubters and Bloodmen.

Of the country of the Doubters, and of the Bloodmen where they lie.

10

20

30

15 *as long as a short-for-ever*: i.e., each day seemed endless.
38 The Bloodmen represent oppressors of Nonconformists in Restoration times. In *Antichrist and His Ruin*, (*Works*, ed. Offor, II, 65-68), Bunyan suggests

derived from the malignity of their nature, and from the fury that is in them to execute it upon the town of Mansoul; their land lieth under the Dog-star, and by that they are governed as to their intellectuals. The name of their country is the Province of Loathgood: the remote parts of it are far distant from the Land of Doubting, yet they do both butt and bound upon the hill called Hellgate-hill. These people are always in league with the Doubters, for they jointly do make question of the faith and fidelity of the men of the town of Mansoul, and so are both alike qualified for the service of their prince.

Now of these two countries did Diabolus by the beating of his drum raise another army against the town of Mansoul, of five and twenty thousand strong. There were ten thousand Doubters, and fifteen thousand Bloodmen, and they were put under several captains for the war; and old Incredulity was again made general of the army.

The number of his new army.

As for the Doubters, their captains were five of the seven that were heads of the last Diabolonian army, and these are their names, Captain Beelzebub, Captain Lucifer, Captain Apollyon, Captain Legion, and Captain Cerberus; and the captains that they had before, were some of them made lieutenants, and some ensigns of the army.

But Diabolus did not count that in this expedition of his, these Doubters would prove his principal men, for their manhood had been tried before; also the Mansoulians had put them to the worst: only he did bring them to multiply a number, and to help, if need was, at a pinch. But his trust he put in his Bloodmen, for that they were all rugged villains, and he knew that they had done feats heretofore.

His chief strength lies in the Bloodmen.

---

that the two final attacks against the saints will be made by the Doubters upon their faith and by the Bloodmen upon their bodies. See W. Y. Tindall, *John Bunyan, Mechanick Preacher* (New York, 1934), p. 155.

3   *Dog-star*: Sirius, the bright star in the constellation of the Greater Dog (*Canis Major*), which supposedly exercised a malignant influence upon the earth.

4   *intellectuals*: intellectual faculties.

As for the Bloodmen, they also were under command, and the names of their captains were Captain Cain, Captain Nimrod, Captain Ishmael, Captain Esau, Captain Saul, Captain Absalom, Captain Judas, and Captain Pope.

The captains of the Bloodmen.

1. Captain Cain was over two bands, to wit, the zealous and the angry Bloodmen; his standard-bearer bare the red colours, and his scutcheon was the murdering club.

Gen. 4:8.

2. Captain Nimrod was captain over two bands, to wit, the tyrannical and encroaching Bloodmen; his standard-bearer bare the red colours, and his scutcheon was the great bloodhound.

Gen. 10:8-9.

3. Captain Ishmael was captain over two bands, to wit, over the mocking and scorning Bloodmen; his standard-bearer bare the red colours, and his scutcheon was one mocking at Abraham's Isaac.

4. Captain Esau was captain over two bands, to wit, the Bloodmen that grudged that another should have the blessing; also over the Bloodmen that are for executing their private revenge upon others; his standard-bearer bare the red colours, and his scutcheon was one privately lurking to murder Jacob.

Gen. 21:9-10.
Gen. 27:42-45.

5. Captain Saul was captain over two bands, to wit, the groundlessly-jealous, and the devilishly furious Bloodmen; his standard-bearer bare the red colours, and his scutcheon was three bloody darts cast at harmless David.

I Sam. 18:10;
19:10; 20:23.
II Sam. 15:17.

6. Captain Absalom was captain over two bands, to wit, over the Bloodmen that will kill a father or a friend, for the glory of this world; also over those Bloodmen that will hold one fair in hand with words, till they shall have pierced him with their swords; his standard-bearer did bear the red colours, and his scutcheon was the son a-pursuing the father's blood.

7. Captain Judas was over two bands, to wit, the Bloodmen that will sell a man's life for money, and those also that will betray their friend with a kiss; his standard-bearer bare the red colours, and his scutcheon

Matt. 26:14-16.

10

20

30

32   *hold one fair in hand with words*: delude, deceive.

was thirty pieces of silver, and the halter.

8. Captain Pope was captain over one band, for all these spirits are joined in one under him; his standard-bearer bare the red colours, and his scutcheon was the stake, the flame, and the good man in it.

Rev. 13:7-8.
Dan. 11:33.

Now the reason why Diabolus did so soon rally another force after he had been beaten out of the field, were for that he put mighty confidence in this army of Bloodmen; for he put a great deal of more trust in them, than he did before in his army of Doubters, though they had also often done great service for him in the strengthening of him in his kingdom. But these Bloodmen, he had proved them often, and their sword did seldom return empty. Besides, he knew that these, like mastiffs, would fasten upon any; upon father, mother, brother, sister, prince, or governor—yea, upon the Prince of princes. And that which encouraged him the more was for that they once did force Emmanuel out of the kingdom of Universe. And why, thought he, *may they not also drive him from the town of Mansoul?*

The conditions of the Bloodmen, their stoutness, and valor.

So this army of five-and-twenty thousand strong, was by their general the great Lord Incredulity, led up against the town of Mansoul. Now Mr. Prywell the Scoutmaster-general, did himself go out to spy, and he did bring Mansoul tidings of their coming. Wherefore they shut up their gates, and put themselves in a posture of defence against these new Diabolonians that came up against the town.

They sit down before Mansoul.

So Diabolus brought up his army, and beleaguered the town of Mansoul; the Doubters were placed about Feelgate, and the Bloodmen set down before Eyegate and Eargate.

How they dispose of themselves.

Now when this army had thus encamped themselves, Incredulity did in the name of Diabolus, his own name, and in the name of the Bloodmen, and the rest that were with him, send a summons as hot as a red-hot iron to Mansoul, to yield to their demands; threat'ning that if they still stood it out against them, they would presently burn down Mansoul with fire. For you must know that as for the Bloodmen, they

They summon the town with a threat'ning.

were not so much that Mansoul should be surrend'red, as that Mansoul should be destroyed, and cut off out of the land of the living. True, they send to them to surrender, but should they so do, that would not stanch or quench the thirsts of these men. They must have blood, the blood of Mansoul, else they die; and it is from hence that they have their name. Wherefore these Bloodmen he reserved while now that they might, when all his engines proved ineffectual, as his last and sure card be played against the town of Mansoul.

Ps. 29:10.
Isa. 59:7.
Jer. 22:17.

Now when the townsmen had received this red-hot summons, it begat in them at present some changing and interchanging thoughts; but they jointly agreed in less than half an hour to carry the summons to the Prince, the which they did when they had writ at the bottom of it, *Lord, save Mansoul from bloody men!*

Ps. 59:2.

So he took it, and looked upon it, and considered it, and took notice also of that short petition that the men of Mansoul had written at the bottom of it and called to him the noble Captain Credence, and bid him go and take Captain Patience with him, and go and take care of that side of Mansoul that was beleaguered by the Bloodmen. So they went and did as they were commanded, the Captain Credence went and took Captain Patience, and they both secured that side of Mansoul that was besieged by the Bloodmen.

Heb. 6:12,15.

Then he commanded that Captain Goodhope and Captain Charity, and my Lord Willbewill, should take charge of the other side of the town. 'And I,' said the Prince, 'will set my standard upon the battlements of your castle, and do you three watch against the Doubt-ers.' This done, he again commanded that the brave captain, the Captain Experience, should draw up his men in the market-place, and that there he should exercise them day by day before the people of the town of Mansoul. Now this siege was long, and many a fierce attempt did the enemy, especially those called

5   *stanch*: appease, allay.

the Bloodmen, make upon the town of Mansoul; and many a shrewd brush did some of the townsmen meet with from them, especially Captain Self-denial; who, I should have told you before, was commanded to take the care of Eargate and Eyegate now against the Bloodmen. This Captain Self-denial was a young man, but stout, and a townsman in Mansoul, as Captain Experience also was. And Emmanuel at his second return to Mansoul, made him a captain over a thousand of the Mansoulians, for the good of the corporation. This captain, therefore, being an hardy man, and a man of great courage, and willing to venture himself for the good of the town of Mansoul, would now and then sally out upon the Bloodmen, and give them many notable alarms, and entered several brisk skirmishes with them, and also did some execution upon them; but you must think that this could not easily be done, but he must meet with brushes himself, for he carried several of their marks in his face; yea, and some in some other parts of his body.

So after some time spent for the trial of the faith, and hope, and love of the town of Mansoul, the Prince Emmanuel upon a day calls his captains and men of war together, and divides them into two companies; this done, he commands them at a time appointed, and that in the morning very early, to sally out upon the enemy, saying, 'Let half of you fall upon the Doubters, and half of you fall upon the Bloodmen. Those of you that go out against the Doubters, kill and slay, and cause to perish so many of them as by any means you can lay hands on; but for you that go out against the Bloodmen, slay them not, but take them alive.'

So at the time appointed, betimes in the morning the captains went out as they were commanded against the enemies. Captain Goodhope, Captain Charity, and those that were joined with them, as Captain Innocent, and Captain Experience, went out against the Doubt-

Sidenotes:
Captain Self-denial the last of those that were put in office in the town of Mansoul.

His valor.

His signs of manhood.

Emmanuel prepares to give the enemy battle. How he ordereth his men.

The captains go out.

2   *shrewd brush*: short but sharp encounter.
18   *brushes*: wounds.

ers; and Captain Credence, and Captain Patience, with Captain Self-denial, and the rest that were to join with them, went out against the Bloodmen.

Now those that went out against the Doubters, drew up into a body before the plain, and marched on to bid them battle. But the Doubters, rememb'ring their last success, made a retreat, not daring to stand the shock, but fled from the Prince's men; wherefore they pursued them, and in their pursuit slew many, but they could not catch them all. Now those that escaped went some of them home, and the rest by fives, nines, and seventeens, like wanderers, went straggling up and down the country, where they upon the barbarous people showed and exercised many of their Diabolonian actions; nor did these people rise up in arms against them, but suffered themselves to be enslaved by them. They would also after this show themselves in companies before the town of Mansoul, but never to abide it; for if Captain Credence, Captain Goodhope, or Captain Experience did but show themselves, they fled.

Those that went out against the Bloodmen, did as they were commanded: they forbore to slay any, but sought to compass them about. But the Bloodmen, when they saw that no Emmanuel was in the field, concluded also that no Emmanuel was in Mansoul; wherefore they, looking upon what the captains did, to be, as they called it, a fruit of the extravagancy of their wild and foolish fancies, rather despised them, than feared them. But the captains minding their business, at last did compass them round; they also that had routed the Doubters came in amain to their aid. So, in fine, after some little struggling, for the Bloodmen also would have run for it, only now it was too late—for though they are mischievous and

The Doubters put to flight.

The unbeliever never fights the Doubters.

The Bloodmen are taken, and how.

10

20

30

12 *fives, nines, and seventeens:* "Five infernal spirits were the leaders of the Satanic army. It consisted of nine companies of Doubters, and eight of Bloodmen, or persecutors. First, five fallen angels; second, nine classes of doubts, and if this was not enough to enslave the soul, they were to be aided by eight classes of persecutors. This may account for the grouping of these dangerous enemies in fives, nines, and seventeens.' (*Works,* ed. Offor, III, 364).

cruel, where they can overcome, yet all Bloodmen are chicken-hearted men, when they once come to see themselves matched and equall'd. So the captains took them, and brought them to the Prince.

Now when they were taken, had before the Prince, and examined, he found them to be of three several countries, though they all came out of one land.

They are brought to the Prince, and found to be of 3 sorts.

1. One sort of them came out of Blindmanshire, and they were such as did *ignorantly* what they did.

2. Another sort of them came out of Blindzealshire, and they did *superstitiously* what they did.

3. The third sort of them came out of the town of Malice in the county of Envy, and they did what they did *out of spite and implacableness*.

For the first of these, to wit, they that came out of Blindmanshire, when they saw where they were, and against whom they had fought, they trembled, and cried as they stood before him; and as many of these as asked him mercy, he touched their lips with his golden sceptre.

I Tim. 1:13-15.
Matt. 5:44.
Luke 6:22.
John 16:1,2.
Acts 9:5,6.
Rev. 9:20,21.
John 8:40-43,
etc.

They that came out of Blindzealshire, they did not as their fellows did, for they pleaded that they had right to do what they did, because Mansoul was a town whose laws and customs were diverse from all that dwelt thereabouts. Very few of these could be brought to see their evil; but those that did, and asked mercy, they also obtained favour.

Now they that came out of the town of Malice, that is in the county of Envy, they neither wept, nor disputed, nor repented, but stood gnawing of their tongues before him for anguish and madness, because they could not have their will upon Mansoul. Now these last, with all those of the other two sorts that did not unfeignedly ask pardon for their faults—those he made to enter into sufficient bond to answer for what they had done against Mansoul, and against her King, at the great and general Assizes to be held for our Lord the King, where he himself should appoint for the country and kingdom of Universe.

The Bloodmen are bound over to answer for what they have done at the Assizes. The day of Judgment.

So they became bound each man for himself to

come in when called upon to answer before our Lord the King for what they had done as before.

And thus much concerning this second army that were sent by Diabolus to overthrow Mansoul.

But there were three of those that came from the land of Doubting, who after they had wand'red and ranged the country a while, and perceived that they had escaped, were so hardy as to thrust themselves, knowing that yet there were in the town Diabolonians—I say, they were so hardy as to thrust themselves into Mansoul among them. (Three, did I say? I think there were four.) Now to whose house should these Diabolonian Doubters go, but to the house of an old Diabolonian in Mansoul, whose name was Evil-questioning; a very great enemy he was to Mansoul, and a great doer among the Diabolonians there. Well, to this Evil-questioning's house, as was said, did these Diabolonians come (you may be sure that they had directions how to find the way thither); so he made them welcome, pitied their misfortune, and succoured them with the best that he had in his house. Now after a little acquaintance (and it was not long before they had that), this old Evil-questioning asked the Doubters if they were all of a town (he knew that they were all of one kingdom); and they answered, *No, nor not of one shire, neither.* 'For I,' said one, 'am an Election-doubter.' 'I,' said another, 'am a Vocation-doubter.' Then said the third, 'I am a Salvation-doubter,' and the fourth said he was a Grace-doubter. 'Well,' quoth the old gentleman, 'be of what shire you will, I am persuaded that you are down boys: you have the very length of my foot, are one with my

Marginal notes:

Three or four of the Doubters go into Mansoul, are entertained, and by whom.

What sort of Doubters they are.

Line numbers: 10, 20, 30

---

31   *down boys:* the second and third editions alter to *town boys,* a form apparently maintained until 1720, when the first edition reading was restored. The emendation is not unattractive contextually, for it catches up the earlier question of the Doubters' being "all of a town"; but that is really all that can be said for it. There is no evidence that the phrase *town boys* is meant to qualify the Doubters with any degree of sophistication. On the other hand, *down boys* is not only fitting in context but is meaningful in itself, since "down" was quite commonly employed in vulgar English as an intensive with the sense of "plain and direct" or "blunt and determined," e.g., "He's a down good fellow." Cf. modern "downright."

32   *have the very length of my foot:* fully understand me, know my predilec-

heart, and shall be welcome to me.' So they thanked him, and were glad that they had found themselves an harbour in Mansoul. Then said Evil-questioning to them, 'How many of your company might there be that came with you to the siege of Mansoul?' And they answered, there were but ten thousand Doubters in all, for the rest of the army consisted of fifteen thousand Bloodmen. 'These Bloodmen,' quoth they, 'border upon our country; but, poor men! as we hear, they were every one taken by Emmanuel's forces.' 'Ten thousand!' quoth the old gentleman, 'I'll promise you that's a round company. But how came it to pass, since you were so mighty a number, that you fainted, and durst not fight your foes?' 'Our general,' said they, 'was the first man that did run for't.' 'Pray,' quoth their landlord, 'who was that your cowardly general?' 'He was once the Lord Mayor of Mansoul,' said they. 'But pray call him not a cowardly general, for whether any from the East to the West has done more service for our Prince Diabolus, than has my Lord Incredulity, will be a hard question for you to answer. But had they catched him they would for certain have hanged him, and we promise you hanging is but a bad business.' Then said the old gentleman, 'I would that all the ten thousand Doubters were now well armed in Mansoul, and myself in the head of them; I would see what I could do.' 'Ay,' said they, 'that would be well if we could see that. But wishes, alas! what are they?' And these words were spoken aloud. 'Well,' said old Evil-questioning, 'take heed that you talk not too loud: you must be quat and close, and must take care of yourselves while you are here, or I'll assure you, you will be snapped.'

'Why?' quoth the Doubters.

'Why!' quoth the old gentleman, 'why, because both the Prince, and Lord Secretary, and their captains and soldiers are all at present in town; yea, the town

Talk betwixt
the Doubters,
and old Evil-
questioning.

---

tions and weaknesses. The allusion is doubtless to the shoemaker's measuring of feet.

12   *round*: large.
33   *snapped*: seized suddenly.

is as full of them as ever it can hold. And besides,
there is one whose name is Willbewill, a most cruel
enemy of ours, and him the Prince has made keeper
of the gates, and has commanded him that with all
the diligence he can, he should look for, search out,
and destroy all, and all manner of Diabolonians.

'And if he lighteth upon you, down you go,
though your heads were made of gold.'

And now to see how it happened, one of the
Lord Willbewill's faithful soldiers, whose name was
Mr. Diligence, stood all this while list'ning under old
Evil-questioning's eaves and heard all the talk that had
been betwixt him and the Doubters that he enter-
tained under his roof.

The soldier was a man that my lord had much
confidence in, and that he loved dearly, and that both
because he was a man of courage, and also a man that
was unwearied in seeking after Diabolonians to apprehend them.

Now this man, as I told you, heard all the talk
that was between old Evil-questioning, and these Diabolonians; wherefore, what does he but goes to his
lord, and tells him what he had heard. 'And sayest
thou so, my trusty?' quoth my lord. 'Ay,' quoth
Diligence, 'that I do; and if your lord shall be pleased
to go with me, you shall find it as I have said.' 'And
are they there?' quoth my lord. 'I know Evil-questioning well, for he and I were great in the time of our
apostasy. But I know not now where he dwells.' 'But
I do,' said his man, 'and if your lordship will go, I will
lead you the way to his den.' 'Go!' quoth my lord,
'that I will. Come, my Diligence, let's go find them
out.' So my lord and his man went together the direct
way to his house. Now his man went before to show
him his way, and they went till they came even under
old Mr. Evil-questioning's wall. Then said Diligence,
'Hark! My lord, do you know the old gentleman's
tongue when you hear it?' 'Yes,' said my lord, 'I
know it well, but I have not seen him many a day.
This I know, he is cunning; I wish he doth not give
us the slip.' 'Let me alone for that,' said his servant

They are over-
heard.

They are dis-
covered.

10

20

30

40

Diligence. 'But how shall we find the door?' quoth my lord. 'Let me alone for that too,' said his man. So he had my Lord Willbewill about, and showed him the way to the door. Then my lord without more ado, broke open the door, rushed into the house, and caught them all five together, even as Diligence his man had told him. So my lord apprehended them, and led them away, and committed them to the hand of Mr. Trueman, the gaoler, and commanded, and he did put them in ward. This done, my lord Mayor was acquainted in the morning with what my Lord Willbewill had done over night, and his lordship rejoiced much at the news, not only because there were Doubters apprehended, but because that old Evil-questioning was taken; for he had been a very great trouble to Mansoul, and much affliction to my Lord Mayor himself. He had also been sought for often, but no hand could ever be laid upon him till now.

They are apprehended, and committed to prison.

The Lord Mayor is glad at it.

Well, the next thing was to make preparation to try these five that by my lord had been apprehended, and that were in the hands of Mr. Trueman, the gaoler. So the day was set, and the Court called and come together, and the prisoners brought to the bar. My Lord Willbewill had power to have slain them when at first he took them, and that without any more ado, but he thought it at this time more for the honour of the Prince, the comfort of Mansoul, and the discouragement of the enemy, to bring them forth to public judgment.

They are brought to trial.

But, I say, Mr. Trueman brought them in chains to the bar, to the town-hall, for that was the place of judgment. So to be short, the jury was panelled, the witnesses sworn, and the prisoners tried for their lives: the jury was the same that tried Mr. No-truth, Pitiless, Haughty, and the rest of their companions.

And first old Questioning himself was set to the bar; for he was the receiver, the entertainer and comforter of these Doubters, that by nation were outlandish men. Then he was bid to hearken to his charge, and was told that he had liberty to object, if he had aught to say for himself. So his indictment was read; the manner and form here follows—

'Mr. Questioning, thou art here indicted by the His indictment. name of Evil-questioning, an intruder upon the town of Mansoul, for that thou art a Diabolonian by nature, and also a hater of the Prince Emmanuel, and one that hast studied the ruin of the town of Mansoul. Thou art also here indicted for countenancing the King's enemies, after wholesome laws made to the contrary. For, 1. Thou hast questioned the truth of her doctrine and state. 2. In wishing that ten thousand Doubters were in her. 3. In receiving, in entertaining and encouraging of her enemies, that came from their army unto thee. What sayest thou to this indictment? Art thou guilty or not guilty?'

'My lord,' quoth he, 'I know not the meaning of His plea. this indictment, forasmuch as I am not the man concerned in it. The man that standeth by this charge accused before this bench, is called by the name of Evil-questioning, which name I deny to be mine, mine being Honest-enquiring. The one indeed sounds like the other, but I trow, your lordships know that between these two there is a wide difference; for I hope that a man even in the worst of times, and that too amongst the worst of men, may make an honest enquiry after things, without running the danger of death.'

WILLBE. Then spake my Lord Willbewill, for he The Lord Willbewill's testimony. was one of the witnesses: 'My lord, and you the honourable bench, and magistrates of the town of Mansoul, you all have heard with your ears that the prisoner at the bar has denied his name, and so thinks to shift from the charge of the indictment. But I know him to be the man concerned, and that his proper name is Evil-questioning. I have known him, my lord, above this thirty years, for he and I—a shame it is for me to speak it—were great acquaintance, when Diabolus that tyrant had the government of Mansoul; and I testify that he is a Diabolonian by nature, an enemy to our Prince, and an hater of the blessed town of Mansoul. He has in times of rebellion been at, and lain in my

10

20

30

40

21   *trow*: believe.

house, my lord, not so little as twenty nights together, and we did use to talk then, for the substance of talk, as he and his Doubters have talked of late. True, I have not seen him many a day. I suppose that the coming of Emmanuel to Mansoul, has made him to change his lodgings, as this indictment has driven him to change his name; but this is the man, my lord.'

Then said the Court unto him: 'Hast thou any more to say?'   The Court.

EVIL. 'Yes,' quoth the old gentleman, 'that I have; for all that as yet has been said against me, is but by   His plea. the mouth of one witness, and it is not lawful for the famous town of Mansoul, at the mouth of one witness to put any man to death.'

DILIG. Then stood forth Mr. Diligence, and said, 'My lord, as I was upon my watch such a night at the   Mr. Diligence's head of Bad Street in this town, I chanced to hear a   testimony. muttering within this gentleman's house. Then thought I, *What's to do here?* So I went up close, but very softly to the side of the house to listen, thinking, as indeed it fell out, that there I might light upon some Diabolonian conventicle. So, as I said, I drew nearer and nearer, and when I was got up close to the wall, it was but a while before I perceived that there were outlandish men in the house; but I did well understand their speech, for I have been a traveller myself. Now hearing such language in such a tottering cottage as this old gentleman dwelt in, I clapped mine ear to a hole in the window and there heard them talk as followeth. This old Mr. Questioning asked these Doubters what they were, whence they came, and what was their business in these parts; and they told him to all these questions, yet he did entertain them. He also asked what numbers there were of them, and they told him ten thousand men. He then asked them why they made no more manly assault upon Mansoul, and they told him; so he called their general coward for marching off when he should have fought for his

---

22   *conventicle*: although the term usually referred to such illegal meetings as those held by the Scottish Covenanters in the seventeenth century, it was often applied contemptuously (as here) to any "hole-and-corner" meeting.

prince. Further, this old Evil-questioning wished, and
I heard him wish, would all the ten thousand Doubters
were now in Mansoul, and himself in the head of
them. He bid them also to take heed and lie quat, for
if they were taken they must die, although they had
heads of gold.'

The Court.   Then said the Court, 'Mr. Evil-questioning here
is now another witness against you, and his testimony
is full: 1. He swears that you did receive these men
into your house, and that you did nourish them
there, though you knew that they were Diabolonians,
and the King's enemies. 2. He swears that you did
wish ten thousand of them in Mansoul. 3. He swears
that you did give them advice to be quat and close
lest they were taken by the King's servants. All which
manifesteth that thou art a Diabolonian; but hadst
thou been a friend to the King, thou wouldest have
apprehended them.'

His plea.   EVIL. Then said Evil-questioning, 'To the first of
these I answer: the men that came into mine house
were strangers, and I took them in; and is it now
become a crime in Mansoul for a man to entertain
strangers? That I did also nourish them is true; and
why should my charity be blamed? As for the reason
why I wished ten thousand of them in Mansoul, I
never told it to the witnesses, nor to themselves. I
might wish them to be taken, and so my wish might
mean well to Mansoul, for aught that any yet knows.
I did also bid them take heed that they fell not into
the captains' hands, but that might be because I am
unwilling that any man should be slain, and not because I would have the King's enemies as such escape.'

My Lord Mayor then replied, that though it was
a virtue to entertain strangers, yet it was treason to
entertain the King's enemies. 'And for what else thou
hast said, thou dost by words but labour to evade, and
defer the execution of judgment. But could there be
no more proved against thee but that thou art a
Diabolonian, thou must for that die the death by the
law; but to be a receiver, a nourisher, a countenancer,
and a harbourer of others of them, yea, of outlandish

Diabolonians, yea, of them that came from far on purpose to cut off and destroy our Mansoul—this must not be borne.'

Then said Evil-questioning, 'I see how the game will go: I must die for my name, and for my charity.' And so he held his peace.

His conclusion.

Then they called the outlandish Doubters to the bar, and the first of them that was arraigned, was the Election-doubter. So his indictment was read, and because he was an outlandish man, the substance of it was told him by an interpreter; to wit, *that he was there charged with being an enemy of Emmanuel the Prince, a hater of the town of Mansoul, and an opposer of her most wholesome doctrine.*

The Election-doubter tried.

Then the Judge asked him if he would plead; but he said only this, *that he confessed that he was an Election-doubter, and that that was the religion that he had ever been brought up in.* And said, moreover, 'If I must die for my religion, I trow, I shall die a martyr; and so I care the less.'

His plea.

JUDG. Then it was replied, 'To question election is to overthrow a great doctrine of the Gospel—to wit, the Omnisciency, and Power, and Will of God; to take away the liberty of God with his creature, to stumble the faith of the town of Mansoul, and to make salvation to depend upon works and not upon grace.' It also belied the Word, and disquieted the minds of the men of Mansoul; therefore by the best of laws he must die.

The Court.

Then was the Vocation-doubter called, and set to the bar; and his indictment for substance was the same with the other, only he was particularly charged with denying the calling of Mansoul.

The Vocation-doubter tried.

The Judge asked him also what he had to say for himself.

So he replied, *that he never believed that there was any such thing as a distinct and powerful call of God to Mansoul; otherwise than by the general voice of the Word, nor by that neither otherwise than as it exhorted them to forbear evil, and to do that which is good, and in so doing a promise of happiness is annexed.*

Then said the Judge, 'Thou art a Diabolonian, and hast denied a great part of one of the most experimental truths of the Prince of the town of Mansoul; for he has called, and she has heard a most distinct and powerful call of her Emmanuel, by which she has been quick'ned, awakened, and possessed with heavenly grace to desire to have communion with her Prince, to serve him, and do his will, and to look for her happiness merely of his good pleasure. And for thine abhorrence of this good doctrine, thou must die the death.'

Then the Grace-doubter was called, and his indictment was read, and he replied thereto, *that though he was of the land of Doubting, his father was the offspring of a Pharisee, and lived in good fashion among his neighbours, and that he taught him to believe—* 'and believe it I do, and will, that Mansoul shall never be saved freely by grace.'

Then said the Judge: 'Why, the law of the Prince is plain: 1. Negatively, *not of works*; 2. Positively, *by grace you are saved.* And thy religion settleth in and upon the works of the flesh. Besides, in saying as thou hast done, thou hast robbed God of his glory, and given it to a sinful man; thou hast robbed Christ of the necessity of his undertaking, and the sufficiency thereof, and hast given both these to the works of the flesh. Thou hast despised the work of the Holy Ghost, and hast magnified the will of the flesh, and of the legal mind. Thou art a Diabolonian, the son of a Diabolonian; and for thy Diabolonian principles thou must die.'

The Court then, having proceeded thus far with them, sent out the jury, who forthwith brought them in guilty of death. Then stood up the Recorder, and addressed himself to the prisoners: 'You, the prisoners at the Bar, you have been here indicted, and proved

The Grace-doubters tried.

Rom. 3.
Eph. 2.

10

20

30

4f. *experimental truths*: truths thoroughly grounded in or derived from religious experience.

guilty of high crimes against Emmanuel our Prince, and against the welfare of the famous town of Mansoul—crimes for which you must be put to death; and die ye accordingly.'

So they were sentenced to the death of the cross. The place assigned them for execution was that where Diabolus drew up his last army against Mansoul, save only that old Evil-questioning was hanged at the top of Bad Street, just over against his own door.

When the town of Mansoul had thus far rid themselves of their enemies, and of the troublers of their peace, in the next place a strict commandment was given out that yet my Lord Willbewill should, with Diligence his man, search for and do his best to apprehend what town Diabolonians were yet left alive in Mansoul. The names of several of them were Mr. Fooling, Mr. Letgoodslip, Mr. Slavishfear, Mr. Nolove, Mr. Mistrust, Mr. Flesh, and Mr. Sloth. It was also commanded that he should apprehend Mr. Evil-questioning's children, that he left behind him, and that they should demolish his house. The children that he left behind him were these: Mr. Doubt, and he was his eldest son; the next to him was Legal-life, Unbelief, Wrong-thoughts-of-Christ, Clip-promise, Carnal-sense, Live-by-feeling, Self-love. All these he had by one wife, and her name was Nohope; she was the kinswoman of old Incredulity, for he was her uncle; and when her father, old Dark, was dead, he took her and brought her up; and when she was marriageable, he gave her to this old Evil-questioning to wife.

Now the Lord Willbewill did put into execution his commission, with great Diligence, his man. He took Fooling in the streets, and hanged him up in Wantwit Alley, over against his own house. This Fooling was he that would have withdrawn his force out of the town. He also took Mr. Letgoodslip one day as he was busy in the market, and executed him according to law. Now there was an honest poor man in Mansoul, and his name was Mr. Meditation, one of no great account in the days of apostasy, but now of repute with the best of the town. This man, therefore, they were willing to prefer. Now Mr. Letgoodslip had a great deal of wealth heretofore in Mansoul, and at Emmanuel's coming it was sequest'red to the use of the Prince; this therefore was now given to Mr. Meditation to improve for the common good, and after him to his son, Mr. Thinkwell; this Thinkwell he had by Mrs. Piety his wife, and she was the daughter of Mr. Recorder.

Clip-promise taken. After this my lord apprehended Clip-promise, now because he was a notorious villain (for by his doings much of the King's coin was abused), therefore he was made a public example. He was arraigned and judged to be first set in the pillory, then to be whipped by all the children and servants in Mansoul, and then to be hanged till he was dead. Some may wonder at the severity of this man's punishment, but those that are honest traders in Mansoul, are sensible of the great abuse that one clipper of promises in little time may do to the town of Mansoul. And truly, my judgment is that all those of his name and life should be served even as he.

Carnal-sense taken. He also apprehended Carnal-sense, and put him in hold; but how it came about I cannot tell, but he brake prison and made his escape. Yea, and the bold villain will not yet quit the town, but lurks in the Diabolonian dens a-days, and haunts like a ghost honest men's houses a-nights. Wherefore there was a proclamation set up in the market-place in Mansoul, signifying that whosoever could discover Carnal-sense, and apprehend him and slay him, should be admitted daily to the Prince's table, and should be made keeper of the treasure of Mansoul. Many therefore did bend themselves to do this thing, but take him and slay him they could not, though often he was discovered.

Wrong-thoughts-of-Christ taken. But my lord took Mr. Wrong-thoughts-of-Christ, and put him in prison, and he died there; though it was long first, for he died of a lingering consumption.

Self-love taken. Self-love was also taken and committed to custody; but there were many that were allied to him in Man-

---

3   *sequest'red*: confiscated.

soul, so his judgment was deferred. But at last Mr. Self-denial stood up and said, 'If such villains as these may be winked at in Mansoul, I will lay down my commission.' He also took him from the crowd, and had him among his soldiers, and there he was brained. But some in Mansoul muttered at it, though none durst plainly, because Emmanuel was in town. But this brave act of Captain Self-denial came to the Prince's ears, so he sent for him, and made him a lord in Mansoul. My Lord Willbewill also obtained great commendations of Emmanuel for what he had done for the town of Mansoul.

Then my Lord Self-denial took courage, and set to the pursuing of the Diabolonians with my Lord Willbewill; and they took Live-by-feeling, and they took Legal-life, and put them in hold till they died. But Mr. Unbelief was a nimble Jack; him they could never lay hold of, though they attempted to do it often. He therefore, and some few more of the subtlest of the Diabolonian tribe, did yet remain in Mansoul, to the time that Mansoul left off to dwell any longer in the kingdom of Universe. But they kept them to their dens and holes: if one of them did appear or happen to be seen in any of the streets of the town of Mansoul, the whole town would be up in arms after them; yea, the very children in Mansoul would cry out after them as after a thief, and would wish that they might stone them to death with stones. And now did Mansoul arrive to some good degree of peace and quiet; her Prince also did abide within her borders; her captains also, and her soldiers did their duties; and Mansoul minded her trade that she had with the country that was afar off; also she was busy in her manufacture.

When the town of Mansoul had thus far rid themselves of so many of their enemies, and the troublers of their peace, the Prince sent to them, and appointed a day wherein he would at the market-place, meet the whole people, and there give them in

Captain Self-denial made a lord.

Live-by-feeling taken.

The peace of Mansoul, she minds her trade. Isa. 33:17. Phil. 3:20. Prov. 31.

17   *nimble Jack*: slippery rascal, tricky knave.

charge concerning some further matters, that, if observed, would tend to their further safety and comfort, and to the condemnation and destruction of their home-bred Diabolonians. So the day appointed was come, and the townsmen met together; Emmanuel also came down in his chariot, and all his captains in their state attending of him, on the right hand and on the left. Then was an 'O yes!' made for silence; and after some mutual carriages of love, the Prince began, and thus proceeded—

'You my Mansoul, and the beloved of mine heart, many and great are the privileges that I have bestowed upon you. I have singled you out from others, and have chosen you to myself, not for your worthiness, but for mine own sake. I have also redeemed you, not only from the dread of my Father's law, but from the hand of Diabolus. This I have done because I loved you, and because I have set my heart upon you to do you good. I have also, that all things that might hinder thy way to the pleasures of Paradise might be taken out of the way, laid down for thee for thy soul, a plenary satisfaction, and have bought thee to myself— a price not of corruptible things, as of silver and gold, but a price of blood, mine own blood, which I have freely spilt upon the ground to make thee mine. So I have reconciled thee, O my Mansoul, to my Father, and entrusted thee in the mansion-houses that are with my Father in the Royal City, where things are, O my Mansoul, that eye hath not seen, nor hath ent'red into the heart of man to conceive.

'Besides, O my Mansoul, thou seest what I have done, and how I have taken thee out of the hands of thine enemies; unto whom thou hadst deeply revolted from my Father, and by whom thou wast content to be possessed, and also to be destroyed. I came to thee first by my law, then by my Gospel to awaken thee, and show thee my glory. And thou knowest what thou wast, what thou saidst, what thou didst, and

10

Emmanuel's speech to Mansoul.

20

30

8   *O yes*: an anglicised form of Fr. *oyez*, hear ye; the call by which the public crier commands silence and attention.
29f.   See I Cor. 2:9.

how many times thou rebelledst against my Father
and me; yet I left thee not, as thou seest this day,
but came to thee, have borne thy manners, have
waited upon thee, and after all accepted of thee, even
of my mere grace and favour; and would not suffer
thee to be lost as thou most willingly wouldst have
been. I also compassed thee about, and afflicted thee on
every side, that I might make thee weary of thy ways,
and bring down thy heart with molestation to a will-
10   ingness to close with thy good and happiness. And
when I had gotten a complete conquest over thee, I
turned it to thy advantage.

'Thou seest also what a company of my Father's
host I have lodged within thy border: captains and
rulers, soldiers and men of war, engines and excellent
devices to subdue and bring down thy foes—thou
knowest my meaning, O Mansoul. And they are my
servants, and thine too, Mansoul. Yea, my design of
possessing of thee with them, and the natural tendency
20   of each of them is to defend, purge, strengthen, and
sweeten thee for myself, O Mansoul, and to make thee
meet for my Father's presence, blessing and glory; for
thou, my Mansoul, art created to be prepared unto
these.

'Thou seest, moreover, my Mansoul, how I have
passed by thy backslidings, and have healed thee. Indeed, I was angry with thee, but I have turned mine
anger away from thee, because I loved thee still, and
mine anger and mine indignation is ceased in the de-
30   struction of thine enemies, O Mansoul. Nor did thy
goodness fetch me again unto thee, after that I for
thy transgressions have hid my face, and withdrawn
my presence from thee. The way of backsliding was
thine, but the way and means of thy recovery was
mine. I invented the means of thy return; it was I that
made an hedge and a wall, when thou wast beginning
to turn to things in which I delighted not. 'Twas I
that made thy sweet, bitter; thy day, night; thy
smooth way, thorny, and that also confounded all that

10   *close with*: accept, adhere to.

sought thy destruction. 'Twas I that set Mr. Godly-fear to work in Mansoul. 'Twas I that stirred up thy conscience and understanding, thy will and thy affections, after thy great and woeful decay. 'Twas I that put life into thee, O Mansoul, to seek me, that thou mightest find me, and in thy finding find thine own health, happiness and salvation. 'Twas I that fetched the second time the Diabolonians out of Mansoul; and 'twas I that overcame them, and that destroyed them before thy face.

'And now, my Mansoul, I am returned to thee in peace, and thy transgressions against me are as if they had not been. Nor shall I be with thee as in former days, but I will do better for thee than at thy beginning. For yet a little while, O my Mansoul, even after a few more times are gone over thy head, I will (but be not thou troubled at what I say) take down this famous town of Mansoul, stick and stone, to the ground. And will carry the stones thereof, and the timber thereof, and the walls thereof, and the dust thereof, and the inhabitants thereof, into mine own country, even into the Kingdom of my Father; and will there set it up in such strength and glory, as it never did see in the kingdom where now it is placed. I will even there set it up for my Father's habitation, for, for that purpose it was at first erected in the kingdom of Universe; and there will I make it a spectacle of wonder, a monument of mercy, and the admirer of its own mercy. There shall the natives of Mansoul see all that of which they have seen nothing here; there shall they be equal to those unto whom they have been inferior here. And there shalt thou, O my Mansoul, have such communion with me, with my Father, and with your Lord Secretary, as is not possible here to be enjoyed. Nor ever could be, should-est thou live in Universe the space of a thousand years.

'And there, O my Mansoul, thou shalt be afraid of murderers, no more; of Diabolonians, and their

I Chron. 29:30.

10

20

30

23f.   Cf. II Cor. 5:1; Rev. 21:2-3.
29   *admirer*: one who marvels.

threats, no more. There, there shall be no more plots, nor contrivances, nor designs against thee, O my Mansoul. There thou shalt no more hear the evil tidings, or the noise of the Diabolonian drum. There thou shalt not see the Diabolonian standard-bearers, nor yet behold Diabolus his standard. No Diabolonian mount shall be cast up against thee there, nor shall there the Diabolonian standard be set up to make thee afraid. There thou shalt not need captains, engines, soldiers, and men of war. There thou shalt meet with no sorrow, nor grief, nor shall it be possible that any Diabolonian should again (for ever) be able to creep into thy skirts, burrow in thy walls, or there last longer, than here you are able to desire it should, and yet it shall always be sweet and new, nor shall any impediment attend it for ever.

'There, O Mansoul, thou shalt meet with many of those that have been like thee, and that have been partakers of thy sorrows; even such as I have chosen, and redeemed and set apart as thou for my Father's Court and City Royal. All they will be glad in thee, and thou when thou seest them, shalt be glad in thine heart.

'There are things, O Mansoul, even things of thy Father's providing and mine, that never were seen since the beginning of the world, and they are laid up with my Father, and sealed up among his treasures for thee, till thou shalt come thither to enjoy them. I told you before that I would remove my Mansoul, and set it up elsewhere, and where I will set it, there are those that love thee, and those that rejoice in thee now, but how much more when they shall see thee exalted to honour. My Father will then send them for you to fetch you; and their bosoms are chariots to put you in. And you, O my Mansoul, shall ride upon the wings of the wind. They will come to convey, conduct, and bring you to that, when your eyes see more, that will be your desired haven.   Ps. 68:17.

'And thus, O my Mansoul, I have showed unto

8   *to make thee afraid*: cf. Isa. 35:9-10.
17ff. Cf. Heb. 12:23.

thee what shall be done to thee hereafter, if thou canst hear, if thou canst understand. And now I will tell thee what at present must be thy duty and practice, until I shall come and fetch thee to myself, according as is related in the Scriptures of truth.

'First, I charge thee that thou dost hereafter keep more white and clean the liveries which I gave thee before my last withdrawing from thee. Do it, I say, for this will be thy wisdom. They are in themselves fine linen, but thou must keep them white and clean. This will be your wisdom, your honour, and will be greatly for my glory. When your garments are white, the world will count you mine. Also when your garments are white, then I am delighted in your ways; for then your goings to and fro will be like a flash of lightning, that those that are present must take notice of; also their eyes will be made to dazzle thereat. Deck thyself, therefore, according to my bidding, and make thyself by my law straight steps for thy feet; so shall thy King greatly desire thy beauty; for he is thy Lord, and worship thou him.

'Now that thou mayest keep them as I bid thee, I have, as I before did tell thee, provided for thee an open fountain to wash thy garments in. Look, therefore, that thou wash often in my fountain, and go not in defiled garments; for as it is to my dishonour, and my disgrace, so it will be to thy discomfort, when you shall walk in filthy garments. Let not therefore my garments, your garments, the garments that I gave thee, be defiled or spotted by the flesh. *Keep thy garments always white, and let thy head lack no ointment.* My Mansoul, I have ofttimes delivered thee from the designs, plots, attempts, and conspiracies of Diabolus, and for all this I ask thee nothing, but that thou render not to me evil for my good, but that thou bear in mind my love, and the continuation of my

Zech. 3:1,2.
Jude 23.

---

7   Cf. Rev. 16:15; 19:8.
15f.   *a flash of lightning*: see Ezek. 1:14.
21   See Ps. 45:11.
24   Cf. Ezek. 13:1; John 13:10; Rev. 7:14.
30ff. See Eccles. 9:8.

kindness to my beloved Mansoul, so as to provoke thee
to walk in thy measure, according to the benefit bestowed on thee. Of old the sacrifices were bound with
cords to the horns of the golden altar. Consider what
is said to thee, O my blessed Mansoul.

'O my Mansoul, I have lived, I have died; I live,
and will die no more for thee. I live that thou mayest
not die. Because I live, thou shalt live also. I reconciled thee to my Father by the blood of my Cross; and
being reconciled, thou shalt live through me. I will
pray for thee, I will fight for thee, I will yet do thee
good.

'Nothing can hurt thee but sin; nothing can
grieve me but sin; nothing can make thee base before
thy foes but sin: take heed of sin, my Mansoul.

'And dost thou know why I at first, and do still
suffer Diabolonians to dwell in thy walls, O Mansoul?
It is to keep thee wakening, to try thy love, to make
thee watchful, and to cause thee yet to prize my noble
captains, their soldiers, and my mercy.

'It is also that yet thou mayest be made to remember what a deplorable condition thou once wast
in. I mean when, not some, but all did dwell, not in
thy walls, but in thy castle, and in thy strong-hold,
O Mansoul.

'O my Mansoul, should I slay all them within,
many there be without that would bring thee into
bondage; for were all those within cut off, those without would find thee sleeping, and then as in a moment
they would swallow up my Mansoul. I therefore left
them in thee, not to do thee hurt (the which they yet
will, if thou hearken to them, and serve them), but
to do thee good, the which they must if thou watch
and fight against them. Know, therefore, that whatever they shall tempt thee to, my design is that they
should drive thee, not further off, but nearer to my

3f.   See Ps. 118:27.
10   Cf. Col. 1:20.
35ff.   *my design*, etc.: this notion of the moral necessity of evil lies at the heart of
Bunyan's doctrine and is symptomatic of an unwavering concern with man
in the here-and-now, with his condition as it now is. A concept at once nobly

Father, to learn thee war, to make petitioning desirable to thee, and to make thee little in thine own eyes. Hearken diligently to this my Mansoul.

'Show me then thy love, my Mansoul, and let not those that are within thy walls, take thy affections off from him that hath redeemed thy soul. Yea, let the sight of a Diabolonian heighten thy love to me. I came once and twice, and thrice to save thee from the poison of those arrows that would have wrought thy death; stand for me, thy friend, my Mansoul, against the Diabolonians, and I will stand for thee before my Father, and all his Court, love me against temptation, and I will love thee notwithstanding thine infirmities.

'O my Mansoul, remember what my captains, my soldiers, and mine engines have done for thee. They have fought for thee, they have suffered by thee, they have borne much at thy hands to do thee good, O Mansoul. Hadst thou not had them to help thee, Diabolus had certainly made a hand of thee. Nourish them, therefore, my Mansoul. When thou dost well, they will be well; when thou dost ill, they will be ill, and sick, and weak. Make not my captains sick, O Mansoul, for if they be sick, thou canst not be well; if they be weak, thou canst not be strong; if they be faint, thou canst not be stout and valiant for thy King, O Mansoul. Nor must thou think always to live by sense: thou must live upon my Word. Thou must believe, O my Mansoul, when I am from thee, that yet I love thee, and bear thee upon mine heart for ever.

'Remember therefore, O my Mansoul, that thou

---

comforting and inspiriting, it distills the essence of Puritanism. It is implicit in all of Milton's major works and explicit in such remarks as these: "That which purifies us is trial, and trial is by what is contrary" (*Areopagitica*, in *Complete Poetry and Selected Prose*, ed. M. Y. Hughes [New York, 1957], p. 728); "For it is by evil that virtue is chiefly exercised" (*Of Christian Doctrine*, in *Complete Poetry*, ed. Hughes, p. 993); "For if there were no opposition, where were the trial of an unfeigned goodness and magnanimity? Virtue that wavers is not virtue, but vice revolted from itself and after a while returning" (*Reason of Church Government*, in *Complete Poetry*, ed. Hughes, p. 662).

19   *made a hand of*: ruined, destroyed, done for. The second edition reads "made an end of," but the third edition restores the earlier reading which makes perfectly good sense.

are beloved of me; as I have therefore taught thee to watch, to fight, to pray, and to make war against my foes, so now I command thee to believe that my love is constant to thee. O my Mansoul, how have I set my heart, my love upon thee, watch! Behold, I lay none other burden upon thee, than what thou hast already. Hold fast till I come.'

7   *Hold fast till I come*: see Rev. 2:24-25.

AN ADVERTISEMENT TO THE READER

Some say the *Pilgrim's Progress* is not mine,
Insinuating as if I would shine
In name and fame by the worth of another,
Like some made rich by robbing of their brother.
Or that so fond I am of being sire,
I'll father bastards: or if need require,
I'll tell a lie in print to get applause.
I scorn it: *John* such dirt-heap never was,
Since God converted him. Let this suffice
To show why I my *Pilgrim* patronize.
    It came from mine own heart, so to my head,
And thence into my fingers trickled;
Then to my pen, from whence immediately
On paper I did dribble it daintily.
    Manner and matter too was all mine own,
Nor was it unto any mortal known,
'Till I had done it. Nor did any then
By books, by wits, by tongues, or hand, or pen,
Add five words to it, or wrote half a line
Thereof: the whole, and ev'ry whit is mine.
    Also for *this*, thine eye is now upon,
The matter in this manner came from none
But the same heart, and head, fingers and pen,
As did the other. Witness all good men;
For none in all the world without a lie,
Can say that this is mine, excepting I.
    I write not this of any ostentation,
Nor 'cause I seek of men their commendation;
I do it to keep them from such surmise,
As tempt them will my name to scandalize.
Witness my name, if anagram'd to thee,
The letters make, *Nu hony in a B.*

JOHN BUNYAN